DISCARD

CALVIN COOLIDGE

CASTLETON STATE COLLEGE · VERMONT ·

LIBRARY

D1600655

The Theoretical Foundations of Chinese Medicine

Systems of Correspondence

M.I.T. East Asian Science Series
Nathan Sivin, general editor

Volume III

The Theoretical Foundations of
Chinese Medicine

編著者：Manfred Porkert

發行所：南 天 書 局 有 限 公 司

登記證字號：行政院新聞局局版臺業字第一四三六號

出版者：南 天 書 局 有 限 公 司

台北市羅斯福路三段二八一號三樓之二

電　話：（〇二）三九二〇一九

郵政劃撥帳戶一〇八〇五三號

印刷者：文 大 印 刷 有 限 公 司

台北市西園路二段二八一巷六弄二二號

中 華 民 國 七 十 年 十 月 景 印

SOUTHERN MATERIALS CENTER, INC.

P. O. Box 13-342 Taipei, Republic of China.

The Theoretical Foundations
of Chinese Medicine

Systems of Correspondence

Manfred Porkert

The MIT Press
Cambridge, Massachusetts, and London, England

610.951
P825+

First MIT Press paperback edition, 1978
Second printing, 1979
Copyright © 1974 by
The Massachusetts Institute of Technology

All rights reserved. No part of this book may be reproduced in any form or by any means, electronic or mechanical, including photocopying, recording, or by any information storage and retrieval system, without permission in writing from the publisher.

This book was set in Monotype Baskerville,
printed on Mohawk Neotext Offset
by Halliday Lithograph Corp.
and bound by Halliday Lithograph Corp.
in the United States of America.

Library of Congress Cataloging in Publication Data

Porkert, Manfred.
    Theoretical foundations of Chinese medicine.

(M.I.T. East Asian science series, v. 3)
Bibliography: p.
1. Medicine—China. I. Title. II. Series: Massachusetts Institute of Technology. M.I.T. East Asian Science Series, v. 3. [DNLM: 1. Medicine, oriental. WB 50 JC6 P8t 1973]
R601.P64 1973   610'.951   73–4960
ISBN 0–262–16058–7

Contents

Tables

The M.I.T. East Asian Science Series

One of the most interesting developments in historical scholarship over the past two decades has been a growing realization of the strength and importance of science and technology in ancient Asian culture. Joseph Needham's monumental exploratory survey, *Science and Civilisation in China*, has brought the Chinese tradition to the attention of educated people throughout the Occident. The level of our understanding is steadily deepening as new investigations are carried out in East Asia, Europe, and the United States.

The publication of general books and monographs in this field, because of its interdisciplinary character, presents special difficulties with which not every publisher is fully prepared to deal. The aim of the M.I.T. East Asian Science Series, under the general editorship of Nathan Sivin, is to identify and make available books which are based on original research in the Oriental sources and which combine the high methodological standards of Asian studies with those of technical history. This series will also bring special editorial and production skills to bear on the problems which arise when scientific equations and Chinese characters must appear in close proximity, and when ideas from both worlds of discourse are interwoven. Most books in the Series will deal with science and technology before modern times in China and related Far Eastern cultures, but manuscripts concerned with contemporary scientific developments or with the survival and adaptation of traditional techniques in China, Japan, and their neighbors today will also be welcomed.

Volumes in the Series

Ulrich Libbrecht, *Chinese Mathematics in the Thirteenth Century: The Shu-shu chiu-chang of Ch'in Chiu-shao*

Shigeru Nakayama and Nathan Sivin (eds.), *Chinese Science: Explorations of an Ancient Tradition*

Manfred Porkert, *The Theoretical Foundations of Chinese Medicine: Systems of Correspondence*

Sang-woon Jeon, *Science and Technology in Korea: Traditional Instruments and Techniques*

Foreword

A rather suspect paradox is responsible for much of the difficulty of understanding Chinese science. We define what we are looking for and what is promising to study by analogy with modern science. Even in China today historians of science lean heavily on contemporary European science in order to pick out Chinese priorities. It takes some knowledge of optics to recognize that the Mohists in the fourth century B.C. dealt seriously with the problems of image formation in mirrors of various shapes; only a man familiar with the principles of engineering could have perceived in the mechanism of the water-driven metallurgical bellows the basic structure of the reciprocating steam engine. The historian of science used to be concerned primarily with the identification and chronological arrangement of priorities, but in recent years this obsession has begun to die away, for more than one reason. The most obvious is that man's prodigious creativity seems to be based on the permutations and recastings of a rather small stock of ideas; tracing back the ancestry of a concept, if done with true erudition and any degree of sophistication, generally leads one back to the very beginnings of scientific thought. (I remember with pleasure a seminar of Giorgio de Santillana's on existentialism which spent considerably more time on Democritus than on Kierkegaard, and never got round to Heidegger.) What is more damaging, a fixation on finding knowledge in the past which merits recognition in the light of the present, leads to a seriously distorted understanding of the past. Once one forms the habit of dividing the thought of ancient scientists into a "scientific" part and an "unscientific" part, there is no reason to put it back together again. Leaving aside the question of how much of today's science will be obsolete in a few decades, how can we claim to comprehend ancient science until we understand integrally how the early investigator saw his problems, how he related them to the theories he knew, how he coined concepts to extend those theories or tie them to new ones, and how he decided when he was right and when he was wrong? Only when we have understood to that depth are we prepared to isolate the significant analogies and dissimilarities between the world's scientific traditions.

There is hardly a field in all of historical scholarship of which we know so little as the development of Chinese medical thought. A mountain of books which treat this subject has accumulated in the West since the sixteenth century. Some are written by European practitioners, since acupuncture is now a flourishing enterprise in the Occident, and some by scholars. But most of these writings, regardless of origin, obscure rather than illuminate the beautiful Chinese theoretical system. This is because they tend to view the traditional art as a crude and eccentric precursor of modern medicine rather than seeking first to comprehend its own inner logic. Thus they are generally based on certain crippling assumptions about the Chinese medical tradition—for instance, that its anatomical ideas are in essence not unlike those of modern medicine, merely less accurate; and that it treats the same disease entities. One usually finds an acknowledgment that classical medicine is a highly abstract and theoretical doctrine, based on such concepts as yin and yang, and that acupuncture was almost always used in combination with such elements as drugs, massage, calisthenics, and breathing disciplines, in a therapeutic program worked out by extremely recondite arguments about the phased flow of *ch'i* energy through the body. One is never told precisely how to reconcile this metaphysical basis with the equally prominent notion that acupuncture is an empirical science which grew out of early discoveries that needles stuck in the flesh produce effects upon organs normally at some distance from the site of penetration—even upon organs which according to modern anatomy do not exist. After trying to dig out of all this writing a serious overview of what the Chinese were after, all one can do is agree with J. R. Hightower's remark about one of the most overrated works on early medicine: "The only valid idea which [an] Occidental medical historian could bring from the most careful reading . . . would be that the Chinese had some peculiar concepts of medicine, an idea he may well have had before beginning to read the book."

I do not think it excessive to say that Manfred Porkert
has written the first truly scholarly book on Chinese medicine
in a Western language. (I think of scholarship as a matter of
intellectual responsibility rather than of footnotes and brackets.)
Dr. Porkert combines knowledge of modern medicine with
an extremely sound grasp of philology, the lamentably dying
art of digging out what words really mean. He has earned the
gratitude of every student of Chinese thought, for instance, by
systematically addressing for the first time the precise meanings
of many fundamental technical terms of Chinese philosophy—
yin and yang, *ch'i* (which he usually renders as "configurational
energy"), *wu hsing* (which he calls the Five Evolutive Phases,
mercifully laying to rest the idea that they are material elements), and so on. For this reason even those who have no
inherent interest in medicine will find much to learn from this
book. Dr. Porkert's working knowledge of the literature of
theoretical medicine is orders of magnitude greater than that of
any previous European writer. He has applied these resources to
explain with great care how the body, its dynamics, and its
relation to the psyche and the macrocosm are envisioned in the
classical tradition down to the present day. At last report,
after all, the bequest of the Yellow Emperor still guards over
the health of the Chinese people as it did two thousand years
ago when the first books were written.

It is difficult to choose the most significant new perceptions
from a book which offers so many. I will merely point out two
examples of particular value in untangling old confusions.

The first is Dr. Porkert's insistence that the classical understanding of the interior of the body, which he calls "orbisiconography," is not the counterpart of Western anatomy but its
antithesis. Anatomy is concerned with the organism as a
structure of parts, and orbisiconography (*tsang-hsiang*) with the
dynamic interplay of what is best described as a number of
functional systems. Any normal Chinese-English dictionary, for
instance, will define *kan* simply as "liver." In medicine (as
opposed to, say, cooking) this word seldom refers to the physical
organ, but rather to the energetic sphere ("orb") which the

organ serves as material substratum. Each orb is defined, not by physical properties, but by its specific roles in the processing, storage, and distribution of vital energy and thus in the maintenance of life. It is further distinguished by special qualities which, corresponding to phases of the great cosmic cycles, determine the orb's special responsibilities for keeping the body temporally in resonance with Nature. Thus the hepatic orb *(kan)* is most economically defined as the functional representative within the body of the Evolutive Phase Wood and all that stands for: the activity of spring within the year cycle, of morning in the day cycle, of quickening and germination. Modern medicine deals with material structures and tissues which are able to perform certain functions. Chinese medicine deals with functions to which physically demonstrable organs happen to be attached. But that is only a general rule. The *san-chiao* 三焦, that source of endless frustration for historians of anatomy unable to definitely locate it, is simply a functional system without a physical organ. Once this Chinese approach to the workings of the body is understood, as a perceptive reader of this book remarked, one is no longer surprised that despite the acuity of Chinese doctors, comparative anatomy was so little developed. The concept of anatomy is a prerequisite for comparative anatomy. It is significant that the modern Chinese word for anatomy, *chieh-p'ou-hsüeh* 解剖學, is not redefined from some traditional concept of the body, but means literally "dissection science."

A second point corrects a serious misconception common in Western writing about acupuncture. In classical medical theory energy is distributed throughout the body, from the inmost orbs to the tips of the fingers and toes, by a series of conduits or "sinarteries" (*ching-luo*, often translated "meridians" in the literature). On the parts of this system which run near the periphery of the body are located hundreds of sensitive points or "foramina" *(hsüeh)*. By inserting needles (acupuncture) or burning small cones of punk (moxibustion) at these sites the doctor attempts by his interference to restore proper phasing of the energetic flow, to restore it to that dynamic balance in the order of time which for Chinese defines health. Much ink has been spilled over whether the existence of this network of conduits can be scientifically demonstrated. These arguments are based on a remarkable variety of investigative methods, ranging from electrical measurement of skin potentials to the microscopic search for special subcutaneous structures. The resulting hypotheses have in general had extremely short half-lives outside the circle of acupuncturists and their devotees. Unfortunately, to carry the radioactive metaphor a step further, none of them ever seems to disappear entirely.

Dr. Porkert has made a considerable contribution to the promotion of more systematic and more self-critical scientific investigation of acupuncture by his assertion that the fundamental *empirical* constituents of the conduit system are not the conduits but the points. The foramina are what the archaic discoverers of acupuncture discovered. Each is precisely located and is believed to induce specific somatic reactions when stimulated. Nowhere in the system of medicine does any empirical procedure involve the sinarteries except to the extent that it involves sensitive points on them. In other words, the notion of a surgical operation on a conduit is simply irreconcilable with the conceptual system of Chinese medicine. The parts of the network which have no points of their own, either because they share the sensitive points of other sinarteries or because they do not lie near the surface of the body, cannot be said to have precise locations, and indeed we find much ambiguity and confusion in classical attempts to describe their courses. The obvious conclusion is that laboratory study of the physical basis of acupuncture is best furthered by concentration on the points, if we recognize that the physical description of the conduit network is on the whole a mnemonic for a web of very abstract functional relations. Some of these relations, to be sure, are localized in space, but many others, as Dr. Porkert has demonstrated in his ground-breaking chapter on phase energetics, are directly concerned with no parameter but time. Dr. Porkert's systematic description and terminology are meant to be as useful to medical researchers as to sinologists.

Magdalen Goffin once said that there are no Cesarean operations in the history of thought. The remarkable advance in the state of our understanding which Dr. Porkert has achieved with this book will lead many students of Chinese medicine to consider it an exception. I see in it not so much the main force of the Cesarean scalpel as the quintessential virtues of sound midwifery: patience, sympathy, and skill.

Nathan Sivin
May 1971

Introduction: Systems of Correspondence in Chinese Medicine

Chinese medicine, like the other Chinese sciences, defines data on the basis of the inductive and synthetic mode of cognition.[1] Inductivity corresponds to a logical link between two effective positions existing at the same time in different places in space. (Conversely, causality is the logical link between two effective positions given at different times at the same place in space.) In other words, effects based on positions that are separate in space yet simultaneous in time are mutually inductive and thus are called *inductive effects*. In Western science prior to the development of electrodynamics and nuclear physics (which are founded essentially on inductivity), the inductive nexus was limited to subordinate uses in protosciences such as astrology. Now Western man, as a consequence of two thousand years of intellectual tradition, persists in the habit of making causal connections first and inductive links, if at all, only as an afterthought. This habit must still be considered the biggest obstacle to an adequate appreciation of Chinese science in general and of Chinese medicine in particular. Given such different cognitive bases, many of the apparent similarities between traditional Chinese and European science which attract the admiration of positivists turn out to be spurious.

The Swiss psychologist C. G. Jung and the English historian of Chinese science Joseph Needham have made an important contribution to defining the essential quality of Chinese thought.[2] Jung has coined the term "synchronicity" (*Synchronizität*) to designate the particular logical principle that forms the basis of Chinese thinking; Needham states that what

[1]The complementary function of the inductive and synthetic as opposed to the causal and analytic mode of cognition has been examined by us in detail in the course of epistemological investigations since 1963. As the greater part of the results of these investigations still awaits publication, it has seemed useful to summarize their essentials here, even though condensation invariably leads to overgeneralization. The qualifier "inductive" was first used as an antonym of "causal" to characterize the connective axiom of Chinese science in our introduction to the German edition of *La pensée chinoise* (*Das chinesische Denken*; Munich, 1963).

[2]C. G. Jung, *Synchronizität als ein Prinzip akausaler Zusammenhänge* in *Naturerklärung und Psyche* (Zurich, 1952); Joseph Needham, *Science and Civilisation in China*, Vol. II, pp. 216ff. See the bibliography for full references.

he calls "correlative thinking" underlies all Chinese science, and has defined the basic action concept "resonance." In so doing, each of these scholars has pinpointed one important aspect of Chinese logic, but they have only partially delineated what constitutes inductivity, the complement to causality.

The aim of all science—and the principal criterion for the scientific quality of any statement—is to define effective positions as unequivocally as possible. No effective position may be defined by itself; its definition calls for comparative references to some other position. If, moreover, it is intended that certain definitions have universal significance, all statements which they embody must be explicitly referred to conventional standards. Quantitative statements (i.e., measurements of universal significance) presuppose conventional standards of measure just as qualitative statements (i.e., evaluations of universal significance) rest upon conventional standards of value.

Modern Western science deals with inductive as well as causal relations. It has at its disposal not only a highly diversified array of conventional metric standards—in the cgs system and its technical derivations—but also makes use of crude standards of value in distinguishing positive–negative, left spin–right spin, and so on.

If systematic inductive links are established between data defined in accordance with conventional standards of value, the result is a system of correspondences. In other words, all systems of correspondence—of which that of Chinese medicine is a particularly impressive example—are diversified out of elementary standards of value.

Basic standards of value used in common by all Chinese science are the polar combination yin-yang and the cycle of the Five Evolutive Phases (abbreviated E.P.; *wu-hsing*). Logical and methodological consistency requires that we begin our investigations by taking a closer look at these standards (Chapter 1). By combining and intertwining these basic standards of quality, it is of course possible to obtain a practically endless scale of universally defined qualities, such as first E.P. of the first E.P., second E.P. of the first E.P., third E.P. of the first E.P., and so on; or yin of the first E.P., yang of the first E.P., yin of the second E.P., and so on. The scale of values so derived permits subtle and precise qualitative definitions, yet it is uniform and abstract. Absolute conventional standards of this kind may find their natural application in theoretical disciplines. In applied science, however—and Chinese medicine decidedly must, as a whole, be considered a practical science which applies theory—any qualitative definition must have quantitative implications, and vice versa. Technical measures based on exact causal and analytic definitions and couched in terms of derived conventional standards of measurement as a rule provide in addition a hint of the quality of the substratum[3] measured, and vice versa.

Centigrade, Fahrenheit, and Réaumur represent good examples in point. Technical measurements expressed in degrees primarily give quantitative information on the relative energy level at stated positions; yet at the same time they call forth certain "physiological" qualities that may be either experienced directly or inferred. On the other hand, temperatures given on the Kelvin scale suggest that these energy levels lie (or at least extend) beyond physiological experience.

As an example of the inverse relation, the basic standards of value, yin-yang and the evolutive phases, are not confined to a perceptive level of phenomenal dimension; they may therefore be said to be free of quantitative implications. Technical standards of value, however, always carry such implications. Thus, *yün, circuitus,* "circuit phase" (abbreviated C.P.) defines a value corresponding to an E.P. that manifests itself in cosmic dimensions; *mo,* "sinartery" indicates an analogous effect on the microcosmic level.

It is these technical standards of value which in essence make up the system of correspondences of Chinese medicine. In Chapter 2, devoted to "phase energetics" (*yün-ch'i*), we shall therefore first deal with technical standards of value applicable to effects of macrocosmic dimension, i.e., with value standards used for the qualitative definition of meteorological, climatic, and immunological effects. We shall then focus our attention in Chapter 3 on the general standards of value employed to describe microcosmic phenomena, such as the functional relationships within the body—epitomized in the Chinese discipline called "imagery of functional orbs" (*tsang-hsiang,* orbisicono-

---

[3]The substratum, positively definable in space, is the carrier or concrete support of functions. The hepatic orb (*kan* 肝), as we shall see, is a functional entity in Chinese medicine, and the liver is merely its substrate.

graphy). In Chapter 4 we shall consider the functional relationships manifest at the surface of the body as developed in the disciplines concerned with the energetic conduits (*ching-luo, sinarteriae*) and with the sensitive points (*shu-hsüeh, foramina inductoria*).

In each case our account will, as a rule, be based primarily on the Inner Classic of the Yellow Sovereign *(Huang-ti nei-ching su-wen* 黃帝內經素問 and *Ling-shu* 靈樞), which contains the first systematic description of the system of correspondences that has remained valid in Chinese medicine to this day. The picture we shall assemble from these sources will be supplemented by quotations from writings up to the present time, for details of which the reader is referred to the notes and the bibliography.

Our approach is philological in method, with greater stress on semantics and etymology than on historical analysis. The present state of our control of Chinese medical literature requires that, with few exceptions, statements on the probable time at which a certain text or theory was originated be made with a margin of at least plus or minus one century, and often much more. Moreover, it must be taken for granted that our present versions of all important medical classics (including, of course, the *Huang-ti nei-ching*) are vitiated by interpolations, lacunae, and corruptions ignored by Chinese commentators.[4]

The transmission of the principal medical texts (including the *Nei-ching*) is submerged in utter darkness from the end of the Han well into the Sui period, that is, for a span of ten generations. The history of textual transmissions remains defective far into the Sung. Consequently controversies on the historical priority of a particular textual variant are largely beside the point. Instead, our efforts must be concentrated on the task of assembling a coherent and logical picture, of giving a phenomenological account of the system of correspondences underlying the whole of Chinese medicine, and of obtaining a clear-cut representation of its technical standards of value.

[4]Particularly impressive examples are given on pp. 117–118 of this volume.

For if the transmission of medical texts for many centuries remains obscure to our understanding, it is equally true that their transmission was far too broad to allow their extinction. Such fundamental works as the *Mo-ching* and the *Chen-chiu chia-i-ching* according to all evidence were compiled during the fourth century A.D., and the vast compendium of pathology, the *Chu-ping yüan-hou lun,* was submitted to the throne in A.D. 610. Consequently, during those centuries quite a number of people must have taken a keen interest in the healing disciplines and had a good command of the theories and axioms set forth in the first classics. If today's text of the first classics is silent, obscure, or contradictory on any subject, we can draw on other texts of the same didactic tradition written perhaps centuries later.

Our phenomenological approach to the subject matter of this book has been determined, aside from personal inclination, by a situation of topical interest: in contradistinction to other branches of the Chinese scientific heritage, Chinese medicine still flourishes today. We have reason to deny the label of "scientific technique" to what a small number of fashionable practitioners in the West make of acupuncture, which is but one of a large array of coordinate therapeutic weapons in the arsenal of Chinese medicine. On the other hand, there is no reason why therapeutic disciplines that have shown their effectiveness through more than two millennia and that today provide one-quarter of the world's population with most of its common remedies should continue to be confined to China. Medical men everywhere should have access to the premises and results of this medical knowledge.

It is thus necessary that we be provided with a methodologically adequate, coherent, and comprehensible account of the Chinese theories in a Western language. Such an account in turn requires consistent use of a precise Western terminology to stand for that of the Chinese authors. Since no such terminology has been available, much of our effort during the past decade has gone into its development.

Let us briefly put on record the principles that have guided us in evolving this terminology. In translating the elements of any text from one language into another, one has a choice of three different procedures, each of which has its uses: literary translation, flexible translation adapted to the context, and normative translation.

If we strive for literary qualities in a translation, our choice of the equivalent for a given word are governed equally by logical, etymological, and aesthetic (melodious, rhythmic) motives. In a flexible translation adapted to the context, our foremost concern is to render logically as precisely and as completely as possible the meaning or meanings of a given expression without losing sight of the clarity and easy comprehensibility of the equivalents chosen. This may require that a single foreign term be rendered by different words in different contexts.

A translation may be called normative if a given term of the foreign language is always rendered by one and the same word (or by the same few words) of our own language. Such an invariant combination of terms in two languages is prone to obscure subtle shades of meaning and allusion. To reduce this danger, care must be taken when choosing a normative equivalent that all contexts are examined in which the original term is used with different nuances of meaning. The choice of a normative equivalent is determined solely by semantic, etymological, and grammatical criteria. For translating technical terms and texts, only the two latter modes, flexible translation and normative translation, can be considered. Our choice between these two alternatives is based on our definition of "technical term." To start with, there is the difference between technical terms in the narrow sense and technical words in a wider sense. By technical terms in a narrow sense, keeping in mind the character of our sources, we understand expressions that have been used consistently and unequivocally by all authorities of the science—if not at all times, at least through many centuries. Technical terms in the wide sense have a precise meaning for some particular author, or only in one particular place in his writings, or else they have been used with ever-changing meanings throughout the ages and by many authors.

For all technical terms in the narrow sense we have developed and used normative Latin equivalents, and for the majority normative English equivalents as well. The qualifier "normative" here is intended to suggest not only that in this investigation we use these standard translations consistently, but that in addition they are capable of serving as the basis of a general Western nomenclature for all disciplines of Chinese medicine. With the latter aim in mind we have systematically examined the meanings of each technical term in all the branches of Chinese medicine, and over a period of several years have tested our Latin and other equivalents for suitability in the interpretation of texts. In the course of this procedure certain normative equivalents originally chosen have been repeatedly modified. Our normative terminology thus is different from previous attempts in that it takes into full account the inductive and synthetic mode of cognition that underlies Chinese technical terminology, and as a rule[5] renders each technical term by a single Latin equivalent that can be used consistently and logically in writing about all the disciplines of Chinese medicine—in sinarteriology as well as in pathology, in phase energetics as well as in internal medicine, in diagnostics as well as in orbisiconography, in gymnastic therapy as well as in pharmacology.

For a majority of Chinese technical terms we have also established English normative equivalents—not by retranslating the Latin term but directly from the original. In the Latin and English equivalents shades of meaning often differ to varying extents in order to translate important connotations of the Chinese that could not be rendered by any single Latin or English word. In a few rare cases we have abstained from introducing an English equivalent, either because the Latin

---

[5]The exceptions to this rule may be counted on the fingers of one hand, and are marked accordingly. It goes without saying that in inflecting languages all forms derived from the same stem are counted as one single equivalent, e.g., *algor, algidus, calor, calidus.* . . .

term, being sufficiently close in form and meaning to the English, is self-explanatory, or because, to the contrary, any normative equivalent would be able to give but a glimpse of the connotations of the Chinese term, whose precise meaning becomes clear only in a flexible English translation. For a very restricted group of technical words we have completely refrained from coining normative equivalents; instead we have put forward either normative or flexible definitions, depending upon the context.[6]

Let us say that this book, like our previous investigations, is based exclusively on Chinese sources. The limited secondary literature in Western languages, although acknowledged in our bibliography and notes, has had no direct bearing on our studies. Limited use has been made of secondary literature in Chinese, on which we have drawn to the extent indicated in the notes for orientation and, in some cases, for a better understanding of the sources. This is particularly true of Chapter 4. In view of the vast literature on acupuncture,[7] frequent reference to secondary writing has greatly aided in distinguishing the salient lines without in any way obscuring the classical core of the theories.

Finally, a note on citations: All Chinese works are cited initially by full title, but subsequent references for many works are abbreviated forms of the romanized titles. Cross references for these short citations are provided in the bibliography.

[6]Examples may in particular be found in the section on energetics discussed on pp. 166–196.
[7]The same holds true for pharmacology, with which, however, the following account is not concerned even indirectly.

1

Basic Standards of Value: Yin and Yang and the Five Evolutive Phases

Yin and Yang

PRELIMINARY REMARKS

Yin and *yang* are the elementary terms used to express a fundamental premise of Chinese thought: they convey the idea of the polar quality of all effects. A polarization of reality had consciously been accomplished *avant la lettre* by the priests of the Shang period (second millennium B.C.). As Hentze[1] points out, motifs and position of the ornamentation on numerous cult bronzes of that period, especially those of the *kuang* vessels, show the epiphany of polar forces.

Some songs of the *Shih-ching* (Book of songs)[2] are considered as the earliest literary mention of the words yin and yang; whereas for first *locus classicus* showing the philosophical and speculative aspects of the paired notion one usually quotes the passage *i yin i yang chih wei tao* 一陰一陽之謂道 (one yin and one yang being called the Tao) in the "Great Commentary" to the *I-ching* (Book of changes).[3] Finally, in the *Li-chi* (Record of rites, considered to have been compiled at the beginning or in the course of the former Han), the words yin and yang (yin-yang), blended into a technical combination, are used frequently.[4]

Granet[5] has investigated and set forth in great detail the original meaning of the terms yin and yang as well as the ideas later associated with them in the Confucian classics: yin and

---

[1]Hentze, *Das Haus als Weltort der Seele* (Stuttgart, 1961), pp. 50ff, 60f *et passim*.
[2]Cf. Granet, *Fêtes et chansons anciennes de la Chine*, songs XIV, 2, XXI,1, and others.
[3]*Hsi-tz'u* 繫辭, *shang* 7, p. 148.
[4]See especially Chapters 6 (*Yüeh-ling*), 9 (*Li-yun*), 11 (*Chiao t'e-sheng*), 19 (*Yüeh-chi*), and 26 (*Chi-t'ung*).
[5]In *Fêtes et chansons anciennes de la Chine*, pp. 244f *et passim*, and especially in the chapter devoted to yin and yang in his *La pensée chinoise*.

yang were used at the outset to designate the shady and the sunny slope of a mountain, respectively; they were names of topographic aspects. By extension of meaning they were also used for the northern and southern banks of a river, for the dark and the sunny seasons, and so on. Because of continual interplay between natural and social events in the rural society of ancient China, the terms yin and yang had, at a very early stage, also acquired a somewhat more general meaning in denoting the *complementary aspects* of social groups, including the complementarity of the sexes. This latter meaning adhered to the terms yin and yang when, from Chan-kuo times, they were increasingly used in technical or speculative contexts. In the course of Granet's sociological argumentation we meet with this clear statement: "Yin and yang may be defined neither as purely logical entities nor as simple cosmogonic principles. They are neither substances nor forces nor genera. To the common consciousness they appear to be indistinctly all this, and no technician would consider them under one particular aspect only, excluding all others."[6] Granet here gives what may well pass for a standard definition of the emblematic[7] significance attributed to the words yin and yang in ritual as well as in everyday speech.

Needham, whose approach is that of the modern scientist rather than the anthropologist, is especially interested in the philosophical and technical connotations of the paired expression *yinyang*.[8] In spite of his awareness of Granet's work, however, he excessively restricts the meaning of these terms in philosophical and even technical texts by referring to them in his chapter on yin and yang as the "two fundamental forces."

Discussions of the terms yin and yang, which are of basic

[6]Granet, *La pensée chinoise*, p. 146. This statement is preceded by a passage in which Grant expounds the classical passage of the *Hsi-tz'u* mentioned in Note 3 above.

[7]See the Index to Granet's *La pensée chinoise* and, for our interpretation of the term "emblem," Porkert, "Farbemblematik in China," *Antaios*, 1962, 4. 2: 154–167.

[8]In *Science and Civilisation in China*, Vol. II, pp. 273ff.

importance for all Chinese thought, are of course not limited to the two authors quoted but may be found in any Western work on Chinese philosophy. Even without the résumé just given it may therefore be assumed that our readers are familiar with the most general meaning of the two terms.

However, a precise interpretation of Chinese medical writings that is consistent under all circumstances calls for a more thorough and detailed knowledge of the technical connotations of these terms. The following paragraphs will be devoted to clearing up these significations. We shall begin by examining the syntactic inflections of the two terms. We shall then analyze their numerous semantic facets and shall finally turn to their technical inflections.

For this kind of investigation ample material may be found in the Inner Classic of the Yellow Sovereign (Huang-ti nei-ching), several chapters of which are devoted essentially to the systematic exposition of correspondences classed by yin and yang in the extant text of the Huang-ti nei-ching su-wen, sections 3 (Shen-ch'i t'ung-t'ien-lun), 4 (Chin-kuei chen-yen-lun), 5 (Yin-yang ying-hsiang ta-lun), 6 (Yin-yang li-ho lun), 7 (Yin-yang pieh-lun), 67 (Wu-yün-hsing ta-lun), 68 (Liu-wei-chih ta-lun), and 74 (Chih-yen-yao ta-lun); and in the Huang-ti nei-ching ling-shu, sections 41 (Yin-yang hsi jih-yüeh) and 72 (T'ung-t'ien). Of these sections the fifth chapter of the Su-wen, bearing the significant title "Great Treatise on the Phenomena Corresponding to Yin and Yang" 陰陽應象大論, is by far the most useful toward gaining a systematic total view of the subject matter. However, we shall occasionally quote sources other then the Nei-ching.

SYNTACTIC INFLECTIONS OF THE TERMS YIN AND YANG

In regard to the syntactic function of the terms yin and yang, three syntactical—and thus semantic—shades of meaning can be distinguished in Chinese texts:

1. The two terms are most frequently employed as qualifiers, in which case they occur, sometimes each by itself, in conjunction with the term qualified, e.g., yang-ch'i 陽氣, yang-yün 陽運, yang-ping 陽病, yang-hsing 陽性, yin-ch'i 陰氣. We may call this the "adjective" use and function.

2. More rarely we find the words used as (apparently) independent syntactical elements. If, in such a case, outward appearance makes us inclined to speak of a "nominal" func-

tion of the terms, it is in better keeping with Chinese interpretations (at least up to the nineteenth century) to say that yin and yang are here used as pregnant expressions which may implicitly always be completed by some qualified term, usually *ch'i* 氣. This should be kept in mind when translating expressions such as *chih-yin* 治陰, *pu-yang* 補陽, *hsieh-yang* 泄陽, *pu-yin* 補陰, as well as *yin-hsü* 陰虛, *yin-shih* 陰實. And, of course, in no Chinese text may the words yin and yang so used be understood as the expression of any abstract principle (such as "fundamental yin").[9]

3. We find the terms yin and yang quite frequently united into a combination of antonyms that usually forms an independent syntactical element[10] but that, in a few set expressions, is subordinated to a subsequent part.[11] In the vocabulary of traditional Chinese science and Chinese philosophy this independent double term occupies the place of such modern expressions as polarity, polar, polarized energy, balance of forces (balanced forces), configuration of forces. When in this third function, the Chinese double term will be transcribed as a single word: yinyang. This double term yinyang has never served as an abstract notion completely stripped of concrete associations. Nevertheless, in comparison to similar composite expressions, such as *t'ien-ti* (heaven and earth → the cosmos), *jih-yüeh* (sun and moon → the luminaries), *nan-nü* (male and female → people, relatives), it has always held a position apart. In contradistinction to the expressions just enumerated, no generally accepted metonym may be found in Chinese literature for the composite expression yinyang.

In general as well as in technical literature one looks in vain for expressions such as *liang-li* 兩力 or *liang-shih* 兩勢 (or *erh-li* 二力, *erh-shih* 二勢) likely to support Needham's terminology and interpretation ("two forces"). On the other hand, an analysis of corresponding contexts in the universal concordance *P'ei-wen yün-fu* 佩文韻府 (1710) shows that typical locutions such as *liang-cheng* 兩正, *liang-ch'üan* 權, *liang-chu* 株, *liang-chi* 極, *liang-k'ai* 楷, *liang-chiao* 角, *liang-wei* 位, *liang-hsing* 行, *liang-yü* 隅, *liang-piao* 表, *liang-pen* 本, *liang-kuan* 觀, *liang-shu* 屬, used for various twofold distributions, are

---

[9] Of this Granet (*La pensée chinoise*, p. 146) has reminded us.

[10] 陰陽不測, 辯陰陽, 卜陰陽.

[11] 陰陽家, 陰陽生, 陰陽學.

never used metonymically in place of "yinyang." There remains the expression *liang-i* 兩儀 (variant form: *erh-i* 二儀) which literally means "the two instruments." Traditionally *liang-i*, in Confucian as well as in the majority of Taoist texts, is used metonymically for *t'ien-ti* (heaven and earth→the cosmos).[12] Classical examples for this equation are found in the remnants of cosmogonic speculations of the Chan-kuo period.

A rather direct one may be found in the philosophical compilation *Lü-shih ch'un ch'iu* 呂氏春秋 5/217: "Great Unity produces the Two Instruments, the Two Instruments produce the yinyang." Because of the clear statement in this sentence one may not equate yinyang with the Two Instruments. This is why the Han commentator Kao Yu 高誘 states explicitly: "By the 'Two Instruments' Heaven and Earth [are meant]." A less precise formula is that of the "Great Commentary" (*Hsi-tz'u* 繫辭) to the *I-ching* 7/156f: 易有太極, 是生兩儀, 兩儀生四象, "In the Changes there is the Supreme Pole which produces the Two Instruments; the Two Instruments produce the Four Emblems."[13] Wang Pi 王弼 makes no comment on this fundamental statement; K'ung Ying-ta 孔穎達, T'ang dynasty author of the *Cheng-i* 正義 commentary, quotes the approximate parallel in the *Lao-tzu* 44: "Tao produces One [= unity], One produces Two [=polarity], Two produces Three, Three produces the Myriad Beings [that is, the diversity of empirical phenomena]. The Myriad Beings carry yin on their backs and embrace yang." He explains: " 'Tao produces One' refers to the Supreme Pole [*t'ai-chi*]. 'The Supreme Pole produces the Two Instruments' in the *Lao-tzu* corresponds [to the sentence] 'One produces Two.' " Unfortunately, the commentators are far from agreement on the meaning of the passage from *Lao-tzu* here adduced by K'ung Ying-ta (cf. *Lao-tzu chiao-shih*, p. 112; *Lao-tzu pen-i*, p. 36).

TECHNICAL CONNOTATIONS OF THE TERMS YIN AND YANG

THE POLAR ASPECTS OF YIN AND YANG

Yin and yang are universal designations for the polar aspects of effects. As such they are untranslatable and have been adopted directly into many languages.[14] If Chinese technical

[12]This lets us modify a statement made more than a decade ago in "Untersuchungen einiger philosophisch-wissenschaftlicher Grundbegriffe und Beziehungen im Chinesischen," *ZDMG*, 1961, *110*. 2: 438, in connection with a passage of the Sung Taoist encyclopedia *Yün-chi ch'i-ch'ien* 雲笈七籤 12/3a: "Yellow is the right color of the Two Instruments." Our supposition then was that "Two Instruments" as a rule was used to mean yinyang, but that equation has been used by leading philosophers (in particular by Chou Tun-i and Shao Yung) only since the Sung era); cf. Feng Yu-lan, *Chung-kuo che-hsüeh shih* 中國哲學史 (Shanghai, 1931), pp. 824 and 831.
[13]易有太極, 是生兩儀, 兩儀生四象.
[14]See p. 423 of "Untersuchungen."

terms are to be left untranslated in any modern Western context, it is imperative that we have a clear idea of the notion at the base of these terms in their original setting. This is all the more necessary in view of the need for an authoritative and sensible interpretation of the achievements of Chinese science in such fields as medical theory.

Over the course of two millennia, the terms yin and yang have acquired a multiplicity of connotations. Hence, their rendition (or description) in Western languages requires a variety of seemingly unrelated equivalents chosen to correspond to meanings that emerge in various Chinese contexts. No smaller assortment of definitions can successfully mediate between the traditional and sometimes archaic connotations of the original words and the conceptual system of modern science.

To start with, the basic and overall definitions of the terms may be given as:

yang = active aspect of an effective position,
yin = structive aspect of an effective position.

Whereas the qualifier "active" at first sight seems self-explanatory, the complementary term "structive" does call for elucidation. Taking Chinese as well as Western findings into account, we introduce the term *structio* ("struction"), derived from the Latin *struere*, to construct, to form concretely, to express the ideas associated with the logical complement of *actio* ("action"). *Structio* (English derivatives: struction, to struct, structive) defines a positive effect given at or within a certain effective position and directly perceptible there.

By contradistinction, *actio* (and the reflexion of *actio, re-actio*) defines an effect taking place outside or beyond a given effective position, and indirectly perceptible only when some "structing" position (an object or subject) is interposed. To cite one example out of several which we shall examine in detail, a stimulus is *actio*, and a response is *structio*. Only through the response do we perceive the stimulus.

FUNDAMENTAL ASSOCIATIONS OF YANG (OF THE ACTIVE ASPECT)
1. Yang signifies something incipient, something inchoative—in Chinese *sheng* 生. One can easily conceive of the beginning of an effect or change as being identical with some action. Consequently, the *Su-wen* 5/46 passage: "Yang produces (gives rise to) . . . " may be considered typical in that incipience implies production.
2. Yang signifies something setting loose (something inducing) —in Chinese *kan* 感. It is a familiar idea both in China and in

the West that effects and changes are set loose or induced by some sort of action. The Chinese term *kan* signifies inductive[15] stimulation that can be defined in time, not in space. In the *Yüeh-chi* of the *Li-chi*,[16] *kan* is conceived as something coming from without, an agency inducing motion.

3. Yang signifies something setting in motion (something dynamizing, something dynamic); something moving, communicating motion; something live—in Chinese *tung* 動, *tsao* 躁, and again *sheng* 生. This chain of semantic associations again is practically self-explanatory. Examples for these meanings are found in the *Su-wen* 7/83: "That which moves is yang"; in the *Su-wen* 5/46: "Yang moves . . . " and so on.

4. Yang signifies something transforming (something causing change)—in Chinese *hua* 化, *pien* 變. "Perceptible change" is the epistemological criterion that lets us infer that "action" takes place (or has taken place). In other words, there is an axiomatic identification of the active with that which transforms. In the *Su-wen* 5/46 we find the statement: "Yang transforms the configurational [i.e., determinate in quality] energy (*ch'i*)."

In this connection it should be remarked that as a rule the Chinese term rendering this nuance is *hua*. *Hua* denotes a fundamental and essential change → a transformation. However, sometimes one also encounters the word *pien*, denoting external, momentary, or apparent change. A *locus classicus* for this distinction is in the *Kuan-tzu* 管子 49/270: "The exemplary man (*sheng-jen*) changes (*pien*) in accordance with the times without transforming [the essence of his being]."[17] This in turn permits us to understand the passage in the *Su-wen* 66/583: "When the beings take rise (*sheng*, the term cited under item 1 above), this is called *hua* (transformation); when the beings have reached their full development (in Chinese *chi* 極: "to arrive at the ridge or summit") [and consequently have taken on a different appearance], this is called *pien* (change)."[18] The terms *pien* and *hua* seem to suggest the idea of complementary antonyms. In the passage of the *Su-wen* 66/583 just quoted where yin and yang are called the father and the mother of change and transformation (*pien-hua*), the compound *pien-hua* may be

---

[15]See the Introduction to this volume.
[16]*Li-chi* 19–38/679.
[17]聖人與時變而不化. Needham, in *Science and Civilisation* in China, Vol. II, p. 74f gives the inverse explanation, philologically as well as logically untenable, for this passage.
[18]物生謂之化, 物極謂之變.

understood as a composite of synonyms and therefore be translated by "changes"; yet, on the other hand, the parallelism between yin/yang and *pien/hua* shows that *pien* and *hua* can be conceived as the two aspects of an action polarized in turn—*pien* as its iterative, active, *hua* as its perfective, structive aspect.

5. Yang signifies something developing, expanding—in Chinese *chang* 長 (also *shu* 舒). A shade of meaning implicit in the definition of the term "action" is that action tends to expand in all directions from its supposed point of origin. Consequently, in the *Su-wen* 2/17, where we find a complete enumeration of the characteristic influences of the seasons, summer, or major yang, is put in line with the technical term *chang*,[19] meaning "to ripen" (literally: to grow up). And in the *Su-wen* 70/659 we find the statement: "Yang expands."

6. Yang signifies something dissolving, dispersing (something subtilizing)—in Chinese *san* 散. This is an ambiguous inflection related to the preceding nuance, yet more comprehensive in meaning. Action not only changes or transforms[20] positions that exist positively;[21] in fact it dissolves, cancels, or annihilates such positions. In another way, action may be conceived as something "subtilizing" because any active influence or any action becomes diluted, is burned up; it consumes itself in the course of time. The passage in the *Su-wen* 5/50: "Of the *sapores* (flavors), the bitter and the sweet ones are of dispersing [tendency] and of yang [polarity]" is explained by the commentator Wang Ping 王冰 (p. 51): "The bitter *sapor* disperses, the sweet *sapor* relaxes; thus [foods and drugs] that make something expand and disperse are yang."[22]

7. Yang signifies something indeterminate yet determining—in Chinese *tan* 淡, *ch'ing* 清; *shen* 神. These seemingly paradoxical qualifications of activity become intelligible if we recall two axioms. The first is that the quality of any action is beyond direct positive experience: it can only be perceived indirectly either in the struction of some perceptive and valuating sub-

[19]In the corresponding text of the *Lei-ching* 類經 1/33, Chang has a diacritical mark of the third tone.
[20]See statement 4 above.
[21]I.e., prior to the action viewed.
[22]辛散, 甘緩, 故發散爲陽.

ject or in the struction of the reaction of a second object by a valuating subject.

These apparently complex epistemological relationships are really quite unequivocal. An illustrative example may help to a better understanding of what has here been sketched only summarily. Let us suppose that the sun (= effective position A) emits rays. On the quality (i.e., determination) of these rays absolutely no positive statement is possible as long as these rays do not strike another object. If they strike another object (=effective position B) and if this happens to be identical with a valuating subject (a condition fulfilled if, for example, the object is an intelligent human being) those specific qualities of the sun's radiation which man is constitutionally capable of perceiving are positively and directly perceived as the result of a struction within the perceptive subject. For the radiation striking the object brings about changes that can be positively determined. Let us now suppose that the sun's rays strike a technical or biological object (=effective position B). This object, of course, will in turn struct certain determinate qualities which perhaps are different from those structed in a human subject, but which correspond to the specific structive capacity of the object. In this case a human observer (=effective position C), perceiving and valuating consciously, can apprehend the effects at position B only indirectly through perceived reactions which he in turn (partly) structs at his position C. From these (subjective) structions he may indirectly, by way of rational deduction, define some qualities of the sun's rays that he is incapable of perceiving through his own sense organs.

This example also serves to illustrate the second axiom: regardless of how many valuating objects are interposed between the source of action (= effective position A) and the final valuating subject (= effective position C), the range of qualities of a given action thus defined cannot exceed those which the valuating objects are capable of structing on the basis of their inherent dispositions. This, in brief, explains the absolute epistemological impossibility of totally defining action and activity.

The foregoing development permits us to understand why, e.g., in the *Su-wen* 74/832, food without definite taste ("something flavorless"; *tan*) is considered one of the *sapores yang*; or why in the *Su-wen* 5/47 and 67 yang may be syntactically qualified by *ch'ing* 清. The term *ch'ing* (which, in common speech, means "pure," "clear," speaking of water) in Taoist technical terminology represents one among several designations of the "neutral point,"[23] i.e., a speculative position in

---

[23]See p. 449 of "Untersuchungen."

which all attributes are supposed to coincide, the quality of which, consequently, cannot be properly characterized by any single attribute.

The *Su-wen*'s connection of *ch'ing* with yang merely reflects the doctrine generally accepted at the time of the compilation of this classic. Thus, in the cosmogonic treatise of the *Huai-nan-tzu* 淮南子 3/52 we similarly find *ch'ing-yang* (literally, the clear yang) as the formative base of "Heaven," corresponding in cosmogony to the determining yet undeterminable pole. The indetermination or, in positive terms, the relative, partial, and haphazard definition of action and activity has been universally accepted by philosophers and scientists, as their writings show, since the first millennium B.C. Its influence conditioned the deep-seated preference for the structive position, a preference voiced in the Han philosophical classic *Huai-nan-tzu* 17/111: "The Exemplary Man dwells in yin, the crowd dwells in yang." In this context, of course, all other connotations and inflexions of yin and yang implicitly come into play.

The necessity, as exemplified in Western science, that any positive statement on any activity depend empirically upon observations made at or through structive positions, is compensated for—and usually obscured by—systematic speculation. However, in disciplines such as orbisiconography,[24] an early halt to this kind of speculative compensation is evidently the main reason for a weakness of the active (yang) positions as compared to the structive (yin) positions. This leads us to the point that yang not only corresponds to something beyond empirical definition and therefore indeterminate but that it constitutes at the same time a determinative factor. This semantic facet has more speculative than practical importance and thus remains implicit in the majority of technical (and medical) treatises. Shades of meaning 2 ("something setting loose") and 4 ("something transforming"), and in an indirect way also meaning 1 ("something beginning"), suggest a determinative influence. The terms "beginning," "setting loose," and "transforming" presuppose that at given effective positions determinate qualities are different at different times or, more simply, that action conditions a new determination.

The final aspect of meaning involves the precise connotation of the Chinese word *shen* 神, which we have examined in previous writings.[25]

---

[24]See pp. 107ff and especially p. 152 below.
[25]See "Untersuchungen," pp. 429–432, and additional articles by the author:

Shen comprises several concepts which in other contexts are contradictory. Insofar as it has polar aspects, *shen* corresponds to yang.[26] The structure of *shen*'s polar energies, we are told, cannot be sounded out or localized.[27] Since *shen* determines the characteristic structure of energetic configurations (*ch'i* 氣), we have defined *shen* as "configurative force."[28]

FUNDAMENTAL ASSOCIATIONS OF YIN (OF THE STRUCTIVE ASPECT)

1. Yin signifies something completing (something perfective)· —in Chinese *ch'eng* 成. Struction, the substantiation of effects, is conceived as the completion, accomplishment, or conclusion of some operation initiated actively. In this respect the statement in the *Su-wen* 5/46, "Yin accomplishes," is representative.

2. Yin signifies something confirming (something corresponding), something responsive—in Chinese *ying* 應. It has been explained (number 7 of the significations of yang) that an action (*actio*) can be positively perceived only to the extent that it strikes an object corresponding to and structing certain of its qualities. Thus the effect stimulated (*kan*) by an action is confirmed (*ying*) structively. The Chinese term *ying* in everyday language means "to reply," "to respond," "to correspond," and in technical contexts constitutes the polar complement of *kan*, to stimulate. The double term *kan-ying* since its first technical use in the commentary upon the Thirty-First Hexagram of the *I-ching*[29] designates the inductive relationship of an (active) stimulus (*kan*) and a (structive) response (*ying*).[30]

3. Yin signifies something reposing, quiescent (something static)

"Wissenschaftliches Denken im alten China...," *Antaios*, 1961; *2.6*: 537ff; "Die energetische Terminologie in den chinesischen Medizinklassikern," *Sinologica*, 1965, *8*.4: 189ff and 203.

[26]"Untersuchungen," p. 429; "Wissenschaftliches Denken," p. 538.

[27]"Wissenschaftliches Denken," p. 538; "Untersuchungen," pp. 429f. See also the text of the *I-ching (Hsi-tz'u)*, p. 147: 神無方, "*Shen* cannot be localized," as well as the parallel passage in *Su-wen* 66/583: 陰陽不測之謂神, "Something the polarity of which is unfathomable is called *shen*."

[28]"Untersuchungen," p. 435; "Wissenschaftliches Denken," p. 539.

[29]*I-ching*, p. 82 (Hexagram *hsien* 咸 → *kan* 感 ["Influence"]: 二氣感應以相與, "The energies of setting loose and responding unite [in a total effect]." See also the *Yüeh-chi* of the *Li-chi* 38/679 and the *Huai-nan-tzu* 7/65.

[30]Since the nineteenth century *kan-ying* has been the Chinese term for electromagnetic induction.

—in Chinese *ching* 靜; something substantiative, consolidating —in Chinese again *ch'eng* 成; something becoming rigid, dying off, fading away—in Chinese *szu* 死, *ch'ü* 去. Yin as the counterpart of dynamic action corresponds to a quiescent effective position at which effects that spread dynamically seem to be precipitated and substantiated, thus becoming perceptible. In the *Su-wen* 5/46 and 7/87 we find the same idea: "Yin is quiescent," and "the quiescent is yin." The structive substantiation of an effect looks like the substantiation of an action whose extent cannot be defined in space. This is why struction (yin) may be conceived of as the stabilization or consolidation of an active effect (*ch'eng*).[31] Repose, quiescence, and other static states are equivalent to death, to cessation or fading away of a given effect. Anything static is sooner or later subject to transformatory or deteriorative action. That is why the "yin hours" correspond to an "expiring configuration."[32] In the *Su-wen* 7/83 the decrescendo pulse (*ch'ü-mo* 去脈) is qualified as yin.

4. Yin signifies something sustaining (sustentative)—in Chinese *yang* 養; something conserving (conservative), something preserving—in Chinese *shou* 收, *ts'ang* 藏. This semantic aspect of yin is less subtle and closer to everyday experience than the preceding one. Every struction implies the tendency to transform a momentary effect into a persistent one, to let endure and to maintain unchanged fleeting qualities. The word *yang*, which, according to its etymology and everyday usage, is translated "to nourish," "to enhance," or "to promote," often is used somewhat more abstractly in technical contexts, where it means "to sustain."

Something may be sustained or propped up (yang) not only by means of food but also by contact with configurations (*ch'i*) of specific affinity. That is why the *Huai-nan-tzu* 20/66 refers not only to sustaining the *shen* (configurative force) and the body (*yang-hsing* 養形) but also to sustaining the transforming influence of the Sovereign (*yang-hua* 養化). The passage continues: "An untrammeled (*ch'ing*)[33] *shen* (configurative force), emotions in equi-

---

[31]As a matter of fact one of the meanings given for "*ch'eng* 成" in the modern dictionary *Han-yü tz'u-tien* 漢語辭典 is *ting* 定, "to fix."
[32]See pp. 25 and 32 below.
[33]See note 23 above.

librium, relaxation in all joints are basic to the sustenance of one's essential nature (*hsing* 性)."[34] Clearly, in the exercises here described there can be no question of food introduced into the organism from outside; the aim is strengthening inductively, by meditation, certain mental images or influences.

Of the two other Chinese terms adduced here the first, *shou* 收, is suggestive of ideas associated with the fall season (to bear fruit, to gather, to harvest, to put away); the second, *ts'ang* 藏, points to ideas associated with winter (to store, to lock up, to hide).[35]

5. Yin signifies something condensing (concentrating); something closing in—in Chinese *shou* 收, *chi* 積, *lien* 斂, *pu* 布. Again, this semantic shading is partly contained in sense 4. Both share the Chinese term *shou*, which in everyday language is translated "to gather together," "to collect," "to put away."

The passage of the *Su-wen* 70/659 already quoted may be rendered as "yang and yin spread" 陽舒陰布. But although both verbs indicate an active effective mode, *pu* 布 suggests the idea of covering → shielding or closing off. The inverse combination (*yin shu, yang pu*) would be inappropriate.[36]

6. Yin signifies something awaiting organization, yet, at the same time, something determinate—in Chinese *ching* 精 (*chuo* 濁), and again *ch'eng* 成. The concept of struction implies[37] that a postulated but previously indefinable effect substantializes into a positive, perceivable one. If the influence conditioning a specific quality is external, this (structing) position must lack this particular determination, and thus be "awaiting specific organization."[38] *Ching,* structive potential, is without perceptible qualitative determination; it receives such a determination under the influence of *shen,* configurative force. In medical texts, *ching* is explicitly qualified as yin, *shen* as yang, e.g., in the commentary of the *Ling-shu* 8/965: "If we speak of *ching* as opposed to *shen, ching* is yin (structive), and *shen* is yang (active)." Anything perfected (inflection 1, above) or sub-

---

[34]神清志平百節皆寧養性之本.

[35]See *Su-wen* 2/17.

[36]See the commentary in *Su-wen* 5/67.

[37]See above, p. 14.

[38]This implication of *ching,* "structive potential," is discussed on pp. 176–179 below.

stantiated (inflection 3, *ch'eng*) implies some kind of perceptible determination.

In this connection we should note the qualification of murkiness (*chuo*) as yin.[39] In murky media it is hard to perceive any clear-cut determination. Such a determination appears only after contact with "clearness" (*ch'ing*), whose yang quality thus becomes manifest. From the *Ling-shu* 40/1178ff. we learn, on the other hand, that yin should be considered to be *ch'ing* 'clear') and yang, *chuo*. That paragraph refers, however, to the orbs and sinarteries:[40] The yang sinarteries receive murky forms of energy in order to clear them, the yin sinarteries receive clear forms of energy in order to recharge the functional orbs and to substantiate subtle forms of energy.

COMPARATIVE SUMMARY OF THE FUNDAMENTAL ASSOCIATIONS OF YIN AND YANG

The senses of the terms yin and yang just discussed compose the semantic perimeter of these terms in technical contexts. Use of the qualifiers yin or yang always brings into play all of their fundamental associations. A comparative table based on the unequivocal Chinese terminology provides an overall view of these semantic complexes.

The meaning of the word yin, defined as structive aspect, comprises the concepts of:	The meaning of the word yang, defined as active aspect, comprises the concepts of:
completion (perfectiveness)	incipience (inchoation)
confirmation, correspondence	setting loose (induction)
quiescence (stasis)	setting in motion (dynamization)
condensation (substantialization);	moving (dynamic)
consolidation, solidification; dying off	inducing change (inducing transformation)
condensation, concentration	development (expansion)
awaiting organization yet determinate	dissolution, dispersion determining yet indeterminate.

[39] In *Su-wen* 5/47 and 67.
[40] See chapters 3 and 4 of this volume.

If we now try to transpose these Chinese notions into the vocabulary of modern science, the following table results:

Yin corresponds to all that is	Yang corresponds to all that is
structive	active
contractive	expansive
intrasusceptive (absorbing into or within the individual)	extraversive (bringing to the surface)
centripetal	centrifugal
responsive	aggressive
conservative	demanding
positive	negative.

Thus prepared, we may now proceed to a discussion of the principal correspondences of yin and yang. We call those correspondences primary that result from a sensuous experience of values and consequently concern natural phenomena; and we qualify as secondary those that are evidently derived from the primary experiences by a speculative process. This distinction is not absolute, and in some cases its application is a question of perspective.

PRIMARY CORRESPONDENCES OF YIN AND YANG

The division of phenomena and effects into two polar groups may be traced back to the archaic beginnings of Chinese culture. It is a safe guess that the conventional value standards of yin and yang, which came into general use in protoscientific literature about the fourth century B.C., had already served to regulate the order of the cults and of society as much as a millennium earlier. From those early times practically to the present, they constitute an element of Chinese consciousness. The primary correspondences of yin and yang have therefore been given extensive treatment in sinological literature.[41] Here we

[41]Among the more important recent accounts are the chapter on yin and yang in Granet's *La pensée chinoise* and Vol. 11, pp. 273ff of Needham's *Science and Civilisation in China*.

simply recapitulate those which are found in medical texts and which form the sensuous basis of the secondary correspondences.

Primary correspondences of yin	Primary correspondences of yang
Earth	Heaven
moon (major yin)	sun (major yang)
autumn, winter	spring, summer
things female	things male
cold, coolness	heat, warmth
moisture	dryness
the inside, interior	the outside, surface
darkness	brightness
things small and weak	things big and powerful
the lower part	the upper part
water, rain	fire
quiescence	movement
night	day
the right side	the left side

The logical connection between these primary correspondences and the overall definition given above[42] can be established without difficulty. The sole exception, the traditional assignations of left and right, is probably due, according to Granet,[43] to early ritualization of certain manual functions.

SECONDARY CORRESPONDENCES OF YIN AND YANG

We qualify as secondary those correspondences which are the result of systematic observation and of systematizing speculation. This is why as a rule the secondary correspondences must be understood as technical qualitative standards in the narrow sense. Since these correspondences have been given only sporadic treatment in sinological literature, we must dwell somewhat on their logical and philological origins.

Secondary correspondences of yin:	Secondary correspondences of yang:
The hours of the day:	
the hours between noon and midnight	the hours between midnight and noon

The power of the sun (=major yang) decreases from noon to midnight and increases from midnight to noon.

aspects:

the *intima* ("inner orb," *li* 裏)	the *species* ("outer orb," *piao* 表)

These common technical terms designate the structive and the active halves of a pair of energetic orbs[44] which will be dealt with in detail in the chapters on orbisiconography and sinarteriology. These aspects have a close affinity to the (primary) correspondences *nei* (inner side, inward things) and *wai* (outside, outward things).

Dynamic tendencies:

sinking, condensing (*chiang* 降)	rising, ascending (*sheng* 升)
sinking, submerging (*ch'en* 沈)	floating, rising (*fu* 浮)

These technical terms used in the iconography of the pulse, in diagnostics, and in pharmacology are related to the primary correspondences *hsia*, *shang* (lower, upper part).

Regions of the body and functional areas:

the abdomen (*fu* 腹)	the back (*pei* 背)

The classical statement of this correspondence may be found in the *Su-wen* 4/39. Its systematic rationale is by no means self-evident, but commentators prior to Chang Chih-ts'ung 張志聰(Ch'ing) accept it uncritically. Chang reminds us that *Lao-tzu* 42: "The Myriad Beings carry yin on their backs and embrace yang" most probably refers to "heavenly" (macrocosmic) phenomena, whereas *Su-wen* 4/39 refers to terrestrial (microcosmic) phenomena.[45]

[42]See p. 14.
[43]In his article "La droite et la gauche en Chine," reprinted in *Études sociologiques sur la Chine*, pp. 261–278.
[44]For the definition of this term see p. 107 and p. 114 below.
[45]See *Su-wen-shih* 素問識 1/22.

He then reasons from the medical classics (abdomen = yin, back = yang) that all yang sinarteries (with one exception) extend over the back and all yin sinarteries run over the front side of the body.[46] As a matter of fact the inverse better explains the origin of the *Su-wen* convention. As far as we can ascertain,[47] by the time the *Su-wen* passage here quoted was formulated, the sinarteriology of the *Nei-ching* had already been evolved. In this system every sinartery is defined, as we shall explain later, on the one hand by the sensitive points (*foramina inductoria*) connected by the sinarteries, and on the other by symptoms corresponding to these sensitive points. The foramina whose activity (*tung* 動) corresponds preponderantly to yin symptoms are situated on the front side ("abdomen") of the body, and those whose activity is preponderantly connected with yang symptoms are situated on the back of the body.

Orbs:

the *orbes horreales* (yin orbs, *tsang* 臟)

the *orbes aulici* (yang orbs, *fu* 腑)

Again the *Su-wen* 4/39 may be quoted: "The *orbes horreales* (*tsang*) are yin, the *orbes aulici* (*fu*) are yang." The precise semantic compass of the terms *orbes horreales et aulici* will be described later in the chapter on orbisiconography. For the moment another classical definition from the *Su-wen* 11/127f will suffice: "The so-called five *orbes horreales* (*wu-tsang* 五臟) store structive potential (*ching*)... the six *orbes aulici* (*liu-fu*) transmit and assimilate[48] [food] but do not store [anything]." The depository function of the *orbes horreales* is a typical yin phenomenon; likewise, the transportation and catabolism of food may be viewed as an active effort and consequently as a yang effect.

The evolutive phases:[49]

Metal, Water

Wood, Fire

The evolutive phases are assigned their place in the correspondence system by a speculative convention:[50] The expansive tendency of Wood and Fire is evident to the senses, and the same is true (in a more subtle way) for the structive, action-absorbing tendency of Metal and Water.

[46]See pp. 204ff below.
[47]See, however, our qualifications earlier in this chapter.
[48]*Hua* 化, literally "to transform"; cf. p. 15.
[49]See the section on "The Five Evolutive Phases" in this chapter. We capitalize the names of the evolutive phases to avoid confusion with the substances whose names they borrow.
[50]A fact also recognized by Needham on pp. 243f of Vol. II of *Science and Civilisation in China*.

Forms of energy:

structure potential (*ching* 精)   configurative force (*shen* 神)

The semantic shadings of this polar couple have been discussed above.

Individually specific structure energy (*hsüeh* 血)	individually specific active energy (*ch'i* 氣)
structure substratum (*hsing* 形)	energy of definite quality emanating from the former (*ch'i* 氣)

We shall deal in detail with these terms on pages 174–175. These correspondences are in harmony with conventional definitions of the terms, as in *Su-wen* 24/252.

constructive energy (*ying* 營)   defensive energy (*wei* 衛)

These correspond strictly to the yin and yang aspects of the unattached structure potential (*ching-ch'i* 精氣),[51] by virtue of their structive (*ying*) and exteriorizing (*wei*) character].

structure fluids (*yeh* 液)   active fluids (*chin* 津)

Under certain conditions (see pp. 190–191), individually specific structure energy (*hsüeh*) is polarized into *chin* and *yeh*.

structure aspect of the individually specific (active) configurative force (*p'o* 魄)	active aspect of the individually specific (active) configurative force (*hun* 魂)

These concepts were adopted into medical theory from earlier philosophical speculation.[52] According to *Ling-shu* 8/965 ("What goes and comes with *shen* [the active configurative force] is called *hun*, what enters and leaves with *ching* [structure potential[53]] is called *p'o*"] they are polar aspects of the individually specific configurative force.

---

[51]See pp. 188–190 and p. 179 below.
[52]See, for example, the *Tso-chuan* 左傳, twenty-fifth year of Chao-kung 昭公, or the *Huai-nan-tzu* 7/66. The latter passage is annotated by Kao Yu: "*p'o* = *yin-shen*, *hun* = *yang-shen* 魄陰神, 魂陽神."
[53]See the section on *ching* below.

Energetic aspects:

exhaustion (*inanitas, hsü* 虛)   repletion (*repletio, shih* 實)

This classification of the two important diagnostic concepts is based on *Su-wen* 29/291 and on the more elaborate pulse studies of Li Shih-chen 李時珍 (1518–1593), *Pin-hu mo-hsüeh* 瀕湖脈學, pp. 19f. *Inanitas*, or exhaustion, is "emptiness that ought to be full," an excessive and pathological responsiveness; *repletio*, or repletion, is "excessive fullness," an exaggerated expansiveness. It must, however, be granted that, from a purely speculative point of view, the opposite correspondence would be equally logical and that in the classical convention preference has simply been given to one of two practically equivalent solutions.

murkiness (*chuo* 濁)   clarity (*ch'ing* 清)

This pair of concepts, already mentioned in connection with the fundamental associations, is equally arbitrary. The correspondences of *ch'ing* (clarity) to yang, and of *chuo* (murkiness) to yin, implicit in *Su-wen* 5/47 and 67, is also encountered outside medical literature (e.g. in *Pao-p'u-tzu nei-p'ien* 抱朴子內篇 7/120). If, on the other hand, we have in mind the physiological correspondence, the inverse assignment holds for physiological correspondences (*Ling-shu* 40/1178; see also p. 22).

Effective tendencies:

development (*chang* 長)   incipience (*sheng* 生)

This correspondence, implicit in the basic definitions of yin and yang, may be found in *Su-wen* 5/46 and 66/590.

conservation (*ts'ang* 藏)   destruction (*sha* 殺)
destruction (*sha* 殺)   incipience (*sheng* 生)

Rendered in everyday language by "to kill," in technical contexts the term *sha*, as a rule, has the more general meaning "to destroy"; this interpretation is explicitly confirmed by Ma Shih's 馬時 commentary to *Su-wen* 5/46.[54] In these two pairs, taken together, the ambiguity of *sha* is clear.

The dissolution of something existing is one of the fundamental modes of activity that characterize yang. Thus there is no intrinsic contradiction in the first two pairs immediately above, as given in *Su-wen* 5/46 and 66/590. From a macrocosmic perspective, however, the opposite evaluation of *sha*, coupled with a different complement, becomes possible. This is es-

---

[54] 殺者蕭殺之殺, 非殺戮之謂也.

tablished in *Su-wen* 66/590, a passage we cite repeatedly: "Heaven [i.e., the acting pole of the Cosmos] gives rise by yang, lets develop by yin; Earth [i.e., the structing pole of the Cosmos] destroys by yang, conserves by yin." In this sentence the polarity of Heaven: Earth overlies that of yin: yang, so that *sha* (destruction), although conceived as yang, takes effect in yin

As we have shown,[55] struction implies dying off, fading away, or becoming rigid. When some particular effect initiated by an action has been completely structed and thus stabilized in space, it becomes the object of new actions tending in turn to neutralize, to counteract, or to annihilate it. Viewed in this way, every struction is succeeded within the cyclic, organismic cosmos by eventual (self-)destruction. With this in mind, let us take a look at the frequently quoted yet by no means unambiguous[56] first lines of *Su-wen* 5/45: "The yinyang is the Tao of Heaven and Earth [i.e., of the Cosmos], the father and mother of change and transformation, the root and beginning of inception and destruction."[57] Surely, *sheng* and *sha* here constitute a pair of antonyms; since *sheng* must be a phenomenal mode of yang, we have to conclude that *sha* is conceived as a yin effect.[58]

Wang Ping who, of all the commentators, is here the least equivocal, indirectly confirms this conclusion: " 'Root and beginning of inception and destruction' points to the functions (*yung* 用) of heat and cold. The Myriad Beings take rise from the warmth of yang energy and die from the cold of yin energy." Chang Ching-yüeh 張景岳, author of the *Lei-ching* 類經 (Classified classic, 1624), first acknowledges (2/35) the equivocality of *sha* and makes a similar case for *sheng*. In Taoist-inspired novels one often finds *sha* as a metonym for yin, a usage registered in the common dictionaries.[59]

The *sapores* (flavors):

sour and pungent	sweet and bitter
salty	flavorless (of neutral *sapor*, *tan* 淡)

[55]On p. 20.
[56]The embarrassment of the commentators in *Su-wen* 5/45 as well as *Su-wen-shih* 1/27 deserves to be noted.
[57]生殺之本始.
[58]Cf. *Su-wen* 16/149: "Structive energy commences destruction" 陰氣始殺.
[59]See, for instance, the entry *sha ch'i* 殺氣 in the *Han-yü tzu-tien*.

The qualitative classification of the first group of *sapores* is given in the *Su-wen* 5/50. It is easy to see why the sour *sapor* with its astringent (contractive) effect and the pungent *sapor* of caustic and likewise contractive effect may be classed as yin, why the sweet and bitter *sapores*, having a relaxing or tonifying influence, should be listed as yang. The passage in question runs: "Among the smells and *sapores* the bitter and sweet ones, [which cause] issuing forth and dispersal, are yang, the sour and pungent ones, which cause welling up and flowing off, are yin." Evidently the authors of the *Nei-ching* here, as well as in a more practically oriented passage of chapter 22, are essentially interested in pharmacodynamic effects which the *sapores* indicate.

The clear-cut yinyang polarity of the *sapores* here is out of step with the polar classification derived from the Five Evolutive Phases.[60]

In the *Su-wen* 74/832 the polar opposition of the salty and the neutral *sapores* is again sustained, if somewhat less stringently, by pharmacodynamic arguments: "The salty *sapor* [that causes] welling up and flowing off is yin, the neutral *sapor* [that causes] filtering through[61] is yang." In a much more general way, however, the yang quality of the neutral *sapor* may be traced to the affinity (not equivalence) between the flavorless and the indeterminate, just as the salty *sapor* reflects the structive quality of determinate things.[62]

In pulse images:

pulsus tardus 遲脈
pulsus mersus 沈脈
pulsus asper 澀脈
pulsus inanis 虛脈
pulsus brevis 短脈
pulsus evanescens 微脈
pulsus languidus 緩脈
pulsus tympanicus 革脈
*pulsus firmus** 牢脈
pulsus lenis 濡脈
pulsus invalidus 弱脈

pulsus celer 數脈
pulsus superficialis 浮脈
pulsus lubricus 滑脈
pulsus repletus 實脈
pulsus longus 長脈
pulsus redundans 洪脈
pulsus intentus 緊脈
*pulsus cepacaulicus** 芤脈
*pulsus chordalis** 弦脈
pulsus movens 動脈
pulsus turbulentus(*pulsus rapidus*)促(疾)脈

pulsus diffundens 散脈
pulsus subtilis sive parvus 細 (小) 脈
pulsus subreptus 伏脈
pulsus intermittens 代脈
pulsus haesitans 結脈

[60]See Chapter 3 for the iconography of the *orbes horreales*.
[61]*Shen-hsieh* 滲泄, "to filter through," "to percolate," is a term denoting the excretion of urine.
[62]See above, p. 17.

This detailed classification of pulse images *(mo-hsiang* 脈象), taken from the comparatively recent (late Ming) *Pin-hu mo-hsüeh,* pp. 9 14, may for the greater part be explained by reference to the "fundamental associations" and "primary correspondences" of yin and yang. In the case of the *pulsus diffundens (san-mo* 散脈), which some might be inclined to class with the yang pulses, evidently the impression of pliancy and a receding tendency have decided the classification. Pulses marked with an asterisk are qualified as yang in yin or yin in yang.

In numerology:

even numbers *(ou* 偶)   odd numbers *(chi* 奇)

This polar distinction has probably been retained from mantic thought and may with equal justice be classified among the "primary correspondences." It is explicitly confirmed in the *Nei-ching (Ling-shu* 5/947).

QUALITATIVE OVERLAPS AND QUANTITATIVE GRADATIONS OF THE FUNDAMENTAL VALUE STANDARDS YIN AND YANG

By reviewing the "fundamental associations" we have gained, among other things, a precise understanding of the semantic compass of the terms yin and yang in technical contexts, and by enumerating their essential correspondences we have come to appreciate their universal application in all fields of Chinese culture. The practical usefulness of the two value standards as well as the precision of their application is further enhanced by the introduction of gradations and combinations which, in turn, are integral with the system of qualitative conventions.

1. We obtain *qualitative* overlaps between yin and yang aspects if, for instance, in a yang phenomenon we further distinguish yin and yang aspects, and within these again differentiate new yin and yang aspects, and so on. In this manner

Fig. 1

we may arrive at a continuous, practically endless qualitative gradation of the polar complements which has its practical limits only in the relative significance of the object so qualified (Fig. 1). To illustrate this point, we may simply recapitulate some of the numerous examples of such overlaps given in *Su-wen* 4/38: "In yin there is [again a] yin, in yang there is [again a] yang. [Thus the hours from] sunrise to noon [correspond to the] yang of Heaven (i.e., of day) [and at the same time to] yang in yang [because the hours of daylight are yang and those of darkness yin]; [the hours from] noon to sunset [correspond to] the yang of Heaven [and to] yin in yang [because the hours of the setting sun are yin[63]]; [the hours from] nightfall to the [first] cry of the cock [i.e., midnight] correspond to yin of Heaven and yin in yin; [and the hours from the first] cry of the cock until sunrise [correspond to] yin of Heaven [and to] yang in yin. . . . "—"Speaking of the yinyang of man, [on] the outside [he] is yang, and inside [he] is yin. . . . The back is yang, the front side (abdomen) is yin, . . . the *orbes horreales* (*tsang*) are yin, the *orbes aulici* (*fu*) are yang. . . . If therefore the back is yang, yang in yang [of the body is represented by] the *orbis cardialis*."

The arguments of the Chinese doctors run along the following lines: The *orbis cardialis* among the five structive orbs (*orbes horreales*), which are yin, occupies the relative position of major yang, and thus is yang in yin. In addition the heart—the organ corresponding to the *orbis cardialis*—is situated within the upper half of the body (i.e., above the diaphragm), classified as yang; still more significant, it lies closer to the back (which is yang) than to the front (*Su-wen* 4/39, commentary, and commentary to the *Lei-ching* 2/43). Since in its quality of an *orbis horrealis* the *orbis cardialis* must be classed as yin, the formula just cited seems justified. Similar overlaps of two or more layers of yin-yang polarities may also be found (with only partial explanations,) in the *Su-wen* Chapters 6/76ff. and 66/590. Overlaps of several yinyang polarities also appear outside medical literature, where they may even attain to a higher degree of theoretical

[63]See pp. 17, 24–25 and p. 48 below, as well as p. 442 of "Untersuchungen."

subtlety[64] despite their less immediate practical significance.

2. As for the *quantitative* gradations of yin and yang, they may be derived only partly and conditionally from these overlaps of yinyang polarities. For instance, the distinction of minor and major aspects depends on the definitions of minor yang and major yang (*shao-yang, yang minor* and *t'ai-yang, yang maior*) and of minor yin and major yin (*shao-yin, yin minor* and *t'ai-yin, yin maior*). We can imagine yin and yang as the poles of a continuous cyclic alternation represented by a circle (Fig. 2).

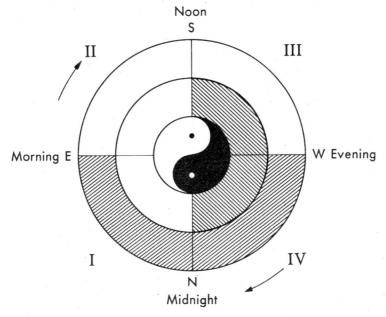

Fig. 2

In such a diagram, as in nature, the transitions between the alternate polarities take place gradually and in unbroken progression: Each polar quality at the outset manifests itself only weakly (with a small quantity of energy) and increases gradually to a maximum, after which it continuously recedes to make room for the opposite polar quality. This alternation

[64]See Needham, Vol. II, p. 276, and Table XIV given there.

is shown schematically in Fig. 2. The outer circle corresponds to the movement of yin and yang in the cycle of day and night, and the intermediate circle follows the polar movement the scribed by the rising and setting sun (cf. pp. 24–25 above and *Su-wen* 4/38f.). If we now consider, with the authors of the *Su-wen* passage quoted, that the outer circle, i.e., the "heavenly cycle," dominates the alternations of the diagram, the following overlaps result in each of the quadrants:

I (first quadrant): yang in yin,
II (second quadrant): yang in yang,
III (third quadrant): yin in yang,
IV (fourth quadrant): yin in yin.

We easily perceive the analogies between

yang in yin and a nascent, budding yang, a yang about to develop = *yang minor*, minor yang;

yang in yang and a fully developed yang = *yang maior*, major yang:

yin in yang and a nascent, budding yin = a yin about to develop = *yin minor*, minor yin;

yin in yin and a fully developed yin = *yin maior*, major yin.

These analogies became fully explicit only in the "Diagram of the Supreme Pole"[65] (Sung) which appears at the center of Fig. 2.

Throughout Chinese medical literature, widespread use is made of a tripartition of yin as well as of yang. Like the bipartite division, this tripartition implies a quantitative gradation of yin and yang that has great significance in both areas in which it is found—sinarteriology and phase energetics. Considerations of systematic numerology must have led to its adoption. The even-numbered cycle obtained by the combination of the tripartite yin and yang complements the odd-numbered cycle of the Five Evolutive Phases and may therefore not be replaced by overlaps of yin and yang (yin within yang, yang within yin, etc.) derived from the linear scheme shown above.[66]

[65]See Granet, *La pensée chinoise*, p. 280, n. 2, and Needham, Vol. II, pp. 460ff.
[66]Fig. 1 and the accompanying explanation.

The hypothesis that the tripartition was introduced primarily to satisfy the desire for numerological symmetry rather than to accommodate empirical data or previous postulates goes far toward explaining contradictions and artificialities that ensue from its application. In order to be able to resolve apparent contradictions and to correct real ones when we encounter them later, we must now take a closer look at classical definitions of the tripartition. These are given in identical passages of the *Su-wen* 6/77 and the *Ling-shu* 5/948 for the yang segments, and of the *Su-wen* 6/79 and the *Ling-shu* 5/949 for the yin segments respectively, namely: "Major yang stands for the opening [functions]." "Resplendence of yang (*splendor yang*) stands for the closing [functions]." "Minor yang stands for the pivot [functions]." And again "major yin stands for the open [functions]." "Shrinking yin (*yin flectens*) stands for the closed [functions]." "Minor yin stands for the pivot [functions]." These statements raise a number of philological and logical problems which we shall examine one by one. Of the foregoing quotations, only the first can be understood directly: "Major yang (*t'ai-yang*) stands for the opening [functions]." Yang signifies something developing, expanding, dispersing.[67] Major yang is also called by commentators[68] "the outside (*species, piao* 表) of yang," "large yang" (*yang amplum, chü-yang* 巨陽), and "flourishing yang" (*yang vigens, sheng-yang* 盛陽).

"Resplendence of yang (*splendor yang, yang-ming*) stands for the closing [functions]."

A few remarks are necessary on the interpretation of the technical term *yang-ming* 陽明, for which we use the normative equivalents *splendor yang* in Latin and "resplendence of yang" in English. In contrast to the remaining five terms of this cycle, in the combination *yang-ming yang* is the qualifier, and *ming* (brightness, clearness) the qualified term. In other words, syntax requires the use of "of" or of the genitive case in the translation. *Yang-ming* as a rule marks the intermediate position at which major and minor yang overlap (Fig. 3). This semantic relationship is confirmed in the *Su-wen* 74/813 and by diverse commentaries (e.g., in the *Su-wen* 6/79: "Where/ when the two yang shine together, this is "*yang-ming*").[69]

---

[67]See p. 16 above.
[68]See *Su-wen* 6/77f.
[69]The German normative term *Überstrahlung des Yang* is still more precise, since it implies the excessive brightness of conjugate sources.

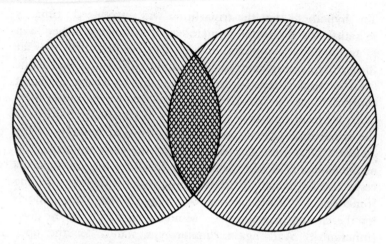

Fig. 3

The rendering "closed" for the rare technical term *ho* 闔 also requires an explanation. In the *Shuo-wen,* p. 594, this graph is explained by "wings of a door." From this meaning, two secondary meanings may be derived: The wings of a door standing between the inside and the outside shut off the interior against the exterior → (1) "to close"; the wings of a door mediate between the interior and the exterior → (2) "to mediate." The first of these derivatives is explicitly given in parallels quoted in the dictionary;[70] moreover, it seems to be the correct translation for the term *ho* used in the obscure tenth section of the *Ṭao-te-ching,* where we have *t'ien-men k'ai-ho* 天門開闔, "The door of Heaven opens and closes." The second derivation, "to mediate," seems to be borne out in the sentences under discussion by the intermediate position of the phase qualified by the term *ho,* by its relationship with "mediating" orbs in sinarteriology, and by the opinions of some highly respected commentators.

Commentators are divided in their opinion on this sentence and—as is only consistent—on those that follow. Wang Ping (T'ang period, *Su-wen* 6/77) remains equivocal: " '*Ho*' is that whereby one wields the power of coercion and consolidation." Ma Shih (Ming, *Su-wen* 6/78) clearly opts for the

---

[70]See, for example, the modern dictionary *Chung-hua ta-tzu-tien* 中華大字典.

meaning 'to mediate': "*Yang-ming* is the second yang, is in the center of [the] yang [phases] and [therefore] signifies '*ho*.' " Chang Chih-ts'ung (Ch'ing, *Su-wen* 6/79), eloquent yet uncommitted, advocates both alternatives with equal vehemence: "*Yang-ming* is a link between the two yang [phases]; it has the effect of [something] *ho* [closing, shutting off?]" and " '*ho*' regulates the penetration toward the inside 闔主內入." Chang Ching-yüeh (Ming, in his *Lei-ching*, 9/205f) on the other hand clearly accepts the sense" to close": " '*Yang-ming* stands for *ho* [the closing functions]' and signifies that it makes the *yang* energies accumulate within; among the three yang it corresponds to the inner side (*li, intima*)."

We will reserve final judgment on this issue until an analysis of the remaining sentences has provided us with a better view of the theory and a wider base for a comparison.

"Minor yang (*shao-yang*) stands for the pivot [functions]." Again, this sentence, like the preceding one, contains an ambiguity which in turn leads to diverse opinions of the commentators. The pivot (*shu* 樞) is prerequisite to any turning movement, yet does not participate in this movement. The pivot may therefore be conceived with equal justice as a *motionless* center or as an organ that controls movement. In the first case one imagines that it is situated within (i.e., at the center) and, to all evidence, does not partake of any motion. In the second case one may suppose that it lies between the poles of a movement and, to a certain degree, does participate in the movement.

Both interpretations are developed in the commentaries. Wang Ping (*Su-wen* 6/77) subtly elucidates: "The pivot stands for the infinitesimally [weak force] regulating a circular motion 樞所以主動轉之微." Ma Shih advocates the first alternative: "Minor yang is the first yang, is the inner side [orb] (*intima, li*) of Yang and signifies the pivotal functions." Chang Chih-ts'ung (*Su-wen* 6/79), as before, seeks to maintain both propositions: "Minor yang is the first *ch'i* to come forth [into positive existence] and therefore has the function of a pivot." This is the first alternative and, by definition, is in harmony with the general qualification given above[71] for minor yang. However, "the pivot regulates [the relations between] inside and outside" [second alternative]. Chang Ching-yüeh (*Lei-ching* 9/205f) clearly pronounces himself in favor of the second alternative in stating: "'Minor yang stands for the pivot [function]' means that it is situated between the inner and the outer side and so is equally capable of sallying forth and of penetrating."

"Major yin (*t'ai-yin*) stands for the opened [functions]." This

[71]See p. 34.

unequivocal sentence makes clear what none of the other definitions of the six parts of the cycle puts beyond doubt: The technical term *k'ai*, to open, *ho*, to close, and *shu*, pivot, do not describe absolute qualities of cyclic phases; they merely indicate qualities relative to other graded standards of the same polarity. As we know, yin itself definitely does not correspond to the aspect of opening.[72] Major yin is qualified as *k'ai* (opened) here because yin the structive aspect is in the phase of maximum actuality,[73] i.e., in its maximum positive manifestation.

"Shrinking yin (*chüeh-yin* 厥陰, *yin flectens*) stands for the closed [functions]."

Chüeh 厥 is an important technical term indicating an inversion of the physiologically normal direction of the energetic current. This inversion always entails the symptom of cold extremities.[74] The word *chüeh* is found as early as the *Shuo-wen* (p. 451) where it is defined as "to dig out or to throw stones" 發石. Graphical derivatives of the character *chüeh* (撅 and 蹶) suggest that *chüeh* 厥 originally expressed the idea of "turning over" or "returning." Thus the technical signification of the word must be directly connected with its archaic meaning. The semantic compass of the Chinese technical term is rendered most satisfactorily by the Latin *flectere*, and the English "to shrink" (and their flectional derivatives). Both simultaneously express the ideas of giving way, receding, and becoming weak that are present in the Chinese expression, which in *Su-wen* 74/813 and in the commentary of Wang Ping to the *Su-wen* 6/79 is explained thus: "*Chüeh* (*flexus*) means 'exhaustion.' When structive energy (*yin-ch'i*) reaches this phase, it is exhausted."

For the interpretation of this passage, our discussion concerning the term *ho* ("wings of a door" → "to close") is relevant, with the big difference that here the commentators are in nearly complete agreement.

Ma Shih (*Su-wen* 6/80) writes: "Shrinking yin is the first yin, is the exhaustion of yin, signifies *ho*, 'something closed.'" Chang Chih-ts'ung in the same place explains: "Shrinking yin is the conjugate exhaustion of the two yin 兩陰之交盡 and therefore has the effect of *ho*, 'something closing [or closed].'" Finally, Chang Ching-yüeh (*Lei-ching* 9/206) asserts: "Shrinking

---

[72]See pp. 22f above. European inflected languages oblige us to choose between perfect and imperfect (iterative) aspects, but this distinction is only latent in the classical Chinese text. "Opening" or "opened"—it is the logical context which lets us decide which is suitable.

[73]For this term see p. 49 below.

[74]For the pathological modalities of *chüeh* 厥 see Chapters 10, 37, and 45 of the *Su-wen*.

yin stands for *ho* [the closed functions]; it dwells at the inner side (*intima, li*) of what pertains to yin."

"Minor yin stands for the pivot [functions]." Here our approach is similar to that for minor yang. The agreement of the commentators, however, is not as complete as with respect to the preceding sentence.

Ma Shih (*Su-wen* 6/80) notes: "Minor yin is the second yin, is [in?] the center of yin, signifies a pivot." Chang Ching-yüeh (*Lei-ching* 9/206) for once is in complete agreement: "Minor yin is the pivot and dwells in the center of what pertains to *yin*." Only Chang Chih-ts'ung (*Su-wen* 6/80) interprets the quality of minor-yin in analogy to that of minor yang: "Minor yin is the first development of all yin; that is why it regulates the pivot functions."

The tripartite yin and yang aspects form a six-phase cycle of derived standards of value with qualitative differences between all phases and quantitative differences within each group of identical polarity. Any conclusion drawn from the foregoing evidence must answer the following questions: (1) Are the various orders of enumeration logically consistent or merely conventional? (2) Which of the opinions put forward by commentators are at variance with these orders and therefore either erroneous, inconsequential, or unconventional? (3) What accounts for the diverging interpretations?

In the following discussion and elsewhere throughout the book these acronyms will be used to refer to the phases of the yinyang cycle:

yin flectens	*yifle*
yin minor	*yimi*
yin maior	*yima*
yang minor	*yami*
splendor yang	*spleya*
yang maior	*yama*

We assume that the order of enumeration of the six-part yinyang cycle found in the *Su-wen* 6/77–79 and in the *Ling-shu* 5/948f (which we have just studied) implies an energetic gradient. We thus are given as first enumeration order (EO 1):[75]

---

[75]Taking into account the conventional premises, we begin our count with the last phase.

yama

spleya   *yimi*

yami   *yifle*

yima

If instead we pay attention to the immediate significance of the qualifiers *k'ai*, *ho*, and *shu*, we arrive at a second enumeration order (EO 2):

yama

yami   *yifle*

spleya   *yimi*

yima

This EO 2 is congruent in respect to the order of its yang phase with the enumeration order advocated by Chang Ching-yüeh, the author of the *Lei-ching*, in his commentary to the passage quoted (*Lei-ching* 9/205f).[76]

If instead we derive the enumeration order of the six energetic positions solely from the semantic significance of the phase names (and especially that of the newly added aspects *chüeh-yin, yin flectens* and *yang-ming, splendor yang*),[77] we obtain a third enumeration order (EO 3):

yama

spleya   *yifle*

yami   *yimi*

yima

[76]Chang Ching-yüeh, who bases his commentary on the qualifier used in the *Su-wen*, is inconsistent in interpreting *ho* 閽 in one place by "inside [function]," in another by "intermediate [function]."

[77]We also take into account clear assertions of the T'ang commentator Wang Ping.

This EO 3 is in complete agreement with the EO consistently advocated by Ma Shih in the *Su-wen* 6/78 and 6/80.

These three paradigms by no means exhaust the number of variants of this cycle that may be encountered in the *Nei-ching*;[78] in fact there are twenty-one theoretically possible variants.[79] They do, however, embody the three heuristically significant enumerative principles: symmetry, inherent systematic order, and harmony between semantic postulate and empirical fact. Hence we may answer the first of our three questions. Positive science demands the agreement of semantic postulates (= meanings of terms) and empirical fact. The fact that EO 3, which best conforms to these conditions, at the same time represents by far the most widely used sequence, strikingly illustrates the inner consistency of Chinese medicine.

EO 3 is mentioned in the *Su-wen* 31/266f and is common in sinarteriology as well as in phase energetics.

In the latter this cycle competes with other (in this context primary) cycles of value standards such as the celestial stems and the terrestrial branches and the evolutive phases. In that area the three phases of each polar quality no longer succeed each other consecutively, but rather alternate with one or two phases of opposite polarity. Nevertheless one may easily perceive why, for instance, the enumeration order resulting from an axiomatic correspondence between terrestrial branches and *configurationes*—*yimi, yima, yami, spleya, yama, yifle*—implies EO 3: in both paradigms all polar axes are studded with the same antithetical values.

yami

yima   *spleya*

yimi   *yama*

yifle

Similarly, the sequence *yifle, yimi, yami, yima, spleya, yama*, second in importance in phase energetics, in spite of interference from the Evolutive Phases, still reflects EO 3; the phases which in EO 3 mark the extremities of the polarities are arranged at the same pole of two of the polar axes, whereas the intermediate phases (*yimi* and *spleya*) occupy opposite poles of the third.[80]

---

[78]See, for instance, the *Su-wen* 9/112.

[79]In keeping with the general aims of this investigation this number includes only cycles in which the three phases of each polarity form a coherent sequence.

[80]See page 73 below.

$$yami$$

$$yimi \qquad yima$$

$$yifle \qquad spleya$$

$$yama$$

In sinarteriology, the situation is further complicated by additional interferences. Besides that due to the E.P.s, we have the polarities of hand/foot, upper half of the body/lower half of the body, back/front, inside/outside, which, at least for the perfunctory investigator, completely mask the cyclical sequence of the six yinyang phases. The six positions of the yinyang cycle are part of the theoretical foundation of the *Shang-han-lun*, 傷寒論 (Treatise on cold lesions, Han), where they are enumerated counterclockwise in EO 3. From the viewpoint of symptomatology, however, the *Shang-han-lun* cycle is based on EO 2.[81]

We can now answer the second and third of our questions. From the early commentaries of the *Su-wen*, those of Wang Ping (T'ang) and perhaps also that of Lin I (Sung), one gains the impression that the six-part yinyang cycle must have been part of an earlier tradition but that the precise qualities of each phase of this cycle had not yet been defined with full clarity. During the Ming, Ma Shih distinctly advocated the universal EO 3; Chang Ching-yüeh and Chang Chih-ts'ung (Ch'ing) tried to establish and to justify the use of EO 3 as well as of EO 2 as normative cyclical sequences.

The reasons for their efforts are easy to understand. Toward the end of the second century A.D., although the tenets of the *Nei-ching* had long been acknowledged,[82] their systematic and practical interpretation was still open. At that moment Chang Chung-ching 張仲景 compiled his famous clinical manual *Shang-han tsa-ping lun* 傷寒雜病論, in which he laid down the general principles of symptomatology.[83] When he chose for the

---

[81]See the *Shang-han-lun chiang-i* 傷寒論講義, p. 21. The correction of EO 3 proposed by the authors of this modern compilation appears not only superfluous but erroneous; at any rate it does not lead to any simplification or amelioration of the theory.

[82]According to a widely accepted hypothesis, the teachings of the *Nei-ching* on the whole were written down, even if not in their present form, toward the end of the third century B.C.

[83]An investigation of pathological and symptomatological theories lies beyond the compass of this book. We should, however, like to draw attention

framework of his symptomatology the six-part yinyang cycle of the *Nei-ching*, he frequently assigned meanings to its phases according to his own judgment and clinical experience, even though these sometimes were in conflict with most qualifications found in the *Nei-ching*.[84] In fact the *Nei-ching* has received a more or less homogeneous interpretation, befitting the status of a classic, only from the Sung period onward. This accomplished, the Ming and Ch'ing commentators undertook to reconcile the qualifications found in the *Shang-han-lun*—a classic in its own right[85]—with those of the *Nei-ching*, a task at which they could not always succeed.

The Five Evolutive Phases (wu-hsing 五行)

PRELIMINARY HISTORICAL AND BIBLIOGRAPHICAL REMARKS

The preceding section closed with a discussion of a cycle of conventional standards of value phased by a triple gradation of yin and yang. This cycle never gained any significance beyond the boundaries of Chinese medicine, out of whose needs it evolved. The role of the cycle of the Five Evolutive Phases (*wu-hsing, quinque transvectus*) in the development of systematic scientific disciplines in China, on the other hand, is second only to that of yin and yang. We shall now turn to the medical aspects of the fivefold cycle.

The fact that in Chinese science the majority of basic standards of value were combined into cycles (all of them since the T'ang and Sung periods, when the yinyang was explicitly represented by a cyclical alternation) is a direct consequence of the inductive and synthetic cognitive mode. We have drawn attention to the fact that the cyclical combination of scientific data is as characteristic of the inductive and synthetic mode as is the linear arrangement of the causal and analytic mode.[86]

---

to the comparative discussion of the various meanings given to the yinyang cycle in different medical disciplines and their sources on pp. 5–11 of Jen Ying-ch'iu's *Shang-han-lun yü-i* 語譯.

[84]See especially Chapters 6, 9, 31, 67, and 70 of the *Su-wen* and Chapters 10 and 12 of the *Ling-shu*.

[85]Which, for traditional Chinese medicine, it remains to this day.

[86]For instance, in "Wissenschaftliches Denken," and in the Introduction to the German edition of Granet's *La pensée chinoise* (*Das chinesische Denken*, Munich, 1963).

Because of their ubiquity in Chinese culture, the conventional standards of the Five Evolutive Phases have been widely discussed in the literature. Perhaps the best-known of these writings are the cursory treatment in Feng Yu-lan's *History of Chinese Philosophy*,[87] the passages in Granet's *La pensée chinoise*,[88] and the detailed and systematic accounts given by Wolfram Eberhard[89] and Joseph Needham.[90] Needham, who writes essentially as a historian of science, gives an elaborate description of the historical beginnings and early ramifications of speculation based on the Five Evolutive Phases. Eberhard presents the most comprehensive collection of correspondences of the Five E.P.s based on extensive studies of the source material and analyzed in the light of modern combinatorial procedures.

According to a still unquestioned tradition, the theory of the Five E.P.s was first formulated explicitly by Tsou Yen 騶衍, who perhaps lived between ca. 350 and 270 B.C., at a time when in certain disciplines, including medicine, the Chinese were about to make the transition between protoscience and science. Since the inception of scientific method in a narrow sense, the cycle of the Five E.P.s has been understood and used as a set of conventional value standards. In many works going back to the third century B.C., and in all philosophical and scientific writing of the Han period, it plays a major role.[91] Naturalists and ritualists, social philosophers and alchemists, Confucianists and Taoists without distinction of philosophic school had recourse to the conventional standards of yin, yang, and of the Five Evolutive Phases. Among the correspondence systems that evolved during the Han, several are remarkable for their elab-

---

[87]On pp. 491–573 of the the original Chinese edition (*Chung-kuo che-hsüeh-shih*). English translation by Derk Boddle, Princeton, 1953.
[88]On pp. 303ff and pp. 375ff *et passim*.
[89]"Beiträge zur kosmologischen Spekulation Chinas in der Han-Zeit," *Baessler-Archiv*, 1933, *16*.1:1–100.
[90]*Science and Civilisation in China*, Vol. II, pp. 232–273 ("Fundamental Ideas of Chinese Science") *et passim*; excellent bibliographies.
[91]For details and sample translations see the works of Needham and Eberhard just quoted.

orateness and for the universal consistency of the systematic links they embody. One of these is the system developed in the *Huang-ti nei-ching.*

At the start we shall therefore analyze and then define epistemologically the energetic qualities of each evolutive phase as they constitute value standards fixed by convention. Notwithstanding the considerable literature on the Five Evolutive Phases this aspect has not hitherto been noted.[92] We will then recapitulate some of the correspondences of the Five E.P.s germane to medicine. We shall conclude this section by considering some of the patterns according to which these conventional values are applied in medicine.

A word should here be inserted on our (normative) translation of the Chinese term *wu-hsing* 五行. Between the sixteenth and the eighteenth centuries, European missionaries aroused interest in and furthered understanding of Chinese culture by alluding, wherever feasible, to familiar notions and concepts. Because of limitations of their philological resources they rendered *wu-hsing* by "Five Elements." That this translation is erroneous and misleading has been pointed out by such scholars as Granet[93] and Needham.[94] It is to be regretted that Needham adduces historical habit[95] to justify continued use of the traditional equivalent, encouraging its perpetuation by authors who will not warn their readers, as he has done. *Hsing* 行 literally means "passage" (or in the active sense, "passing through"); thus in Latin we use the normative equivalent *transvectus*, and in English "evolutive phase."[96]

QUALITATIVE DEFINITION OF THE FIVE CONVENTIONAL VALUES

The Five Evolutive Phases, as their name implies, constitute stretches of time, temporal segments of exactly defined qualities that succeed each other in cyclical order at reference positions defined in space. Or, couched in terms closer to practice, the Five E.P.s define conventionally and unequivocally energetic qualities changing in the course of time. They typify the

[92]In our article "Farbemblematik in China," pp. 154–167, we have briefly encountered the subject.

[93]*La pensée chinoise,* pp. 313f.

[94]Needham, *Science and Civilisation in China,* Vol. II, pp. 243f.

[95]*Ibid.,* p. 244: "The term 'elements' has for so long been used for the *wu-hsing* that it is hardly possible to discard it."

[96]In analogy to the normative German term *Wandlungsphase,* which we have used for more than a decade in publications cited.

qualities of energy by the use of five concepts (wood, fire, earth, metal, water) which, because of the richness of their associations, are ideally suited to serve as the crystallizing core for an inductive system of relations and correspondences.

From the outset the evolutive phases have been laden with meaning that could be only partly explicated rationally. In medicine and other disciplines, with growing diversification, subtlety, and consistency, the system of correspondences came increasingly within the reach of rational explication. In studying, systematically and rigorously, the originally emblematic conventions of value used in Chinese science we are merely moving further in a direction marked out by the best representatives of Chinese scientific medicine more than two thousand years ago. We should always keep in mind that Western science is not more rational than Chinese science, merely more analytical.[97]

The goal of understanding the essence of Chinese thought about nature in the light of modern science can only be attained if on the one hand we abstain from substituting analytical Western equivalents for Chinese synthetic terms[98] (which would destroy their integral significance); and if on the other hand we define and circumscribe these same Chinese terms analytically. Only thus will the scientist, who moves in a radically different sphere of ideas than the sinologist, be able to assimilate and reconstruct the notions expressed by these terms.

There is a reciprocal relation[99] between the conventional standards and the effects they define. The most general concepts implicit in the values of the E.P.s depend not only on their names (Wood, Fire, and so on) but on the whole system of correspondences of which they constitute the core.

There are several geometrical arrangements of the evolutive phases. One of these, particularly close to modern ideas, cor-

[97]We have stressed this essential point in relevant writings since 1957.
[98]See "Untersuchungen" as well as "Wissenschaftliches Denken."
[99]This statement is valid not only for the qualitative standards here discussed but analogously for the quantitative standards so familiar to us. These latter are repeatedly fixed with greater precision as a consequence of the progress of techniques depending on them.

relates four E.P.s to the azimuthal directions and the fifth to the center.[100] In this disposition Wood corresponds to East, Fire to South, Metal to West, Water to North and Earth to the center (Fig 4).

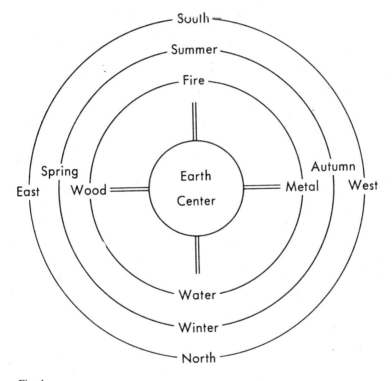

Fig. 4

To each direction and thus each of the four directional E.P.s there is simultaneously correlated one of the Four Seasons:
to the East and to Wood: Spring,
to the South and to Fire: Summer,
to the West and to Metal: Autumn,
to the North and to Water: Winter.

[100]This scheme is also employed in nonmedical contexts. In the *Nei-ching*, it is found in *Su-wen* 5/55–60.

The idea of correspondence between directions and seasons is due to the fundamental experience of the daily or yearly course of the sun, and the connection of the E.P.s to these natural data probably reflects the fact that certain emblems typifying seasonal change were gradually raised to the rank of universal conventions of value. The constant change of the sun's position relative to any point of reference furnishes an impressive and ever-present model for dividing all possible energetic cycles and for characterizing their individual phases. The sun may be considered as the substantiation and emblem par excellence of the active aspect, yang. Where its influence is screened off or momentarily excluded, the opposite polar aspect, structivity or yin, becomes effective. Thus we derive the first of three polarizing criteria that determine the cycle of the Five E.P.s: the polarity of active/structive aspects (yin: yang). The hours and seasons and the azimuth directions in which the sun expands its energy—at noon, in the South, in Summer, but also in the morning, in the East, in Spring— are qualified as yang, as active; inversely, the hours and seasons and the directions in which the sun's energy wanes or seems to disappear altogether—at midnight, in the North, in Winter, but also in the evening, in the West, in Autumn—are conceived as correspondences of the conservative, stabilizing tendency and qualified as yin, structive ones.[101] If we now try to further polarize phenomena that share the same pole, such as morning and noon (parallel to East and South, Spring and Summer) or evening and midnight (parallel to West and North, Autumn and Winter), we find a common difference (which again is evident from everyday experience). Those aspects that at noon or midnight (in the South or North, in Summer or Winter) are fully unfolded and immediately affect nature and the senses, in the morning and evening (in the East and West, in Spring and Autumn) are only intimated and potential. We thus meet with the second of the three polarizing criteria: the polarity of potentiality/actuality (Fig. 5).

[101]See *Su-wen* 3/22ff; 4/38f; 5/48ff *et passim*.

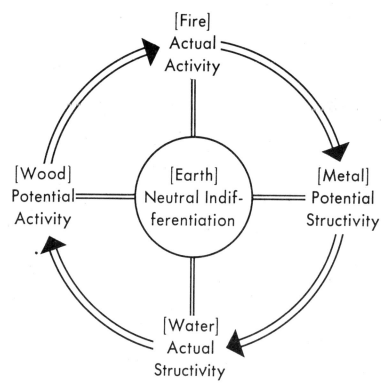

Fig. 5

Wood corresponds to potential activity, to minor yang (*yang minor*),
Fire corresponds to actual activity, to major yang (*yang maior*),
Metal corresponds to potential structivity, to minor yin (*yin minor*),
Water corresponds to actual structivity, to major yin (*yin maior*).

When we compare Figs. 4 and 5, it is evident that positions of potentiality (Wood and Metal) and positions of actuality (Fire and Water), respectively, are combined on common axes; we may thus speak of an axis of potentiality and an axis of actuality. The hours of the day, the azimuth directions, and the seasons arranged consecutively on the arms of a cross correspond to the order indicated by the endless course of the sun. At first in emblematic form, and ultimately as the consequence of scientific abstraction, this becomes the sequence of the Evolutive Phases as positions on a cycle. The center of these four peripheral evolutive phases is marked by the central E.P., Earth. At the intersection of the two polar axes the qualities of the polar phases not only meet but are mutually equalized and neutralized; or, if only a single axis is dynamically considered, commutated. The center of the cycle is at once the pivot, the center of gravity, the point of transition and transformation of the whole structure, its neutral pole, and its point of primordial undifferentiation. We thus realize the last of the polarizing criteria of the E.P. cycle: the polarity of qualitative differentiation/neutral undifferentiation. The evolutive phase Earth represents the conventional sign for this neutral and undifferentiated stage capable of endless struction and reaction. Viewed from the perspective of any differentiated quality, the neutral point assumes qualities complementary to those of the position of perspective; the neutral center is situated on the shortest path to the complementary pole, and spatially in front of it.

VARIOUS SEQUENCES OF THE E.P.S. AND THEIR APPLICATIONS TO MEDICAL THEORY

The phases of a cycle alternate in a set order. A definite order observed repeatedly at each cyclical revolution provides us with an additional element useful for the systematic description of energetic processes: the constant sequence in which effective qualities alternate. A number of such sequences are an integral part of the theory of the Five Evolutive Phases.

Eberhard[102] has assembled all 36 sequences that can be formed with five phases and has checked their mention (or neglect) in the scientific and protoscientific literature of the Han period. Needham[103] gives a detailed account of the five sequences in most extensive use.

We have already acquainted ourselves with a geometrical arrangement of the Evolutive Phases which, since it is chiefly

[102]Eberhard, "Beiträge," pp. 45f.
[103]Needham, *Science and Civilisation in China*, Vol. II, pp. 253–261.

used in the description of macrocosmic processes, we may call the "macrocosmic sequence" or Sequence 0 (see Figs. 4 and 5). It consists of four peripheral phases that alternate clockwise in accordance with their correspondences (the hours, seasons, directions) and of a center occupied by the central and undifferentiated E.P. which subsumes the qualities of the other four.

In an applied science, such as Chinese medicine, preference is given to sequences integrating the neutral E.P. into the cycle. Depending on the level of rationality and the degree of abstraction, this insertion may take place at one, two, or four points of the cycle. In the ancient sections of the *Nei-ching*, compiled at a time when yin/yang outshone the other polarities in the minds of the authors, the central evolutive phase is inserted at one single point, between Fire (major yang, actual activity) and Metal (minor yin, potential structivity). Because of the influence of the classical tradition this has remained to this day the most frequent technical sequence. In the chapters of the *Nei-ching* interpolated later,[104] the central E.P. is realized more clearly as a phase of transition and alternation, and so is consistently inserted into the cycle after each peripheral E.P.[105]

The so-called "production sequence" (*sequentia efficiens, hsiang-sheng-hsü* 相生序)—in which every Evolutive Phase is conceived as the product or "child" (*tzu* 子) of the precedent E. P., which in turn is considered its "mother" (*mu* 母) (Fig. 6)

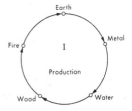

Fig. 6

[104]See pp. 56–58 below.
[105]Refer to the correlation between terrestrial branches and E.P.s in Figs. 11 and 17.

—may be considered the basic sequence (Sequence I). This *sequentia efficiens* starts with Wood and ends with Water. Thus the first Evolutive Phase Wood produces the second Evolutive Phase Fire, which in turn produces the third Evolutive Phase Earth, which in turn produces the fourth Evolutive Phase Metal, which in turn produces the fifth evolutive phase Water, which again produces the first E.P. and so on. We take as Sequence II the "conquest or checking sequence" (*sequentia vincens sive cohibens, hsiang-sheng, hsiang-k'o-hsü* 相勝, 相克), in which each E.P. is considered to check (*k'o* 克) the preceding one (Fig. 7). By using ordinals derived from the numbering

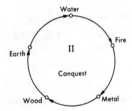

Fig. 7

of Sequence I, we obtain the sequence 1–3–5–2–4.

Sequences I and II may be called physiological in the sense that they operate in all intact, harmonious functions of the living organism. Energies and stimuli (yang) affecting the organism from without tend to advance the body functions and energy circuits in the direction of Sequence I. A structive resistance (yin) ensures that this drive does not overstimulate the metabolism. This resistance, present in the substrative quality (and quantity) of the orbs, engenders a corrective physiological check on the driving yang forces in the direction of Sequence II. Energetic processes are, however, incessantly exposed to a multitude of influences from without and within—so-called heteropathies (*hsieh* 邪)—that disturb the physiological balance of drive and check in single regions (orbs) or throughout the organism. These disturbances become manifest diagnostically as energetic "deficiencies" (*pu-chi* 不及) or "redundancies" (*t'ai-kuo* 太過) at specific positions of the organism, in the *foramina* and *sinarteriae*. If energy (*ch'i* 氣) becomes deficient at a given position of the organism, the energetic quality of this position is overpowered by the qualities of other positions contiguous and connected functionally according to Sequence II. If, inversely, the energy of a given position is redundant (*t'ai-kuo*), its own qualities overpower the qualities of positions functionally connected with it.[106] Under these conditions the "check" (*k'o*) degenerates to become "accroachment" (*ch'eng* 乘). Moreover, the qualities of positions touched by these anomalies are "violated" (*wu* 侮) in accordance with a pathological Sequence III (Sequence II in reverse), which therefore is called the "violation sequence" (*sequentia violationis, hsiang-wu-hsü* 相侮序): 1–4–2–5–3. Thus Wood violates Metal; Metal violates Fire; Fire violates Water; Water violates Earth; Earth in turn violates Wood (Fig. 8).

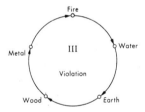

Fig. 8

Examples: If Wood is deficient in energy, its quality will be accroached upon (*ch'eng*) by the E.P. Metal normally checking (*k'o*) it; and it will be violated (*wu*) by the quality of Earth, which in the normal order it keeps in check (*k'o*). If Wood, on the other hand, is redundant in energy, it will encroach on the quality of Earth instead of merely checking it, and will violate Metal by which it should itself be checked.

The distinction between the physiological and the pathological effects just considered is summed up thus:

Physiological relationships:
1. *B* checks (*k'o*) *C*.

[106]Additional details on this subject which fall within the realm of pathology and diagnostics will be given in Chapter 2.

2. *B* is checked by *A*.
3. *C* checks *D*.
4. *C* is checked by *B*, etc.

Pathological relationships:
If *B* shows energetic deficiency (*pu-chi*), there ensues
1. *B* is violated (*wu*) by *C*.
2. *B* is accroached (*ch'eng*) by *A*.
If *B* is energetically redundant (*t'ai-kuo*), there ensues
1. *B* accroaches (*ch'eng*) *C*.
2. *B* violates (*wu*) *A*, etc.

These three sequences, out of a possible 36, express economically the whole gamut of energetic fluctuations within a cycle (deficiency or redundancy of an E.P.). They are able to represent everything of specifically medical significance within the theory of the Five Evolutive Phases.

To conclude, we should explain a few technical terms of pathology that define the transmission (*ch'uan* 傳) of heteropathies (*heteropathia, hsieh* 邪) according to the sequences of the E.P.s. In *Nan-ching* 難經 103[107] distinctions are made among

1. *Heteropathia inanitatis* ("exhaustion heteropathy"), *hsü-hsieh* 虛邪; the heteropathy advances according to Sequence I: the "mother" accroaches on the "child." Example: transmission of a heteropathy originating in the *orbis hepaticus* to the *orbis cardialis*.

2. *Heteropathia repletionis* ("repletion heteropathy"), *shih-hsieh* 實邪; the heteropathy spreads backward; the "child" accroaches on the "mother." Example: transmission of a heteropathy originating in the *orbis cardialis* to the *orbis hepaticus*.

3. *Heteropathia praedatoria* ("predatory heteropathy"), *tsei-hsieh* 賊邪; the heteropathy originates at a position the qualities of which (according to Sequence II) are not checked but, to the contrary, physiologically check those of the reference positions. Example: Transmission of a heteropathy originating in the *orbis hepaticus* to the *orbis lienalis*.

4. *Heteropathia subtilis* ("subtle heteropathy"), *wei-hsieh* 微邪; the heteropathy originates at a position conquered according to Sequence II, and consequently spreads according to Sequence III. Example: transmission of a heteropathy originating in the *orbis lienalis* to the *orbis hepaticus*.

5. *Heteropathia recta* ("direct heteropathy"), *cheng-hsieh* 正邪; the heteropathy is confined to the orb in which it originates.

---

[107]Chapter 4/125f.

2

Standards of Value for Phenomena of Macrocosmic Dimensions: Phase Energetics

General Preliminaries

It is axiomatic in Chinese thought that all realms of Nature—the macrocosm and all microcosms—are interconnected inductively. The energetic processes of the Cosmos unceasingly modulate the changes that take place in every individual organism. For this reason systematic and qualitatively unequivocal descriptions of temporally variable meteorological, climatological, and immunological influences are needed for diagnosis and therapy of both the exogenous (in Chinese *wai-kan* 外感, literally "induced from without") diseases and of the epidemic and pandemic diseases. The latter are designated by the significant technical term *shih-ping* 時病 or *shih-ch'i-ping* 時氣病, i.e., "diseases dependent on the time," "diseases conditioned by the temporal configuration."

The most basic statement of the macrocosmic variation is the calendar. Since the most ancient times the Chinese have used a combined solar-lunar calendar.[1] To this day, farmers and practitioners of traditional medicine take their cues from it.

Reference to the calendar, common in the medical arts of all cultures, permits only rudimentary prognoses of average probability both in immunology and epidemology, since certain diseases occur more often in some seasons than in others; the aggravation of certain symptoms is more frequent at some hours of the day than at others. Although the hours and seasons revolve in endless uniformity, each cycle shows individual meteorological, immunological, and other relevant characteristics. In order to define more precisely the characteristics

---

[1]At least since the second millennium B.C. For the astronomical foundations of the Chinese calendar see the outline in Needham, *Science and Civilisation in China*, Vol. III, pp. 293f and 290ff, as well as his detailed bibliographical data.

of each individual interval and incorporate these influences rationally into diagnostics and therapy, Chinese medicine has evolved the qualitative conventions of phase energetics.

We have adopted the term "phase energetics" to designate a discipline concerned with the changes of energetic configurations (*configurationes, ch'i*) during various intervals (circuit phases, *circuitus, yün*). Its Chinese counterpart is the combined technical term *yün-ch'i* 運氣, a fusion of *wu-yün* and *liu-ch'i* 五運六氣, The Five Circuit Phases and The Six Energetic Configurations, *quinque circuitus et sex configurationes.*

Historical and Bibliographical Preliminaries

The version of the *Huang-ti nei-ching su-wen* (Candid questions in the Inner Classic of the Yellow Sovereign) edited in A.D. 762 by Wang Ping 王氷 is the oldest authority on phase energetics. In this version of the *Su-wen* two chapters—9 and 22—refer in passing, and nine chapters—66 through 74—are devoted entirely to, phase energetics. Because the latter chapters are far longer than other chapters of the *Su-wen,* almost a third of this very widely distributed edition of the Classic is taken up by phase energetics. This illustrates the great importance attributed to phase energetics in certain medical circles and also furnishes increased support for the hypothesis that these oversized chapters containing the whole theory of phase energetics were interpolated into the *Su-wen* by Wang Ping. So far as can be ascertained today, the theory of circuit phases and energetic configurations was not treated in any other version of the *Huang-ti nei-ching* nor by any other author prior to Wang Ping.

It was only in the Sung that Wang Ping's edition of the *Su-wen* displaced all other versions of this text. We have the tables of contents of two earlier versions: (1) of a *Huang-ti su-wen* in 8 *chüan* (sections) annotated by Ch'üan Yüan-ch'i 全元起 of the Liang,[2] and (2) of a *Huang-ti nei-ching t'ai-su* 太素 in 30 *chüan* edited during the Sui by Yang Shang-shan 楊上善.[3] In these tables the headings of Chapters 66 to 74 are not found; moreover, in the surviving fragment of the *T'ai-su* text we also look in vain for any reference to the *yün-ch'i* theory. The same is true for the writings of Chang Chung-ching, who compiled his *Shang-han tsa-ping-lun* during the later Han period; those of Huang-fu Mi 皇甫謐 (ca. A.D. 251–282) who in his *Chia-i-ching* has

---

[2]This table is reprinted in the *Su-wen-shih* and more recently in the *Huang-ti nei-ching su-wen i-shih* 黃帝內經素問譯釋, p. 11.

[3]The fragments of this table of contents may be examined in the modern reprints of this text; see our bibliography.

reproduced verbatim large parts of the *Su-wen;* those of Wang Shu-ho (second half of the third century), whose *Mo-ching* 脈經 is clearly based on the theory and terminology of the *Su-wen;* and even those of Sun Szu-mo (ca. A.D. 581–682) who, in his clinical and pharmacological compendiums *Ch'ien-chin yao-fang* 千金要方 (Prescriptions worth a thousand) and *Ch'ien-chin i-fang* 千金翼方, in many respects pays tribute to the Taoist cosmology which lies at the origin of phase energetics.

Lin I 林億, who together with Kao Pao-heng 高保衡 was charged with re-editing the *Nei-ching* during the period 1068–1077, explains this silence by the hypothesis that the copies of the *Su-wen* used by Huang-fu Mi, Ch'üan Yüan-ch'i, and others lacked *chüan* and that Wang Ping had closed this gap with an opus transmitted independently until his time, the *Yin-yang ta-lun* 陰陽大論 (Great discussion on yin and yang), which had been mentioned earlier by Chang Chung-ching.[4] Lin I thus tries, not very convincingly, to suggest that phase energetics had been part of the classical tradition at least from the later Han period. Taken together, the evidence suggests that it was Wang Ping himself who gave definite form to this theory and inserted it into the *Su-wen.* Such a hypothesis is further supported by the fact that a medico-Taoist treatise in 17 *chüan*, entitled *Hsüan-chu mi-yü* 玄珠密語 (Secret words of [the master of the] mysterious pearl) and devoted to the theory of circuit phases and energetic configurations, is ascribed to him.

Wang Ping submitted his *Su-wen* edition and commentary to the throne in 762, whereas the *Hsüan-chu mi-yü* is said to have been composed during the reign of the Empress Wu (A.D. 685–705). Wang Ping's *Su-wen* commentary is written in a polished style, and the *Hsüan-chu mi-yü* in the rustic *(ts'u-yeh* 粗野) language of the Taoist treatises. It was recognized even in Sung times that the extant version of the *Hsüan-chu mi-yü* was wrongly ascribed. Of course Wang Ping may have been the author of a lost treatise on this subject (see *I-chi-k'ao,* pp. 1390–1393).

A flat statement that Chapters 66 through 71 and 74 are interpolations is not found before the end of the Yüan period. At that time the doctor and philologist Wang Lü 王履 states in a note to his essay "Injuries due to the Four Seasonal Configurations" ("Szu-ch'i so-shang lun" 四氣所傷論):[5] "Of

---

[4]See p. 20 of the *Chung-kuo i-chi-k'ao.*
[5]Contained in his collection *I-ching su-hui-chi* 醫經溯洄集 (Critical essays on the Chinese medical classics), p. 22.

course the seven chapters dealing with the Five Circuit Phases
(wu-yün) and the Six Energetic Configurations *(liu-ch'i)* on the
one hand, and the remaining chapters of the *Su-wen* on the other,
represent two [different] writings coming from the hand of two
different persons. Each of these in his account was following
his own guiding idea; [that is why] one should not confound
them. If, consequently, the seven chapters have been interpolated into the *Su-wen* by Wang Ping, they cannot be the
original text of the *Su-wen*."

We do not exclude the possibility that other chapters of the *Su-wen*—
including 9 and 29, relevant here—also contain interpolations. There is
rarely any conclusive proof of such interpolations, chiefly because we lack
really independent parallel texts. A more thorough knowledge of the form
and content of medical literature should gradually enable us at least to
distinguish between passages supported by multiple traditions and doubtful
ones.[6]

The thesis that phase energetics constitutes a relatively late
innovation is corroborated by the fact that secondary literature
on this subject does not appear before the middle of the Sung
period (1099)[7] and in notable quantity only in the Ming. At
the very beginning of the Ming era, Chu Su 朱橚, a son of the
founder of the dynasty, gave ample space to phase energetics
in the "Universal Prescriptions" (*P'u-chi-fang* 普濟方) edited
under his aegis: sixty synoptic tables accompanied by ex-
plicatory texts show the energetic configurations in the Cosmos
to be expected according to the *yün-ch'i* theory during each year
of the calendaric cycle. In 1624 Chang Chieh-pin(Ching-yüeh)
張介賓 (景岳), highly esteemed as a medical theorist and author
of the *Lei-ching*, published his *Lei-ching t'u-i* 類經圖翼 (Illustrated "wing" to the classified [inner] classic), which opens
with an exposition of the theory of the Five Circuit Phases
and the Six Energetic Configurations. Chang not only
elaborates on the rules laid down in the *Su-wen* by incorporating
ideas suggested by the neo-Confucian Chou Tun-i's concept
of the Supreme Pole (*t'ai-chi* 太極) and its unfoldment in the

[6]See our note on p. 183 below concerning the *Su-wen* 5/54–61.
[7]That was the year in which Liu Wen-shu's *Su-wen ju-shih yün-ch'i lun-ao*
素文入式運氣論奧 appeared. See *I-chi-k'ao*, p. 1394.

sensuous universe, but also introduces a more consistent systematic order. His treatise is valued today as the most succinct and systematic account of phase energetics.

Among the most important of the many dissertations on this subject written under the Ming are the [*Su-wen*] *Yün-ch'i-t'u k'uo-ting-chü li-ch'eng* 運氣圖括定局立成 by Hsiung Tsung-li 熊宗立 (see *I-chi-k'ao*, p. 1398) and the *Yün-ch'i i-lan* 運氣易覽 by Wang Chi 汪機 (Sheng 省) (see ibid., p. 1399).

During the Ch'ing period the theory of phase energetics was summed up in 1749 in Chapter 35 of the *I-tsung chin-chien* 醫宗金鑑 (Golden Mirror of Medicine) in the terms of the "original text," i.e., Wang Ping's *Su-wen* edition. Recently the Nanking College of Chinese Medicine found it appropriate to insert an ample account of phase energetics into the second edition of its *Chung-i-hsüeh kai-lun* 中醫學概論 (Compendium of [traditional] Chinese medicine; Peking, 1959). In the same year Jen Ying-ch'iu 任應秋, author of a colloquial version of the *Su-wen* with commentary, published a small monograph[8] in which he explains medical as well as paramedical aspects of this discipline.

Although, as we have seen, phase energetics has for at least four centuries drawn the attention of the best authorities on Chinese medicine, it is the weakest link within the theoretical structure of China's scientific medicine. Even though we do not admit all the objections levied in the course of time against phase energetics,[9] there is no denying that from the outset speculative combinations have held sway over empirical data. At the same time we believe it to be more than a historical curiosity. Our discussion below cannot hope to be a definitive solution to this difficult and fundamental scientific problem but is better considered as a stimulus and basis for original research in this field (see the conclusion of this chapter).[10]

---

[8] *Wu yün liu ch'i* 五運六氣 (Phase energetics).
[9] A collection of critical opinions may be found in the *I-chi-k'ao*, pp. 1401–1404.
[10] See in particular pp. 105–106 below.

The Basic Conventional Value Standards of Phase Energetics

The qualitative conventions used in phase energetics—yin and yang, the Five Evolutive Phases, as well as the emblems formed by combining the Ten Celestial Stems and the Twelve Terrestrial Branches—had been employed in Chinese science with precise significance for many centuries, but in order to express relationships postulated by this new discipline, they were given a new interpretation between the seventh and eighth centuries.

THE TEN CELESTIAL STEMS AND THE TWELVE TERRESTRIAL BRANCHES

The supporting framework of phase energetics is constituted by two series of numerical emblems: the Ten Celestial Stems (*t'ien-kan* 天干) and the Twelve Terrestrial Branches (*ti-chih* 地支). The designation "emblem" indicates their ambiguous function:[11] they serve simultaneously for the numeration (quantitative designation) and for the classification and qualification (qualitative description) of positions. By pairing the celestial stems with terrestrial branches (see. Table 1, later in this section), 60 composite numerical emblems are obtained, representing the ordinals 1 to 60. These have been used since the middle of the second millennium B.C. for counting and marking the days: to each day there was given one emblem; after the sixtieth emblem had been assigned, a new cycle began. In those early ages the separate characters for celestial stems or terrestrial branches served protocolar and mantic functions. Almost all the names of Shang kings (eighteenth to twelfth centuries B.C.) have a celestial stem as second component. In turn, the terrestrial branches served to mark temporal divisions of the solar year and the spatial arcs of the azimuth.

The development of protoscientific speculation multiplied the applications and interpretations of the cyclical characters. Probably since the middle of the first millennium, the terrestrial branches were also used to mark the divisions of the day

[11]See our article "Farbemblematik in China," and Granet, *La pensée chinoise,* pp. 152f.

into twelve double-hours.[12] About the beginning of our era the ancient day numeration by means of the sexagesimal cycle was extended to the count of years and months, for which purpose the beginning of the year count was pushed back into legendary antiquity, usually to the year 2637 B.C., when the mythical Yellow Sovereign was imagined to have reigned. During the past ninety years sinologists have published a number of investigations and propounded numerous hypotheses concerning the origin and etymology of the stems and branches; the results have been summarized by Otto Franke (*Geschichte des chinesischen Reiches*, Vol. III, pp. 66–69), and more recently by Joseph Needham (*Science and Civilisation in China*, Vol. III, pp. 396–398). By the time phase energetics evolved (eighth century A.D.) the archaic mythical connotations of the stems and branches had completely vanished into the abyss of time, and even the ancient symbolic associations of the characters (still preserved in the *Lü-shu* 律書 of the *Shih-chi* and in the *Lü-li-chih* 律曆志 of the *Ch'ien-Han-shu*[13] had been effaced by rational and systematic interpretation. Only the latter requires our attention here.

The Ten Celestial Stems (*t'ien-kan* 天干) are:
1—*chia*-甲; 2—*i* 乙; 3—*ping* 丙; 4—*ting* 丁; 5—*wu* 戊; 6—*chi* 己; 7—*keng* 庚; 8—*hsin* 辛; 9—*jen* 壬; 10—*kuei* 癸.

The Twelve Terrestrial Branches *(ti-chih* 地支*)* are:
1—*tzu* 子; 2—*ch'ou* 丑; 3—*yin* 寅; 4—*mao* 卯; 5—*ch'en* 辰; 6—*szu* 巳; 7—*wu* 午; 8—*wei* 未; 9—*shen* 申; 10—*yu* 酉; 11—*hsü* 戌; 12—*hai* 亥.

Phonetic transcriptions of the Chinese cyclical emblems for the use of those who do not read characters turn out to be unsatisfactory for methodical as well as for mnemonic reasons. Nor would a translation of the archaic senses of the characters be of any help, even if more than a few of these meanings were known. Because of their multiple associations, the characters cannot simply be replaced by Roman numerals or Greek letters. We therefore propose to replace the Chinese numerical emblems in Western writing by a transparent system of phonemes which reflect the essential technical associations. We thus use for celestial stems an alphabetical series based on the code vowel *u* (=*uranus*), for the Greek sky god:

1—*ust*; 2—*bust*; 3—*cust*; 4—*dust*; 5—*esut*; 6—*fust*; 7—*gust*; 8—*hust*; 9—*just*; 10—*kut*

---

[12]See Needham, *Science and Civilisation in China*, Vol. III, p. 398.
[13]Pp. 491 and 398 respectively. See, for example, Granet, *La pensée chinoise*, pp. 153ff.

and for the terrestrial branches an analogous series based on the code vowel *a* (=*gaia*), for his mother, Earth:

1—*ast*; 2—*bast*; 3—*cast*; 4—*dast*; 5—*esat*; 6—*fast*; 7—*gast*; 8—*hast*; 9—*jast*; 10—*kat*; 11—*last*; 12—*mast*.

Subsequently we shall confine ourselves to these new terms, adding Chinese characters only where they seem indispensable.

By successively pairing stems with branches, we obtain the cycle of sixty emblematic combinations, in which each of the ten stems is used six times and each of the twelve branches five times (see Table 1).

The current cycle for the classificatory count of years began in 1924, a year *ust-ast;* the next will begin in the year 1984, again a year *ust-ast.* Examples of the cyclical terms for recent years are:

1925: *bust-bast*	1930: *gust-gast*	1935: *bust-mast*
1940: *gust-esat*	1945: *bust-kat*	1950: *gust-cast*
1955: *bust-hast*	1960: *gust-ast*	1965: *bust-fast*
1970: *gust-last*	1975: *bust-dast*	1980: *gust-jast*

These and intermediate years may easily be derived from Table 1.

THE FIVE CIRCUIT PHASES AND THE SIX ENERGETIC CONFIGURATIONS

Phase energetics aims to define the medical significance of macrocosmic (i.e., meteorological, climatic, immunological) influences on microcosmic (i.e., physiological) processes. The term *yün* 運 (*circuitus,* circuit phase, abbreviated C.P.) designates the implicit, deductive (not empirically perceptible), and therefore active and incipient aspect. *Ch'i* 氣 (*configuratio,* energetic configuration), its counterpart, is the explicit, perceptible, concrete, and structive aspect of the cosmic situation. In nontechnical contexts the term *yün* has the meanings "to transport," "to circulate," "to move," "(auspicious) fortune." The character *yün* in the *Shuo-wen,* p. 72, represents a moving chariot or travel in a closed chariot. (See the section on *"Ch'i"* in Chapter 3 for the general semantic compass of *ch'i.*)

The polar complementarity of *yün* and *ch'i* is immediately evident in the qualities of their correspondences. The Five Circuit Phases (*wu-yün;* 5 is a yang number) constitute five temporal periods of different quality that form a cycle. Their qualities are quite identical with those of the Five Evolutive

Table 1. The Sixty Emblematic Combinations in Phase Energetics

1 *ust-ast*	21 *ust-jast*	41 *ust-esat*
2 *bust-bast*	22 *bust-kat*	42 *bust-fast*
3 *cust-cast*	23 *cust-last*	43 *cust-gast*
4 *dust-dast*	24 *dust-mast*	44 *dust-hast*
5 *esut-esat*	25 *esut-ast*	45 *esut-jast*
6 *fust-fast*	26 *fust-bast*	46 *fust-kat*
7 *gust-gast*	27 *gust-cast*	47 *gust-last*
8 *hust-hast*	28 *hust-dast*	48 *hust-mast*
9 *just-jast*	29 *just-esat*	49 *just-ast*
10 *kut-kat*	30 *kut-fast*	50 *kut-bast*
11 *ust-last*	31 *ust-gast*	51 *ust-cast*
12 *bust-mast*	32 *bust-hast*	52 *bust-dast*
13 *cust-ast*	33 *cust-jast*	53 *cust-esat*
14 *dust-bast*	34 *dust-kat*	54 *dust-fast*
15 *esut-cast*	35 *esut-last*	55 *esut-gast*
16 *fust-dast*	36 *fust-mast*	56 *fust-hast*
17 *gust-esat*	37 *gust-ast*	57 *gust-jast*
18 *hust-fast*	38 *hust-bast*	58 *hust-kat*
19 *just-gast*	39 *just-cast*	59 *just-last*
20 *kut-hast*	40 *kut-dast*	60 *kut-mast*

Phases (from which they are derived), except that their enumeration order is different:

first circuit phase : Earth
second circuit phase: Metal
third circuit phase: Water
fourth circuit phase: Wood
fifth circuit phase: Fire

The circuit phases are combined with celestial stems (Heaven is yang) so that each C.P. is defined by two celestial stems congruent by 5 which constitute its numerical emblems,[14] thus,

[14]*Ibid.*, p. 197 *et passim.*

first circuit phase Earth: *ust-fust*
second circuit phase Metal: *bust-gust*
third circuit phase Water: *cust-hust*
fourth circuit phase Wood: *dust-just*
fifth circuit phase Fire: *esut-kut*

or, arranged in Sequence 0 of the evolutive phases (see *Su-wen* 66/592; 67/595):

esut-kut

dust-just   *ust-fust*   *bust-gust*

cust-hust

The Six Energetic Configurations (*liu-ch'i, sex configurationes;* 6 is a yin number) constitute six climatic or immunological situations of different quality. These configurations, likewise combined into a cycle, are explicitly determined by the qualities of the Five Evolutive Phases and the tripartite yin and yang (Fig. 9). As may be seen from this figure, the conventional standard Fire is here split into *ignis principis* (*chün-huo* 君火, "princely fire") and *ignis ministri* (*hsiang-huo* 相火, "ministerial fire") to make the qualities of the E.P.s tally with the six-part cycle.

In accordance with the basically structive quality of the energetic configurations they are assigned terrestrial branches

Table 2. Associations of the Six Energetic Configurations

Evolutive Phase	Configuration	Terrestrial Branches
1. *ignis principis*	*yin minoris*	*ast-gast*
2. *humi humidae*	*yin maioris*	*bast-hast*
3. *ignis ministri*	*yang minoris*	*cast-jast*
4. *metalli aridi*	*splendoris yang*	*dast-kat*
5. *aquae algidae*	*yang maioris*	*esat-last*
6. *ligni venti*	*yin flectentis*	*fast-mast*

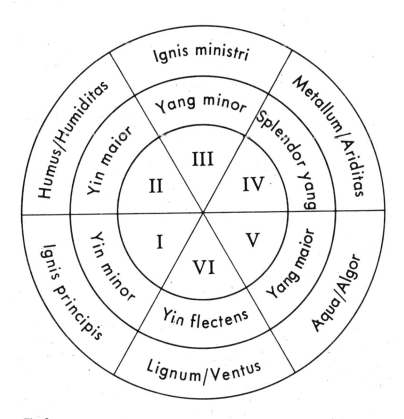

Fig. 9

(Earth is yin) as numerical emblems. Each energetic configuration is defined by two terrestrial branches, as shown in
Table 2. (For the usual cyclical arrangement, see Fig. 10; cf.
also *Su-wen* 66/592ff). A third correlation, also used outside phase
energetics, is made between the Twelve Terrestrial Branches
and the Five Evolutive Phases. It expresses cyclically the basic
evolutive direction of the E.P.s corresponding to Sequence I
(Fig. 11). In this scheme the clockwise gyration begins and ends
with Water (*transvectus aquae*), which is thus assigned the
branches *ast-mast*.[15] To each of the peripheral E.P.s hence there
correspond two consecutive terrestrial branches, always separat-

[15]*Ast* is the first and *mast* the last of the terrestrial branch series.

Fig. 10

cd by a single branch belonging to the central E.P. (*Su-wen* 67/565).[16]

Because of the convention that even-numbered emblems are yin and odd-numbered ones are yang,[17] it is evident that the cyclical characters assigned to each *circuitus* and *configuratio* explicitly indicate its basic polarity. No matter whether the two emblems assigned are directly consecutive (as in the case of the Five E.P.s.), five characters apart (as in the case of the *circuitus*), or six characters apart (as in the case of the *configurationes*), one emblem always corresponds to an even, and the other always to an odd, number.

[16]See also Fig. 15 and the accompanying explanation.
[17]See Chapter 1, section on "Secondary Correspondences of Yin and Yang."

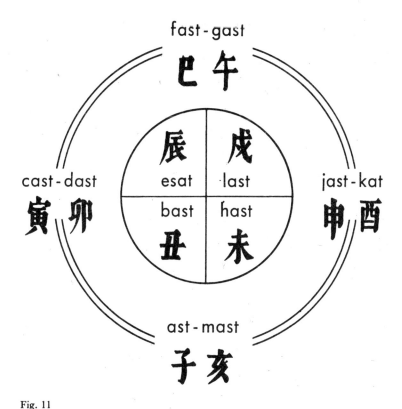

fast-gast

巳 午

cast-dast

辰 | 戌
esat | last
bast | hast
丑 | 未

寅 卯

jast-kat

申 酉

ast-mast

子 亥

Fig. 11

LEVELS OF CIRCUIT PHASES

Circuit phases as well as energetic configurations interact on several levels; in other words, we may define several kinds of circuit phases as well as of energetic configurations. Among circuit phases we may distinguish:

1. Great circuit phases, *ta-yün* 大運, *circuitus magni* (also called central circuit phases, *chung-yün* 中運, *circuitus medii*). The *circuitus magnus* qualifying a year in the Chinese lunar calendar is marked by the cyclical character (celestial stem) corresponding to that year in the sixty-year cycle.

According to the traditional count, the year 1968 is the forty-fifth of the current cycle and is marked by the cyclical characters *esut-jast*. Since circuit phases are determined solely by celestial stems, *esut* 戊 points to the quality Fire. Thus the great circuit phase of 1968 is Fire (*ta-yün wei huo* 大運 爲火).

2. Dominant circuit phases, *chu-yün* 主運, *circuitus dominantes*. In the same way as cycles are divided into five evolutive and circuit phases, each year may be subdivided into five equal periods called "circuit seasons" (*tempora circuitum, yün-chi* 運季) of 365/5 or about 73 days each. The circuit phase in strict correspondence to a given circuit season is called its dominant circuit phase (*circuitus dominans*). Without regard to the celestial stem resulting from the year count, in each and every year:

the first Circuit Season is dominated by the circuit phase Wood
the second Circuit Season is dominated by the circuit phase Fire
the third Circuit Season is dominated by the circuit phase Earth
the fourth Circuit Season is dominated by the circuit phase Metal
the fifth Circuit Season is dominated by the circuit phase Water.

The enumeration order of the *circuitus dominantes* is identical with Sequence I (the "production sequence") of the Evolutive Phases.

3. Deversant circuit phases, *k'o-yün* 客運, *circuitus deversantes*. In addition to its unchanging *circuitus dominans,* each circuit season is attributed a so-called deversant circuit phase (*circuitus deversans, k'o-yün*).[18] This phase changes five times each year in

Table 3. Combinations of Deversant Circuit Phases

Celestial Stem of the Year	Circuit Seasons (*Tempora circuitum*)				
	First	Second	Third	Fourth	Fifth
ust or *fust*	Earth	Metal	Water	Wood	Fire
bust or *gust*	Metal	Water	Wood	Fire	Earth
cust or *hust*	Water	Wood	Fire	Earth	Metal
dust or *just*	Wood	Fire	Earth	Metal	Water
esut or *kut*	Fire	Earth	Metal	Water	Wood

[18]From the Latin *deversor* = "guest," *deversari* = "to be guest," "to act as a guest," in analogy to *dominari* = "to be host," "to act as host."

such a way that the circuit phase corresponding to the celestial stem of the year "deversates" (i.e., is guest) only during the first of the five circuit seasons; during the subsequent four circuit seasons the remaining phases become deversant in Sequence I order. The resulting combinations may be tabulated as in Table 3.

If we depict the three kinds of circuit phases in a circular scheme, the picture in Fig. 12 results. The central or Great

Fig. 12

Circuit Phase inscribed in the central field and subsuming the overall quality of the lunar year is valid throughout the year with which it changes; the central field is encircled by the fixed Five Dominant Circuit Phases; their fixed ring is in turn surrounded by the mobile circle formed by the Five Deversant Circuit Phases; at each New Year (= change of the Great Circuit Phase) this outer ring moves one step to the right.

NOTATION OF THE CIRCUIT PHASES BY MEANS OF THE MUSICAL EMBLEMS

For the sake of completeness we must mention the notation of the C.P.s by means of the five ancient musical emblems.[19] This system was not developed out of scientific necessity but probably arose from traditional Chinese ritual associations.[20] The rules for the notation have been set forth in detail by Chang Ching-yüeh and can be grasped easily.[21] According to an ancient convention, each E.P. *(hsing, transvectus)* corresponds to a characteristic sound emblem:[22]

to the evolutive phase	Wood	Fire	Earth	Metal	Water
the sound emblem	*chüeh* 角	*chih* 徵	*kung* 宮	*shang* 商	*yü* 羽

These same sound emblems may be employed in a derived sense no longer capable of musical reproduction as emblems of the circuit phases, with each split into minor and major components analogous to yin and yang, e.g., *shao-chüeh, t'ai-chüeh* (*chüeh minor, chüeh maior*), and so on. Now it should be recalled[23] that the numeral value of the celestial stems that correspond to a circuit phase implies a polarization of the circuit phases into yin and yang (because odd numbers are yang and even numbers yin). It will be explained below that in principle this polarization indicates redundancy or deficiency.[24] "If the [celestial stem indicative of the polar quality] is yang, the [corresponding musical emblem] must be classed as "major"; if [the celestial stem] is yin [the corresponding musical emblem]

---

[19]See Needham, *Science and Civilisation in China*, Vol. IV:1, p. 140.
[20]It is of central importance in Chapters 70 and 71 of the *Su-wen*.
[21]In his *Lei-ching t'u-i* 2/37f as well as in the *Lei-ching* 26/588.
[22]See Needham, *Science and Civilisation in China*, Vol. II, Table XII, p. 262, as well as Vol. IV:1, pp. 253ff.
[23]See p. 66 above.
[24]See p. 76.

must be classed as "minor."[25] In other words, the musical emblem coupled with a circuit phase whose celestial stem is even (*bust, dust, fust, hust, kut*) is preceded by the qualifier "minor" (*shao*), while that coupled with a phase whose stem is odd (*ust, cust, esut, gust, just*) is preceded by the qualifier "major" (*t'ai*) (Fig. 13). All three kinds of circuit phases (*circuitus*

Fig. 13

magni, dominantes, et deversantes) can be marked by these split (polarized) musical emblems.[26]

LEVELS OF ENERGETIC CONFIGURATIONS

The Six Energetic Configurations (*sex configurationes, liu-ch'i*

[25]*Lei-ching t'u-i* 2/37b.
[26]*Ibid.* 2/38.

Table 4. Periodic Configurations (*chieh-ch'i* 節氣, *Configurationes articulatae*) Grouped into Steps (*pu* 步, *Gradus*)

Designation*	Beginning	Step
1 Great Cold	January 21	First
2 Beginning of Spring	February 5	
3 The Rains	February 20	
4 Awakening from Hibernation	March 7	
5 Spring Equinox	March 22	Second
6 Clear and Bright (Weather)	April 6	
7 Rain on the Grains	April 21	
8 Beginning of Summer	May 6	
9 Lesser Fullness (of Grain)	May 22	Third
10 Grain in Ear	June 7	
11 Summer Solstice	June 22	
12 Lesser Heat	July 8	
13 Great Heat	July 24	Fourth
14 Beginning of Autumn	August 8	
15 End of Heat	August 24	
16 White Dew	September 8	
17 Autumn Equinox	September 24	Fifth
18 Cold Dew	October 9	
19 Hoar Frost	October 24	
20 Beginning of Winter	November 8	
21 Lesser Snow	November 23	Last
22 Great Snow	December 7	
23 Winter Solstice	December 22	
24 Lesser Cold	January 6	

*The Chinese names of the fortngihtly periods may be found in any dictionary, or in Needham, *Science and Civilisation in China*, Vol. III, Table XXXV, p. 405.

六氣), are both semantic[27] and rhythmic[28] complements of the circuit phases. The energetic configurations are temporally linked to the circuit phases by reference to a division of the year into twenty-four "fortnightly periods," possibly in use since Chou times.[29] These fortnightly periods, properly called "nodal configurations" (*configurationes articulatae, chieh-ch'i* 節氣), have an average duration of 15.21 days.[30] If every four consecutive fortnightly periods are grouped into a "step" (*pu* 步, *gradus*; note the primary relationship of this technical term to space), a division of the year into six greater periods results. (See Table 4.)

These steps in turn serve as calendaric substratum for the energetic configurations. And as with the circuit phases, here again dominant and deversant aspects interact, in the form of

1. Dominant energetic configurations (*chu-ch'i* 主氣, *configurationes dominantes*). Each step is assigned a fixed configuration, its *configuratio dominans*, based on the "production sequence" (Sequence I) of the E.P.s (see Table 5).

2. Deversant energetic configurations (*k'o-ch'i* 客氣, *configurationes deversantes*). The assignment of the deversant configurations is somewhat more complicated, because this concept covers qualifying functions on several levels. It is based on the

Table 5. Dominant Configurations for the "Steps"

Step	Configuratio dominans
First	*yin flectentis ligni venti*
Second	*yin minoris ignis principis*
Third	*yang minoris ignis ministri*
Fourth	*yin maioris humi humidae*
Fifth	*splendoris yang metalli aridi*
Sixth	*yang maioris aquae algidae*

[27]The *circuitus* primarily determine qualities effective in time (*t'ien*), and the *configurationes* primarily determine those substantial in space (*ti*).
[28]The six-beat rhythm (= yin) as opposed to the five-beat rhythm (= yang) of the circuit phases.
[29]See *Science and Civilisation in China*, Vol. III, pp. 404ff.
[30]*Ibid.*

correspondence between terrestrial branches and configurations
and has the following aspects:

(a) The energetic configuration corresponding to the terrestrial branch of the year is called (configuratio) imperans caelo
(szu-t'ien chih ch'i 司天之氣, "Heaven-Governing Configuration") and assigned as configuratio deversans to the third of the
six steps.

Since the year 1968 was an esut-jast year, and the terrestrial branch jast
belongs to the configuratio yang minoris, yang minor is the (configuratio) imperans
caelo of that, year.

The deversant configuratio imperans caelo exercises a determination on three levels: It "regulates" the overall character of the

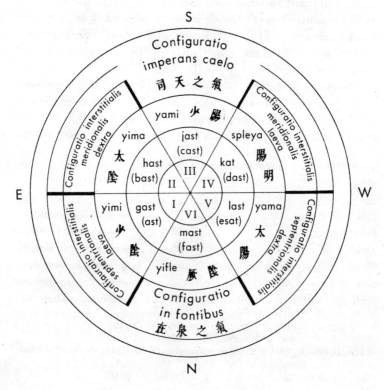

Fig. 14

year;[31] it determines the individual quality of the first (= rising) half of the year comprising the first three of the six "steps"; and it constitutes the specific deversant configuration of the third step (Fig. 14).

(b) *Configurationes deversantes* are assigned to the remaining steps in accordance with their terrestrial branches. Supposing that *jast—yang minor* is the *imperans caelo* of the year, determining the third step, the

configuratio deversans of the fourth step must be (*kat* 酉) *splendor yang*
configuratio deversans of the fifth step must be (*last* 戌) *yang maior*
configuratio deversans of the sixth step must be (*mast* 亥) *yin flectens*
configuratio deversans of the first step must be (*gast* 午) *yin minor*
configuratio deversans of the second step must be (*hast* 未) *yin maior*

(c) The deversor (*configuratio deversans*) of the sixth (= last) step is likewise given additional significance and a special designation: "Configuration in the Sources" (*configuratio in fontibus, tsai-ch'üan chih ch'i* 在泉之氣). The second, "setting" half of the year (steps 4, 5, and 6) shows a specific quality opposed step by step to that of the first half of the year. In the system of phase energetics, if the Six Energetic Configurations (*sex configurationes*) are arranged on the six points of a star in order of their terrestrial branches (see Fig. 5), each of the three axes of the star is studded with one yin configuration and one yang configuration, matched as specific energetic complements. The sixth step (*in fontibus*) always lies diametrically opposite the third step (*imperans caelo;* cf. Fig. 14 as well as Figs. 9 and 10).

(d) The remaining four *configurationes deversantes*[32] are called "intermediate energetic configurations" (*configurationes interstitiales, chien-ch'i* 間氣) because they lie between the configurations determining the characteristics of a given year. They are distinguished as right (*dextrae*) and left (*laevae*), southern and northern (*meridionales et septentrionales*). The reason for these distinctions is easily explained. To each *configuratio imperans*

---

[31]See *Su-wen* 74/776.
[32]That is, besides the *configurationes imperans caelo et in fontibus.*

caelo and *configuratio in fontibus* there are assigned two of the *configurationes interstitiales*, one to its left, the other to its right. Left and right are determined by standing in the pivot position (e.g., the *configuratio imperans caelo*) and facing the center. In any circular disposition of the configurations, the *configuratio imperans caelo* occupies the apex, the southernmost position,[33] and the *configuratio in fontibus* lies at the lowest point of the circle, the north (Fig. 14).

After having in this manner analyzed the basic conventions of phase energetics (*yün-ch'i*), we may take a closer look at their synthetic applications. In so doing we shall see, as in the discussion of yin and yang and the Five Evolutive Phases, that only a small fraction of the inflections and combinations that are logically and combinatorically possible are used; only these will be the object of our investigations.

The Systematic Inflections of the Basic Conventional Standards of Phase Energetics and the Consequences of These Inflections

THE INFLECTION OF THE CIRCUIT PHASES (*CIRCUITUS*)

The circuit phases define the overall quality of temporal periods that, in a way, constitute the cosmic background of meteorological and immunological situations represented in the changing qualities of the Six Energetic Configurations. Within the framework of phase energetics the circuit phases, taken by themselves, suffer only minor inflections, to which, however, there are attributed universal effects.

The inflection of the circuit phases consists in the fact that, as a rule and *a priori*, each such phase is classed either as redundant (*t'ai-kuo* 太過) or as deficient (*pu-chi* 不及) in energy, depending upon the yinyang quality of its celestial stem. In other words, all circuit phases qualified by an odd-numbered celestial stem (*ust, cust, esut, gust, just*) by definition are considered redundant (or *vigens, sheng* 盛) in energy; and all circuit phases qualified by an even-numbered celestial stem

[33]See the standard orientation of the quarters in Sequence 0 in Fig. 4.

(*bust, dust, fust, hust, kut*) are by definition considered energetically deficient (or *dilabens, shuai* 衰).[34]

As a consequence of the redundancy (*t'ai-kuo*) of a given circuit phase, its specific qualities by their duration and intensity tend to overwhelm those of the neighboring phases of the cycle and to diminish their effective duration, for these latter, because of the alternation of odd and even numbers, of yin and yang, of minor and major aspects, are by definition deficient in energy. The consequences of this may be detailed as follows:

(*a*) The specific effect of a *circuitus redundans* will set in some time before its calendaric beginning and will persevere beyond its calendaric end.

This postulate is consistent with logic; it seems doubtful, however, whether its classical legitimization may be sought precisely in the passage (*t'ai-kuo-che hsien-t'ien, pu-chi-che hou-t'ien* 太過者先天, 不及者後天) of the *Su-wen* 69/635, as is done by the commentators Ma Shih[35] and, following him, by Jen Ying-ch'iu.[36] That is why the latter rightly also quotes the *Su-wen* 71/735 (which is identical with *Su-wen* 71/764): "If a circuit phase is redundant [in energy] it sets in prematurely, if it is deficient [in energy] its arrival is postponed." For evident reasons[37] the classics contain no precise data on the temporal advance or lag due to redundancy. Jen Ying-ch'iu, however, thinks that 13 days in either direction would be the shift occasioned by the redundancy of a great circuit phase.

(*b*) The specific quality of a redundant circuit phase affects the qualities of the preceding and of the subsequent (by definition deficient) circuit phases. In the words of Chang Ching-yüeh: "Concerning the 'transformation due to equality' (*transformatio par, ch'i-hua: As* a rule, in the case of the redundancy of a yang year[38] the position of the subject sees luxuriant development (旺). If I then meet with an energetic configuration that ought to check me, it will be unable to conquer me; it will turn out instead that I am its equal (*ch'i* 齊, *par*)."[39]

---

[34]*Lei-ching t'u-i* 2/41f. We repeatedly draw on this book, which is based on the classical traditions but gives a clearer and more lucid account of the theory of phase energetics than the *Nei-ching* and its commentaries.

[35]*Su-wen* 69/636.

[36]*Wu-yün liu-ch'i*, p. 21.

[37]See below, p. 103.

[38]That is, a year qualified by an odd-numbered celestial stem.

[39]*Lei-ching t'u-i* 2/43.

He continues on the subject of circuit phases on equal energetic levels: "In a year of energetic redundancy (*t'ai-kuo chih nien* 太過之年) we inversely witness a transformation due to equality, with the [effects] conquering the position of the subjects. For instance, the *circuitus humi kung maioris* 太宮土運 inversely proves equal to the transformatory influence (*transformatio, hua*) of the *circuitus ligni*."[40]

These explanations show that the effect of a redundant C. P. on neighboring phases is quite similar to the effect defined as "violation" (*violatio, wu*) in regard to the E. P.[41] That the term in phase theory is *ch'i*, "equal," instead of *wu*, "violating," probably reflects the fact that here a constant rather than an abnormal relationship is being described.

The repercussions of energetic redundancy of the circuit phases on the climate, the society, and the microcosm are set forth in great detail in *Su-wen* 69/636f. for the *circuitus magni*, the circuit phases conditioning the overall qualities of the year: "If in a given year Wood is redundant, the energy of Wind will be rampant; the *humus lienalis*[42] will be subject to heteropathies; the people will fall ill with indigestion and subsequent diarrhea; and the intake of food will decrease and great fatigue will ensue.... [43] If in a given year Fire is redundant, the *metallum pulmonale*[44] will be subject to heteropathies; the people will suffer from malaria and subsequent cachexia; cough with bloody sputum and bloody diarrhea will occur.... If in a given year Earth is redundant, rain and humid weather will prevail; the *aqua renalis*[45] will be subject to heteropathies; the people will suffer from abdominal pains; depressions will occur.... If in a given year Metal is redundant, drought will be rampant; the *lignum hepaticum*[46] will be subject to hetero-

[40]*Ibid.*, 2/42.
[41]See above, p. 53.
[42]That is, the quality of the E.P. (Earth) corresponding to the *orbis lienalis*.
[43]This and what follows are only brief extracts from the classical text. A translation of the complete passage would necessitate a more ample explication of pathology and its terminology than the limits of the present study allow.
[44]That is, energy of the quality (Metal) which characterizes the *orbis pulmonalis*.
[45]That is, energy of the quality (Water) which characterizes the *orbis renalis*.
[46]The Wood of the *orbis hepaticus*.

pathics; the people will complain of pains in the flanks and in the abdomen; there will be red and painful eyes, styes, and temporary deafness.... If in a given year Water is redundant, the cold will be rampant and heteropathies will hurt the *ignis cardialis*;[47] the people will suffer from fevers, inner restlessness, rheumatic pains, and cold diseases in all parts of the body...."

Energetic deficiency (*pu-chi*) is the inverse of redundancy; the affected circuit phase becomes recessive in duration and intensity as compared to its neighbors. Hence its qualities are overlaid more or less by the qualities of the *phases* preceding and following it. As Chang Ching-yüeh puts it: "In a year of energetic deficiency that which [ought] to conquer [me] combines[48] with my own transformatory influence (*hua*). For instance, the transformatory [Earth] influence of the *circuitus humi kung minoris* (少宮土運) combines with that of Wood, the transformatory [Wood] influence of the *circuitus ligni chüeh minoris* (少角木運) combines with that of Metal...." and so on.[49]

The relation denoted by the technical term *chien-hua* 兼化, "combined transformation" (*transformatio coalescens*), is identical with that for which in connection with the E.P.s the term *ch'eng*, "accroachment," is used. The designation depends on whether it is viewed as a constant cyclic phenomenon (in the case of the circuit phases) or as an abnormal event (with the evolutive phases).

The repercussions of energetic deficiency on climate, society, and the microcosm are described in the *Su-wen* 69/642f.: "If in a given year Wood is deficient, drought will be rampant; the enlivening energy (*ch'i vitale*) will lack [sufficient] resonance; the vegetation will be retarded in its development... the people will suffer from cold, pains in the flanks and in the abdomen, flatulence, and watery diarrhea. ...If there is a *reversio*,[50] [on the other hand] scorching and sweltering heat will prevail [as an effect of] Fire.... If in a given year Fire is deficient, cold will be rampant; the regime of growth will not assert

---

[47]The Fire of the *orbis cardialis*.
[48]*Chien* 兼, *coalescere*.
[49]*Lei-ching t'ui-i* 2/42.
[50]This term is explained later on in this chapter, under the heading "Variability of Conquest and Return."

itself; plants will bud and then wither...the people will suffer
from pains in the chest, plethora of the midriff, heaviness of
the limbs, ischiatic pains, and sudden aphasia accompanied by
pain in the heart.... If in a given year Earth is deficient, Wind
will be rampant and the energetic configuration required for
the ripening [of the crops] will not establish itself;[51] the vegetation may develop luxuriantly... yet will only show a splendid
appearance, bearing no fruit.... The people will suffer from
intestinal disease and from cholera, heavy limbs, fatigue, and
abdominal pains.... If in a given year Metal is deficient,
scorching heat and Fire will be rampant; the enlivening energy
will assert itself and the energetic configuration favorable to
growth will prevail;[52] beings will develop luxuriantly...
people will suffer from short breath, fatigue of the upper limbs,
colds and hematuria.... If in a given year Water is deficient,
humidity will prevail; the energy favoring growth will assert
itself in a perverted manner; maturation will be accelerated...
the people will suffer from abdominal plethora, fatigue,...
ulcers, and diseases of the joints...."

From what precedes it is evident that—in conformity with the
constant alternation of odd- and even-numbered celestial
stems—the circuit phases librate regularly between redundancy
and deficiency. Eight times in the sixty-year cycle the qualities
of the circuit phases manifest themselves in a balanced way,
at the occasion of the "Year Coincidence" (*conventus annorum,
sui-hui* 歲會), which is accompanied by a "balanced energetic
configuration" (*configuratio aequa, p'ing-ch'i* 平氣).[53] The "Year
Coincidence"[54] occurs when the quality of the celestial stem of
the year (defined according to the C.P.s) tallies with that of the
terrestrial branch of the year (defined according to the correspondence between terrestrial branches and E.P.s). At the
same time the terrestrial branch of the year must correspond

[51]化氣不令.
[52]Rendered in technical usage: "will achieve single-handed conquest."
[53]*Su-wen* 68/620.
[54]Also called *sui-chih* 歲直, *positio recta anni*, or *sui-wei* 歲位. See *ibid.* and
note 3 in the *Su-wen i-shih*, p. 446 (Chapter 68).

to the E.P. Earth or to the "correct" branch of one of the four peripheral evolutive phases.

If the Twelve Terrestrial Branches are arranged on a circle divided into four equal segments, each segment encloses three "positions" (*wei* 位, *positiones*). Listed clockwise, the first of these positions is the "oblique" (*hsieh* 邪) or "wrong" position (*fei-ch'i-wei* 非其位) of the direction and its corresponding E.P.; the second or middle position (which is oriented upon a cardinal point) is the "correct" (*cheng* 正) position; and the third, a transitional position, is called "position of the E.P. Earth"(Fig. 15).[55]

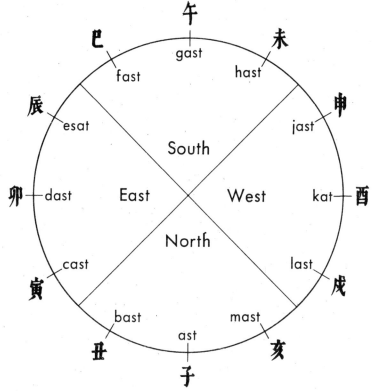

Fig. 15

According to the criteria just defined, a *conventus annorum* occurs in each cycle in the years shown in Table 6. The *Nei-ching* theory that the Year Conicidence involves a balanced energetic

[55]See p. 51 above as well as Fig. 10 in the *Su-wen i-shih*.

Table 6. Occurrence of the *Conventus annorum*

Year	*Transvectus sive circuitus*
dust-dast (4)	*ligni*
ust-last (11)	*humi*
cust-ast (13)	*aquae*
bust-kat (22)	*metalli*
fust-bast (26)	*humi*
ust-esat (41)	*humi*
esut-gast (55)	*ignis*
fust-hast (56)	*humi*

configuration (*configuratio aequa*) seems to rest solely on the passage of the *Su-wen* (68/620, *Su-wen i-shih*, p. 446) already quoted. It implies that the energetic redundancy or deficiency determined by the yinyang quality of the celestial stem assigned to the circuit phase is compensated for or neutralized by the opposite effective tendency of a terrestrial branch (at the same pole in the cycle of the E.P.s). Later experts, led by Chang Ching-yüeh of the Ming period,[56] advocate a theory that is in incomparably better agreement with principle, namely, that the "balanced energetic configuration" results whenever the circuit phase is damped by an energetic configuration in accordance with the conquest sequence (Sequence II) of the E.P.s. This relationship is designated as "Torment of Heaven" (*caeli supplicio*), and will be treated in greater detail in connection with the coupling modes of circuit phases and configurations.[57] The balanced energetic configuration, irrespective of the cyclical combination on which it rests, may be considered the ideal standard of the circuit phases; in *Su-wen* 70/659f, its effects are allotted space out of all relation to its practical significance. From this passage the principal effects of the three circuit phase inflections may be summarized as in Table 7.

---

[56]*Lei-ching t'u-i* 2/43: "If the circuit phase is redundant, it is damped; if it is deficient, it is assisted."
[57]See the following sections.

Table 7. The Three Energetic Configurations of the Circuit Phases

Circuitus	Configuratio aequa	Circuitus deficiens	Circuitus redundans
Wood (lignum)	Spreading harmony	Scanty harmony	Mighty development
Fire (ignis)	Rising brightness	Covered brightness	Flaming light
Earth (hvmus)	Founded transformation	Lowly limitation	Ample profusion
Metal (metallum)	Open arrangement	Subordinate change	Solid accomplishment
Water (aqua)	Silent submission	Meager trickle	Inundation

Based on the *Su-wen i-shih* 70/481; see its table uniting all corresspondences of the *configuratio aequa*.

Redundancy (*t'ai-kuo*), deficiency (*pu-chi*), and balanced energetic configuration (*p'ing-ch'i*), the "three energetic configurations" (*san-ch'i* 三氣) of the circuit phases,[58] cover practically all the inflections that the circuit phases by themselves exhibit in the classical and secondary literature. The interpretation of all the combinations and gradations resulting from the interaction of the great, dominant, and deversant circuit phases is left to the discretion of practitioners with a speculative leaning.

INFLECTIONS OF THE ENERGETIC CONFIGURATIONS

The relationship of energetic configurations (*ch'i*), for which we use the term "inflection," is conjugation or "yoking together"[59] of positions at equal levels but of opposite polarity: a dominant configuration (*configuratio dominans, chu-ch'i*) with a deversant configuration (*configuratio deversans, k'o-ch'i*).

The rhythm of the dominant configurations, immutable through the years, corresponds to the structive, concretive influence of immobile Earth. As "terrestrial configurations" (*ti-ch'i*)[60] they correspond to the structive components of climatic, immunological, and other cosmic situations. The deversant energetic configurations, changing every year, are

[58]*Su-wen* 70/659 *et passim.*
[59]*Chia-lin* 加臨 and *hsiang-lin* 相臨 (*contactus*) are variant designations of this concert of forces.
[60]*Lei-ching t'u-i* 2/47.

emblems of the ever-moving Heavens. As "celestial configurations" (*t'ien-ch'i*) they correspond to the active, dynamizing components of any climatic situation.[61]

Certain notions suggested by the concepts *dominus* and *deversor* are explicitly ruled out by definition, so that the deversant configuration is assigned the determinative and controlling function, and the dominant configuration must abide with a subordinate, associate role. Keeping in mind this particular interpretation will enable us to see, in what follows, the systematic cohesion between postulates and conventions that may otherwise seem irreconcilable. Between deversant and dominant configurations three types of conjugate relations are of prognostic significance: "agreement" (= identity, *t'ung-ch'i* 同氣, *configurationes communes*); "secundovection" or concurrence (= similar sense of flow, *shun* 順, *secundovectio*); "contravection" or contrariety (= opposite sense of flow, *ni* 逆, *contravectio*). Dominant and deversant configurations are "in agreement" if, for a certain "step" (*pu, gradus*) they agree simultaneously in the qualities of their corresponding evolutive phases and in their yinyang polarity.

The configurations must be examined separately for each step. Because there are different enumeration orders of dominant and deversant configurations,[62] "agreement" occurs only in 50 percent of the years; three years in which *configurationes communes* occur in either one or four of the six steps alternate with three years entirely devoid of "agreement."

"Agreement" between deversant and dominant configurations means that active and structive components in the macrocosm are identically oriented. This favors extreme development of the climatic and biotopic (immunological) qualities of the configurations; the inevitable repercussions on neighboring steps are disturbances and an unbalanced meteorological evolution. "Secundovection" and "contravection" presuppose that "if the configurations establish a regular relationship, there is harmony (氣相得則和), if not, a pathological situation ensues (不相得則病)."[63] An additional rule is: "If the *dominus*

[61]*Ibid.*, commentary by Wang Ping in the *Su-wen* 74/807.
[62]See the diagrams on pp. 72–75 above.
[63]*Su-wen* 67/597.

conquers, this is contravection; if the *deversor* conquers, this is secundovection."[64]

A relationship between a dominant and a deversant configuration is "regular" only if it is initiated by the active pole (the deversant configuration) and if it corresponds to a normal, "physiological" order (Sequence I or II) of the E.P.s.[65] Secundovection and a harmonious overall situation ensue if the dynamic energy of the active component (i.e., of the *deversor*) prevails in a productive (*sheng*) or checking (*k'o*) manner over the static energy of the structive component (i.e., the *dominus*).[66] From the inverse relation, with the *dominus* checking the *deversor*, a disharmonious and critical climatic situation ensues. An additional rule is: "If the "sovereign" (*chün* 君) steps into the place of the "minister" (*ch'en* 臣) this is secundovection; if the "minister" steps into the place of the 'sovereign' this is contravection."[67]

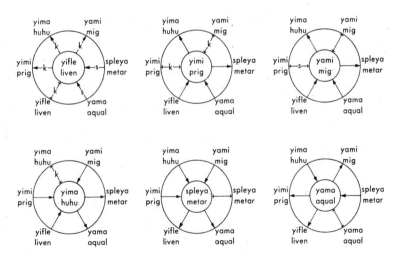

Fig. 16

[64]*Su-wen* 74/806. The word *ts'ung* 從, "following," is used here as a synonym of *shun* 順, *secundovectio.*

[65]Cf. p. 52 above.

[66]*Nei-ching chiang-i* 內經講義, p. 163; *Chung-i-hsüeh kai-lun*, p. 37f.

[67]*Su-wen* 68/620.

This rule applies exclusively to the E.P. Fire, split into *ignis principis* and *ignis ministri*. If, for a given step, the mobile deversant configuration is represented by minor yin (= *ignis principis*) and if this meets with *ignis ministri yang minoris* for *configuratio dominans* (= "in the fixed position" [*wei*]), secundovection ensues; if, in the contrary, the *configuratio deversans ignis ministri* steps into the (fixed) position of the *configuratio dominans ignis principis*, contravection is the consequence.[68]

A comparative view of the inflections of the energetic configurations is given in Fig. 16.

Table 8. *Yin flectens imperat caelo*

Gradus	Configuratio Deversans	Dominans	Meteorology	Pathology
I	spleya metar	yifle liven	First onset of severe cold, onset of the "destructive configuration" (*sha-ch'i*)	Cold in the right side, in the lower parts
II	yama aqual	yimi prig	Persistent cold, hoar frost; spread of the "destructive configuration"; deterioration of the shoots; alternation of cold and rain	Hotness emanating from the center of the body
III	yifle liven	yami mig	Frequent windy days	Spontaneous tears, ringing of the ears, dizziness
IV	yimi prig	yima huhu	Sweltering heat	Icterus, swellings all over the body
V	yima huhu	spleya metar	Alternation of humid and dry weather; finally cool days, rain and wind	
VI	yami mig	yama aquat	Return of warm weather, powerful onset of yang, hatching of the insects; rivers do not freeze; powerful development of the telluric configuration; the vegetation starts to grow; people feel at ease	Fever diseases

Immunology: Disposition for "wind" diseases during the first half, for "heat" diseases during the second half of the year; in the middle of the year alternation of "wind" and "drought."

General Presciptions: For harmonizing the constitution, pungent *sapores* during the first half, salty *sapores* during the second half of the year.

[68]See also *Su-wen* 67/597 and the commentary of Chang Chih-ts'ung on p. 600 of the same text.

Secundovection between the two configurations of a step favors a balanced meteorological and a stable and propitious immunological situation; contravection between the configurations entails a tense, unstable meteorological and an insecure or even dangerous immunological situation.

We sum up in Tables 8–13 the concrete climatic and immunological consequences of a deversant and a dominant energetic configuration, as they are described in Chapter 71 of the *Su-wen*.[69] Here and elsewhere throughout the book these acronyms will be used to refer to the Five Evolutive Phases and their emblems and qualities:

lignum, ventus (Wood and Wind)	*liven*
ignis principis (Sovereign Fire)	*prig*
ignis ministri (Ministerial Fire)	*mig*
humus humida or *humiditas* (Earth and Humidity)	*huhu*
metallum aridum or *ariditas* (Metal and Dryness)	*metar*
aqua algida or *algor* (Water and Cold)	*aqual*

The Coupling (Contactus, hsiang-lin 相臨) of Circuit Phases and Energetic Configurations 運氣相臨

For didactic reasons we have analyzed separately the inflections of circuit phases and energetic configurations. In practice, data of immediate significance are coupled, just as weather always is the combined effect of terrestrial, structive (topological, hydrological, etc.) factors and changing macrocosmic, active influences (temporal variables).

The coupling of circuit phases and configurations may take place on any level, but in practice prognosis is based on a few salient data, which alone are described in great detail. On this premise we shall consider the coupling of (*a*) *circuitus magnus* (Great Circuit Phase) and *configuratio imperans caelo* (Heaven-Governing Configuration); (*b*) Great Circuit Phase, Heaven-Governing Configuration, and the evolutive phase of the terrestrial branch; and (*c*) Great Circuit Phase and *configuratio in fontibus* (Configuration in the Sources).

[69]These tables are based on the summaries in *Su-wen i-shih* 71/519ff.

Table 9. *Yin minor imperat caelo*

Gradus	Configuratio Deversans	Dominans	Meteorology	Pathology
I	yama aqual	yifle liven	Onset of cold, hibernation of insects and animals; freezing of brooks, wind; bitter cold (covered sky)	Arthroses, arthritis, sciatica; if there is a change to "heat," inner ulcers and outward swellings
II	yifle liven	yimi prig	With the onset of the yang configuration: wind; spring weather, budding and thriving of the vegetation interspersed with cold days	Retention of urine; dim sight, inflammations of the eye; plethoric heat
III	yimi prig	yami mig	Great heat, powerful development of the flora and fauna; sporadic cold days.	Circulation troubles, pains in the heart; alternation of heat. and cold; short breath, red eyes
IV	yima huhu	yima huhu	Onset of damp heat; abundant and prolonged rains, alternation of cold and hot weather	Dry throat, icterus; cold in the head, blocked nasal passages, nosebleed; excretion of mucus
V	yami mig	spleya metar	Return of dry (or moderately damp) heat, thriving vegetation; "healthy" weather	(Fever diseases)
VI	spleya metar	yama aqual	Drought; cooler days; finally cloudy and rainy days	Coughs, phthisis (hemoptisis), intestinal diseases

Immunology: Fever diseases during the first, "cold" diseases (that may likewise be accompanied by fever) during the second half of the year. Propensity to short breath, hemoptisis, epistaxis (nosebleed), red eyes, hordeolum, inflammation in the canthus; gastritis; pains in the heart; pains in the back; tympanism, bloody feces, dry throat.

General Prescriptions: For harmonizing the *configuratio ignis* during the first half of the year: salty and cold prescriptions; if energy is to be drained off: pungent *sapores;* during the second half of the year: sour *sapores* for the concentration and pungent *sapores* for the draining off of energy.

Table 10. *Yin maior imperat oaelo*

Gradus	Configuratio Deversans	Dominans	Meteorology	Pathology
I	*yifle liven*	*yifle liven*	Cold recedes, spring comes accompanied by wind, budding vegetation, mild weather; finally alternation of humid and windy weather, yet little rain	Diseases of *hsüeh** and of the muscles and joints; fatigue, atrophies
II	*yimi prig*	*yimi prig*	Regime of sweltering heat; powerful development of the vegetation; timely rains and humidity	Epidemics of diverse origins and symptomatology
III	*yima huhu*	*yami mig*	At first warm weather benefiting the vegetation; timely rains; finally cooler days	Fatigue, swellings of the abdomen and belly
IV	*yami mig*	*yima huhu*	Alternation of sultry, oppressive and cool, windy days; dew, mists, humidity; autumnal overall characteristics of the weather	Hot skin; petechial hemorrhages; malaria; plethora, chiefly abdominal; swellings
V	*spleya metar*	*spleya metar*	Autumnal weather, cold, fog, first hoar frosts; leaves are dropped, early cold periods	Skin diseases
VI	*yama aqual*	*yama aqual*	Severe cold, abundant precipitation; then frost and light snow	Diseases of the joints (rheumatism, sciatica)

Immunology: Abdominal plethora induced by cold and humid weather.
General Prescriptions: Sharp and pungent *sapores*.

*For this term, see p. 185.

Table 11. *Yang minor imperat caelo*

	Configuratio			
Gradus	Deversans	Dominans	Meteorology	Pathology
I	*yimi prig*	*yifle liven*	Stormy weather; the cold recedes; budding vegetation, mild cold reversals	Epidemies; hemorrhages from nose and mouth; red eyes, cough; stagnant circulation; headache; plethora in the chest; ulcerous skin
II	*yima huhu*	*yimi prig*	Cloudy, hazy weather, rain	Cough, contravections of energy [circulatory collapses]; vomiting, sore throat; headache, unconsciousness, fainting; suppurating ulcers
III	*yami mig*	*yami mig*	Great dry heat	Inner heat [heat stroke]; deafness, dim sight, hyperemia in the head; ulcers; cough colds in the head, nosebleed, obstructed nasal passages
IV	*spleya metar*	*yima huhu*	Cooler days, sporadic hot weather; dew	Plethora, fatigue
V	*yama aqual*	*spleya metar*	Further cooling off; transition to rainy cold autumn weather	—
VI	*yifle liven*	*yama aqual*	Stormy and foggy weather (fog, dew)	Heartache, coughs

Immunology: The antagonism of heat and cold induces ulcers without, malaria, diarrhea within; deafness; vomiting; dim eyesight.

General prescriptions: Salty and pungent prescriptions as a general rule; sour *sapores* for draining off energy.

Table 12. *Splendor yang imperat caelo*

Gradus	Configuratio Deversans	Configuratio Dominans	Meteorology	Pathology
I	yima huhu	yifle liven	Early frost, sever cold, ice; finally rain	Plethora accompanied by fever, flushed, puffy face; sleepiness, nosebleed, sneezing; dark colored or red and scarce urine
II	yami mig	yimi prig	Spreading warmth, germinating vegetation	Epidemies and strokes
III	spleya metar	yami mig	Preponderantly cool weather; later drought and heat; then again damp weather	Alternation of chills and heat flushes
IV	yama aqual	yima huhu	Wet and cold weather	Epileptiform symptoms; tremblings, deliriums, shallow accelerated breath; dry throat; thirst, sore throat; ulcers and furuncles; malaria accompanied by shivers; limp extremities; hematuria.
V	yifle liven	spleya metar	Spring weather with flourishing vegetation	
VI	yimi prig	yama aqual	Warm weather, insects emerging again; brooks do not freeze.	Fever diseases

Immunology: Coughs, dry throat; alternation of heat (fever) and frost (shivers); ulcers.
General Prescriptions: Salty prescriptions for harmonizing the constitution.

THE COUPLING OF GREAT CIRCUIT PHASE AND HEAVEN-GOVERNING CONFIGURATION

The Great Circuit Phase covers the active aspect, primarily defined in time, of the overall characteristics of the year; the Heaven-Governing Configuration indicates the structive aspect, primarily based on topological factors of the entire year.[70] Because of the fundamental importance of these two elements, their mutual relationship deserves priority of discussion. When the Great Circuit Phase and the Heaven-Governing Configura-

[70]See the *Su-wen i-shih* 66/418f.

Table 13. *Yang maior imperat caelo*

| | Configuratio | | | |
Gradus	Deversans	Dominans	Meteorology	Pathology
I	yami mig	yifle liven	Powerfully rising warmth, early germination of plants	Epidemies; fevers; headaches; sores and furuncles
II	spleya metar	yimi prig	Cold reversals with damage to the vegetation; cool weather	Plethora, stagnant circulation
III	yama aqual	yami mig	Rain, moist and cool weather	Sensations of outward chills and inner heat; inner ulcers; derangements, depressive states; high fevers with slowed down pulse, limpness; diarrhea
IV	yifle liven	yima huhu	Wind and rain; thriving vegetation	
V	yimi prig	spleya metar	*Reversio* of yang, warm weather, ripening flora	
IV	yima huhu	yama aqual	Moist and cool weather; later frosts, fog; overcast weather with wind	

Immunology: Atrophies, weakness of the muscles; diarrhea; dark or bloody urine. General Prescriptions; Sharp prescriptions for drying and calefaction (to compensate for the cool and moist over-all character of the year).

tion couple as a result of the regular calendaric combinations between celestial stems and terrestrial branches, the qualities and sequences of the evolutive phases generate five kinds of interaction:

1. The Heaven-Governing Configuration produces the Great Circuit Phase *(ch'i sheng yün)*; there prevails *transformatio secundovehens* ("concurring transformation," *shun-hua* 順化.

2. The Heaven-Governing Configuration checks the Great Circuit Phase *(ch'i k'o yün)*; there prevails *caeli supplicium* ("Torment of Heaven," *t'ien-hsing* 天刑).

3. The Great Circuit Phase produces the Heaven-Governing Configuration; there prevails *contravectio parva* ("minor contrariety," *hsiao-ni* 小逆).

4. The Great Circuit Phase checks the Heaven-Governing

Configuration (*yün k'o ch'i*); this is *contactus sine harmonia* ("disharmonious coupling," *pu-ho* 不和).

5. The Great Circuit Phase and the Heaven-Governing Configuration are of identical quality (*yün ch'i hsiang-t'ung*); there prevails *congruentia caelestis* ("Congruence of Heaven," *t'ien-fu* 天符). As may be seen in Fig. 17, each of these five relationships occurs twelve times in the course of a 60–year cycle.

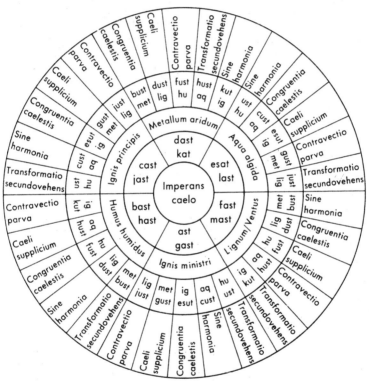

Fig. 17

The technical terms used to designate the five coupling modes suggest their climatic and immunological consequences. As a rule, the decisive role in conditioning positive empirical phenomena is attributed to the energetic configuration (*ch'i*) immanent in the terrestrial (topological, etc.) situation, as opposed to the cosmic influences variable in time (*circuitus, yün*). Now if it happens that these latter influences seem to arise out of and reflect the terrestrial conditions—in other words if the circuit phase proceeds from the ruling energetic configuration (Heaven-Governing Configuration) in accordance with Sequence I of the E.P.s, a harmonious meteorological evolution and a "concurring transformation" ensue. Under any other conditions, tension, critical antagonism, and extreme weather situations must be expected. These tensions and antagonisms will remain within narrow bounds and may eventually be completely counterbalanced or—to the contrary, may indirectly be increased to critical intensity—if the leading influence on the overall energetic setup of the year is exercised by the circuit phase, in other words if the terrestrial situation appears to be determined by the cosmic influences variable in time. In this case there results only a "minor contrariety."

Far more powerful tensions result from inhibitory relationships developing in accordance with the E.P. conquest sequence (Sequence II). This is the case when the Heaven-Governing Configuration checks or restrains the Great Circuit Phase, entailing a "Torment of Heaven," the mutilation of cosmic influences; or, still more critically, when the Great Circuit Phase checks the Heaven-Governing Configuration, thus bringing about a "disharmonious coupling." Analogously, even more critical than the coincidence of equidirectional deversant and dominant configurations is the match called "Congruence of Heaven" (*t'ien-fu* 天符), involving a Heaven-Governing Configuration and a Great Circuit Phase of identical quality; such "singleness of effort" favors extreme meteorological developments.

THE COUPLING OF THE GREAT CIRCUIT PHASE, HEAVEN-GOVERNING
CONFIGURATION, AND EVOLUTIVE PHASE OF THE TERRESTRIAL
BRANCH

We have earlier discussed a situation called "Year Coincidence" (*conventus annorum, sui-hui*), defined as a qualitative coincidence between the celestial stem (of the Great Circuit Phase) and the

Table 14. Occurrence of the *Congruentia caelestis maxima*

Year	*Circuitus/Transvectus/Configuratio imperans caelo*
bust-kat (22)	*metalli*
fust-bast (26)	*humi*
esut-gast (55)	*ignis*
fust-hast (56)	*humi*

terrestrial branch of the year, determined in accordance with the Five E.P.s. The agreement is even more inclusive if the "Year Coincidence" coincides with the "Congruence of Heaven" —in other words, when the qualities of the Great Circuit Phase, Heaven-Governing Configuration, and evolutive phase of the terrestrial branch are congruent. This event, called the Supreme Congruence of Heaven (*congruentia caelestis maxima, t'ai-i*

Table 15. Occurrence of the *Congruentia caelestis communis*

Year	*Transvectus sive circuitus*
gust-gast (7)	*metalli*
just-jast (9)	*ligni*
ust-last (11)	*humi*
gust-ast (37)	*metalli*
just-cast (39)	*ligni*
ust-esat (41)	*humi* *

*It should be noted that the years 41 and 11 have already been enumerated among the ordinary *conventus annorum*.

Table 16. Supervention of the *Conventus annorum communis*

Year	*Transvectus sive circuitus*
hust-hast (8)	*aquae*
kut-kat (10)	*ignis principis*
kut-fast (30)	*ignis ministri*
hust-bast (38)	*aquae*
kut-dast (40)	*ignis principis*
kut-mast (60)	*ignis ministri*

Table 17. Couplings and Inflections of Circuit Phases and Energetic Configurations

Year	Stem/Branch	Configuratio imperans caelo	Circuitus magnus	Configuratio in fontibus
1	ust-ast	yimi, prig	humus redundans	spleya, metar
2	bust-bast	yima, huhu	metallum deficiens	yama, aqual
3	cust-cast	yami, mig	aqua redundans	yifle, liven
4	dust-dast	spleya, metar	lignum deficiens	yimi, prig
5	esut-esat	yama, aqual	ignis redundans	yima, huhu
6	fust-fast	yifle, liven	humus deficiens	yami, mig
7	gust-gast	yimi, prig	metallum redundans	spleya, metar
8	hust-hast	yima, huhu	aqua deficiens	yama, aqual
9	just-jast	yami, mig	lignum redundans	yifle, liven
10	kut-kat	spleya, metar	ignis deficiens	yimi, prig
11	ust-last	yama, aqual	humus redundans	yima, huhu
12	bust-mast	yifle, liven	metallum deficiens	yami, mig
13	cust-ast	yimi, prig	aqua redundans	spleya, metar
14	dust-bast	yima, huhu	lignum deficiens	yama, aqual
15	esut-cast	yami, mig	ignis redundans	yifle, liven
16	fust-dast	spleya, metar	humus deficiens	yimi, prig
17	gust-esat	yama, aqual	metallum redundans	yima, huhu
18	hust-fast	yifle, liven	aqua deficiens	yami, mig
19	just-gast	yimi, prig	lignum redundans	spleya, metar
20	kut-hast	yima, huhu	ignis deficiens	yama, aqual

Contactus sive inflectio	Victoria	Reversio	Transformationes		
			Configuratio imperans caelo	Configuratio in fontibus	Circuitus magnus
1 transformatio secundovehens	—	—	calor	pluvia	ariditas
2 transformatio secundovehens	calor[a]	algor	humor	limpiditas	algor
3 sine harmonia	—	—	ardor	algor	ventus
4 caeli supplicium; conventus annorum	limpiditas	calor	ariditas	ventus	calor
5 caeli supplicium	—	—	algor	calor	humor
6 caeli supplicium	ventus	limpiditas	ventus	humor	ardor
7 caeli supplicium; congruentia caelestis communis	—	—	calor	limpiditas	ariditas
8 caeli supplicium; conventus annorum communis	pluvia	ventus	pluvia	algor	algor
9 contravectio parva; congruentia caelestis communis	—	—	ardor	ventus	ventus
10 sine harmonia; conventus annorum communis	algor	pluvia	ariditas	calor	calor
11 sine harmonia: conventus annorum; congruentia caelestis communis	—	—	algor	humor	humor
12 sine harmonia	calor	algor	ventus	limpiditas	ardor
13 sine harmonia; conventus annorum	—	—	calor	algor	limpiditas
14 sine harmonia	limpiditas	calor	pluvia	ventus	algor
15 congruentia caelestis	—	—	ardor	ardor	ventus
16 contravectio parva	ventus	limpiditas	limpiditas	pluvia	calor
17 contravectio parva	—	—	algor	limpiditas	pluvia
18 contravectio parva	pluvia	ventus	ventus	algor	ardor
19 contravectio parva	—	—	calor	ventus	limpidias
20 contravectio parva	algor	pluvia	pluvia	ardor	algor

Note: Established with the aid of Table 28 in the *Su-wen i-shih*, p. 559.
[a]Latin meteorological terms used in the last five columns may be interpreted as follows: *calor* (hot weather), *humor* (damp weather), *algor* (cold weather), *ventus* (wind), *ariditas* (drought), *limpiditas* (clear weather), *pluvia* (rains), *ardor* (scorching heat).

Table 17 (Continued)

Year	Stem/Branch	Configuratio imperans caelo	Circuitus magnus	Configuratio in fontibus
21	ust-jast	yami, mig	humus redundans	yifle, liven
22	bust-kat	spleya, metar	metallum deficiens	yimi, prig
23	cust-last	yama, aqual	aqua redundans	yima, huhu
24	dust-mast	yifle, liven	lignum deficiens	yami, mig
25	esul-ast	yimi, prig	ignis redundans	spleya, metar
26	fust-bast	yima, huhu	humus deficiens	yama, aqual
27	gust-cast	yami, mig	metallum redundans	yifle, liven
28	hust-dast	spleya, metar	aqua deficiens	yimi, prig
29	just-esat	yama, aqual	lignum redundans	yima, huhu
30	kut-fast	yifle, liven	ignis deficiens	yami, mig
31	ust-gast	yimi, prig	humus redundans	spleya, metar
32	bust-hast	yima, huhu	metallum deficiens	yama, aqual
33	gust-jast	yami, mig	aqua redundans	yifle, liven
34	dust-kat	spleya, metar	lignum deficiens	yimi, prig
35	esul-last	yama, aqual	ignis redundans	yima, huhu
36	fust-mast	yifle, liven	humus deficiens	yami, mig
37	gust-ast	yimi, prig	metallum redundans	spleya, metar
38	hust-bast	yima, huhu	aqua deficiens	yama, aqual
39	just-cast	yami, mig	lignum redundans	yifle, liven
40	kut-dast	spleya, metar	ignis deficiens	yimi, prig

Contactus sive inflectio	Victoria	Reversio	Transformationes		Circuitus magnus
			Configuratio imperans caelo	Configuratio in fontibus	
21 transformatio secundovehens	—	—	ardor	pluvia	ventus
22 congruentia caelestis maxima; conventus annorum	calor	algor	ariditas	limpiditas	calor
23 congruentia caelestis	—	—	algor	algor	pluvia
24 congruentia caelestis	limpiditas	calor	ventus	ventus	ardor
25 congruentia caelestis	—	—	calor	calor	limpiditas
26 congruentia caelestis maxima; conventus annorum	ventus	limpiditas	pluvia	pluvia	algor
27 caeli supplicium	—	ventus	ardor	limpiditas	ventus
28 transformatio secundovehens	pluvia	ventus	limpiditas	algor	calor
29 transformatio secundovehens	—	pluvia	algor	ventus	humor
30 transformatio secundovehens; conventus annorum communis	algor	—	ventus	ardor	ardor
31 transformatio secundovehens	—	algor	calor	pluvia	ariditas
32 transformatio secundovehens	calor	—	humor	limpiditas	algor
33 sine harmonia	—	—	ardor	algor	ventus
34 caeli supplicium	limpiditas	calor	ariditas	ventus	calor
35 caeli supplicium	—	—	algor	calor	humor
36 caeli supplicium	ventus	limpiditas	ventus	humor	ardor
37 caeli supplicium; congruentia caelestis communis	—	—	calor	limpiditas	ariditas
38 caeli supplicium; conventus annorum communis	pluvia	ventus	pluvia	algor	algor
39 contravectio parva; congruentia caelestis communis	—	—	ardor	ventus	ventus
40 sine harmonia; conventus annorum communis	algor	pluvia	ariditas	calor	calor

Table 17 (*Continued*)

Year	Stem/Branch	Configuratio imperans caelo	Circuitus magnus	Configuratio in fontibus
41	ust-esat	yama, aqual	humus redundans	yima, huhu
42	bust-fast	yifle, liven	metallum deficiens	yami, mig
43	cust-gast	yimi, prig	aqua redundans	spleya, metar
44	dust-hast	yima, huhu	lignum deficiens	yama, aqual
45	esut-jast	yami, mig	ignis redundans	yifle, liven
46	fust-kat	spleya, metar	humus deficiens	yimi, prig
47	gust-last	yama, aqual	metallum redundans	yima, huhu
48	hust-must	yifle, liven	aqua deficiens	yami, mig
49	just-ast	yimi, prig	lignum redundans	spleya, metar
50	kut-bast	yima, huhu	ignis deficiens	yama, aqual
51	ust-cast	yamĩ, mig	humus redundans	yifle, liven
52	bust-dast	spleya, metar	metallum deficiens	yimi, prig
53	cust-esat	yama, aqual	aqua redundans	yima, huhu
54	dust-fast	yifle, liven	lignum deficiens	yami, mig
55	esut-gast	yimi, prig	ignis redundans	spleya, metar
56	fust-hast	yima, huhu	humus deficiens	yama, aqual
57	gust-jast	yami, mig	metallum redundans	yifle, liven
58	hust-kat	spleya, metar	aqua deficiens	yimi, prig
59	just-last	yama, aqual	lignum redundans	yima, huhu
60	kut-mast	yifle, liven	ignis deficiens	yami, mig

	Contactus sive inflectio	Victoria	Reversio	Transformationes		
				Configuratio imperans caelo	Configuratio in fontibus	Circuitus magnus
41	sine harmonia; conventus annorum; congruentia caelestis communis	—	—	algor	humor	humor
42	sine harmonia	calor	algor	ventus	limpiditas	ardor
43	sine harmonia	—	—	calor	algor	limpiditas
44	sine harmonia	limpiditas	calor	pluvia	ventus	algor
45	congruentia caelestis	—	—	ardor	ardor	ventus
46	contravectio parva	ventus	limpiditas	limpiditas	pluvia	calor
47	contravectio parva	—	—	algor	limpiditas	pluvia
48	contravectio parva	pluvia	ventus	ventus	algor	ardor
49	contravectio parva	—	—	calor	ventus	limpiditas
50	contravectio parva	algor	pluvia	pluvia	ardor	algor
51	transformatio secundovehens	—	—	ardor	pluvia	ventus
52	congruentia caelestis	calor	algor	ariditas	limpiditas	calor
53	congruentia caelestis	—	—	algor	algor	pluvia
54	congruentia caelestis	limpiditas	calor	ventus	ventus	ardor
55	conventus annorum; congruentia caelestis maxima	—	—	calor	calor	limpiditas
56	conventus annorum; congruentia caelestis maxima	ventus	limpiditas	pluvia	pluvia	algor
57	caeli supplicium	—	—	ardor	limpiditas	ventus
58	transformatio secundovehens	pluvia	ventus	limpiditas	algor	calor
59	transformatio secundovehens	—	—	algor	ventus	humor
60	transormatio secundovehens; conventus annorum communis	algor	pluvia	ventus	ardor	ardor

t'ien-fu[71] 太乙天符), occurs four times during the sixty-year cycle, in the years shown in Table 14.

Because of the qualitative coincidence of three significant elements it is also called "Triple Conjunction" (*coniunctio triplex, san-ho* 三合).[72] Probably because of the harmonizing effect of the *conventus annorum*, it favors an equable evolution of the weather.[73]

THE COUPLING OF GREAT CIRCUIT PHASE AND CONFIGURATION IN THE SOURCES

The "Configuration in the Sources" (*configuratio in fontibus, tsai-ch'üan chih ch'i* 在泉之氣) by its cyclical position and quality always complements the Heaven-Governing Configuration. As ruler of the second half of the year it compensates the energetic quality of the first three "steps." This function comes into particular relief if a qualitative resonance (defined in accordance with the Five E.P.s) is established between this configuration and the Great Circuit Phase (the latter, by definition, always shows either energetic redundancy or energetic deficiency). If the celestial stem of a year is odd-numbered, so that the configuration compensates for energetic redundancy of the Great Circuit Phase, the ensuing qualitative coincidence is called "Shared Congruence of Heaven" (*congruentia caelestis communis, t'ung t'ien-fu* 同天符) (see Table 15). If the celestial stem of the year is even-numbered, so that the configuration compensates for energetic deficiency of the Great Circuit Phase, the coincidence is called "Shared Year Coincidence" (*conventus annorum communis, t'ung sui-hui* 同歲會)(see Table 16).[74] In using musical emblems, yang stems are always signaled by the qualifier "major" (*t'ai, maior*) and yin stems by "minor" (*shao, minor*). Therefore the years of a Shared Congruence of Heaven are collectively called the "Triply Major" (*tres maiores, san-t'ai* 三

---

[71]Literally "*tessera congruens caelestis Uni maioris,*" in which "*Unum maior*" is a name of the Celestial Pole.
[72]In *Su-wen* 66/588.
[73]*Su-wen* 66/588 and the commentaries on p. 589.
[74]*Lei-ching t'u-i* 2/53 *et passim*.

太), and the years of an Agreement in Year Coincidence are designated as the "Triply Minor" (*tres minores, san-shao* 三少).[75] In keeping with the compensatory function of the Configuration at the Source, its resonance with the Great Circuit Phase generally favors balanced meteorological developments.

All the couplings and inflections of circuit phases and energetic configurations are shown in Table 17.

Empirical Inflections in Phase Energetics

The inflections, combinations, and resonances of energetic configurations and circuit phases are deduced from the postulates of the correspondence system. Although this system is founded upon extensive empirical observation, it is far too abstract to be fundamentally alterable by climatic and meteorological variations. Response to eventualities is concentrated in what we call "empirical inflections," expressed as simple "if...then" rules. With their help, "unusual" meteorological phenomena are reconciled with theory. The empirical inflections of phase energetics have no predictive power. We mention them merely as clues to ancient scientific methods.

VARIABILITY OF CONQUEST AND RETURN

By a rule explained above,[76] the Heaven-Governing Configuration determining the overall characteristics of the year in addition has particular significance for the climatic qualities of the first three "steps," that is to say, of the first half of the year. If the quality assigned to this configuration actually turns out to be that of meteorological phenomena observed in the first six months, this event is called "Conquest" (*sheng* 勝, *victoria* [*configurationis imperantis caelo*]). Similarly, the complementary "Configuration in the Sources" holds particular significance for the climatic qualities of the last three "steps," the second half of the year. The pattern conditioned by this configuration counterbalances that established by the Heaven-Governing Configuration, therefore the appearance of phenomena correspond-

[75] *Lei-ching t'u-i* 2/53.
[76] See p. 74–75.

ing in quality to the Configuration in the Sources is called "Return" (*fu* 復, *reversio* [*configurationis in fontibus*]).

The point is that, although the two configurations are both assigned particular qualities and exact temporal extent, these are not modified or even threatened by temporal or qualitative variations in the world of experience.[77]

This separation of theory and empirical reality tends to deprive the system of phase energetics of all scientific conviction; a theory that cannot be stringently tested by reality is empty speculation. The rules by which Conquest and Return are judged establish only a loose link between theory and empirical data.

They may be summarized thus:

1. The Conquest of the Heaven-Governing Configuration during the first half of the year should be relieved during the second half by the complementary Return of the Configuration in the Sources.

2. If the quality corresponding to the Heaven-Governing Configuration is not marked in the meteorological phenomena of the first half of the year—in other words if there has been no Conquest—there should likewise be no Return during the second half of the year.

3. If the Conquest of the Heaven-Governing Configuration is not followed by a Return of the Configuration in the Sources, natural catastrophes and epidemics must be expected.

THE EMPIRICAL DELAY OF THE THEORETICAL DATES OF THE CONFIGURATIONS

A theory developed exclusively in the interpolated Chapter 72 of the *Su-wen*[78] tries to account for the fact that the systematic

[77]*Su-wen* 74/804 and *Su-wen i-shih*, p. 600.

[78]See pp. 881 ff. We know chapters 72 and 73 of the *Su-wen* were missing when Wang Ping edited the work in 762. Nevertheless all of the modern editions of the *Su-wen* furnish (most often as an appendix) a version of those chapters purportedly rediscovered later. The text of Chapter 72 was "found" by Liu Wen-shu (see note 7 above) during the Sung period and published in the Appendix to his *Su-wen ju-shih yün-ch'i lun-ao* 素問入式運氣論奧. There are good reasons to believe that this chapter was written or at least

postulates of phase energetics are frequently out of step with the actual course of the weather. This theory, which refers only to the cycle of the Six Energetic Configurations, supposes that sometimes anomalies are caused by the fact that the Heaven-Governing Configuration (or the Configuration at the Source) does not take its place (*loco non considit, pu ch'ien-cheng* 不遷正) or does not relinquish its place (*locum non dat, pu t'ui wei* 不退位) on the date postulated by theory. Similarly it is supposed that—with the configurations or steps visualized as arranged on a circle[79]—the intermediate energetic configurations likewise shift at the wrong time.

Thus for instance the *configuratio deversans yang maioris* may not ascend (*sheng pu ch'ien* 升不前) in time from the *interstitium dextrum* [*configurationis in fontibus*] into the *configurationis imperantis caelo*; or the *configuratio yin maioris* may not descend (*chiang pu hsia* 降不下) in time into the *configurationis in fontibus*.

The Problematical Scientific Character of Phase Energetics

Phase energetics is by far the weakest link we have so far discerned in the correspondence system of Chinese medicine. Its methodical defects, both practical and theoretical, are due almost without exception to the inadequacy of its technical foundations.

A comprehensive and unequivocal description of the subject matter of phase energetics—energetic processes of worldwide dimensions—requires adequate astronomical instruments, a far-flung network of precisely coordinated observatories, uniform and exact measurements of time, and calibrated instruments, all of which have become generally available in China only in our century. The authors of the theory of phase energetics, living probably 1500 years before our time, had to rely on very fragmentary empirical data to apply and verify their systematic speculations. This explains the two principal defects of their system: (1) It is coupled only to the rhythms of sun and

---

arranged by Liu himself (see *Szu-pu tsung-lu: I-yao-pien* 四部總錄醫藥編, p. 334).

[79]See Fig. 15.

moon and does not permit precise statements on the qualities of events whose temporal dimension exceeds 60 years. (2) It completely disregards geographical coordinates and therefore has nothing to say about the meteorological situation at a definite place. Since all meteorological events happen at definite places, one may feel tempted to reject the scientific value of phase energetics altogether. Such a categoric rejection would be unjustified, for the basic pattern of phase energetics is worth taking seriously as a paradigm for the further development of modern medicine. Taking into account the complex nature of the phenomena described, phase energetics offers a simple, transparent, and rather consistent mode of explanation for climatic and other macrocosmic influences in physiology. It describes systematically unequivocal relationships, which may be tested by experience, between macrocosmic events on the one hand and physiological, immunological, and pathological conditions on the other.

What phase energetics is deficient in—continuous, precise, and extensive data from meteorological observations—may easily be furnished by modern science. Inversely, for the latter the effective relations between climate and immunology remain almost completely unexplored. By combining what Chinese and Western science have to offer, a powerful impulse would be given for the further development of rational therapy.

3

Standards of Value for Phenomena of Microcosmic Dimensions, I: Orbisiconography

General Preliminaries

All medical knowledge is centered on the body and its vital manifestations. Naturally, statements bearing on the bodily substratum and its functions constitute, so to speak, the bone and muscle of any medical theory. As with any other discipline, these medical statements are tinged by the mode of thought of their authors. Whereas in anatomy Western medicine, causal and analytic, primarily describes the aggregate carriers (or substrata) of effects, inductive synthetic Chinese medicine is primarily interested in the fabric of functional manifestations of the different body regions. These manifestations are described systematically by the discipline called "orbisiconography" (*tsang-hsiang* 臟象).

The ambiguity of the technical term "orb" (*orbis*) reflects almost exactly that of the Chinese term *tsang* 臟, which refers on the one hand to a bodily substratum with ill-defined material and spatial contours, and on the other hand to a physiological function associated with the substratum and qualitatively defined in time with precision and subtlety. The Chinese word *fei* 肺 "lungs," for instance, calls to mind only coincidentally and vaguely most of the ideas someone with a Western education associates with the lungs. Instead, *fei* designates primarily and predominantly an orb of functions defined systematically and logically, the *"orbis pulmonalis."* The qualifiers used in orbisiconography (*pulmonalis, cardialis,* and so on) must be understood as definitions of effective relations or functions, not simply as expressions of crude anatomical insights. This is why statements bearing on a certain orb can under no circumstances be made to agree completely with statements bearing on the corresponding organ in Western thought. The better both statements are supported in context by empirical data integrated into their logical systems, the less

reconcilable they turn out to be. Given this fundamental diver-
gence it may happen that for a given orb described by traditional Chinese medicine (e.g., the *orbis tricalorii, san-chiao*),
Western medicine can define no corresponding substratum or,
inversely, that Chinese medicine does not postulate an orb for
an organ (e.g., the pancreas) defined by Western medicine.
Orbisiconography (*tsang-hsiang*), methodologically speaking, is not the close
counterpart of Western anatomy but its antithesis.[1] Illustrations of orbisiconography were, as a rule, meant primarily as diagrams of functions, not
as pictures of anatomical substrata. The attempt to view them as "anatomical figures" inevitably leads to abortive conclusions.

Historical and Bibliographical Preliminaries

In accordance with the importance of orbisiconography in
early Chinese medicine, its explanation is already allotted
ample space in the medical classics (*Huang-ti nei-ching*) *Su-wen*
and *Ling-shu*. The *locus classicus* for the designation of this
discipline is in Chapter 9 of the *Su-wen*,[2] where the Yellow
Sovereign asks: "How about orbisiconography 臟象何如?"
Wang Ping comments on this: "What is called *hsiang*, 'images,'
'phenomena,' is manifest on the outside and may be viewed."
The essentials of orbisiconography are particularly developed
in Chapters 8 through 11 of the *Su-wen* and in Chapter 2 of the
Ling-shu, but numerous supplementary or parallel details are
given in other chapters of these books.[3]

To the problem of the age of orbisiconographic theory there
is no pat answer. Circumstantial evidence supports the guess
that the essence of the theory goes back at least to the Han and
attained definite form before the Sui:

[1] Most European writers still cling to this error (Hüboiter, *Die chinesische
Medizin;* Henri Maspero, "Les Procédés de nourrir le principe vital"; Pierre
Huard and Ming Wong, *Chinese Medicine*). The Chinese authors of the
Chung-i-hsüeh kai-lun (p. 53), who may be said to represent the contemporary
viewpoint of the People's Republic of China, are quite aware of the point
of orbisiconography.
[2] *Su-wen* 9/109 = *Lei-ching* 3/46.
[3] Chapters 1, 4, 5, 19, 21, 23, 24, 29, 38, 44, 61, 67, and 81 of the *Su-wen*,
and Chapters 4, 6, 8, 17, 18, 29–33, 35, 36, 40, 47, 50, 53, 54, 56, 59, 60,
64, 65, 70, and 72 of the *Ling-shu*. We shall refer to these texts as the need
arises.

1. The writings of Chang Chung-ching (of the Later Han, end of the second century A.D.), the *Shang-han-lun* and the *Chin-kuei yao-lüeh* 金匱要畧, repeatedly refer to orbisiconographic data similar to those in the *Nei-ching*; and Chapters 1, 6, 8, and 9 of the *Chen-chiu chia-i-ching* 針灸甲乙經 (compiled in the third century) contain extensive quotations from the *Nei-ching*.
2. In the table of contents of Ch'üan Yüan-ch'i's *Su-wen* edition, all chapters dealing with orbisiconography except 8 and 67 are enumerated.
3. The sixth chapter of the *Huang-ti nei-ching t'ai-su* fragment[4] furnishes highly interesting parallels to the orbisiconographic passages in the *Su-wen* and *Ling-shu*.
Besides the testimony of these authoritative texts, the whole tenor of later medical literature, and mention of orbisiconographic theories in other scientific and philosophical works of the Han tend to support the hypothesis that orbisiconography has played a part in the constitution of science since the end of the third century B.C. Among medical books clear reference to orbisiconography can be found in the early *Nan-ching* and the *Mo-ching* (second half of third century), in the *Chia-i-ching* of about the same period, and in the late seventh-century work of Sun Szu-mo 孫思邈. The *Li-chi* (*Yüeh-ling*), Chapters 4 and 7 of the *Huai-nan-tzu* (ca. 120 B.C.), and the *Po-hu-t'ung-i* 白虎通義 (late first century A.D.),[5] to mention only the more important nonmedical classics of certain date, all mention orbisiconographic elements which correspond to those of the *Nei-ching*.[6]

The Elements of Orbisiconography: Terminology
Orbisiconography (*tsang-hsiang*) is the comprehensive and systematic description of energetic processes taking place in the

[4]Pp. 27–35.
[5]8/321ff.
[6]See also Granet, *La pensée chinoise*, pp. 375–387. Maspero, in his much-quoted "Les Procédés de nourrir le principe vital," pp. 191–197, postulates a specifically Taoist "anatomy" ("internal cosmography" would be a better term) and physiology. In reality the Taoist authors interested in meditational techniques, like masseurs and acupuncturers, simply stressed certain aspects of the common orbisiconographic theory.

microcosm (i.e., within an individual organism) and of the dynamic relations that may be defined or postulated through empirical observation of these processes. Orbisiconography therefore is concerned first with the specific spheres of syndromes (orbs), and second with the qualitatively different forms of energy present in these orbs (energetics).

QUALITATIVE DIVISION OF THE ORBS

The Chinese term for "orb" (*orbis*) is *tsang* 臟 (modern and technical ideogram) or 藏 (ancient character, frequently found in philosophical texts).[7] In technical as well as in nontechnical texts there occurs with quite identical meaning the double term *tsang-fu* 臟腑, composed of two antonyms. The principal orbs are divided into a yin group and a yang group. Hence the narrower technical connotation of *tsang* is yin orb (Latin term: *orbis horrealis*)[8] and of *fu* 腑, yang orb (Latin term: *orbis aulicus*).[9] In *Su-wen* 11/127f. this distinction is explained as follows: "The so-called Five Yin Orbs store structive potential[10] without letting anything drain off; therefore they are 'full' (*pleni, man* 滿) but not 'replete' (*repleti, shih* 實). By contrast, the Six Yang Orbs transmit and assimilate, yet do not store; therefore they are 'replete' yet can never be 'full.'"[11] "Full" (*man, plenus*) and "replete" (*shih, repletus*) are important technical terms, with the antonyms "empty" (*k'ung* 空, *vacuus*) and "exhausted" (*hsü* 虛, *inanis*). Thus this passage indicates that "fullness" (*k'ung-man*) of the *orbes horreales* is a physiological function of the general health of the organism or of a certain orb, while "repleteness" (*hsü-shih*) on the other hand is primarily a clue

[7]See *Su-wen* 8/94 and *Lei-ching* 3/44.
[8]*Tsang* 臟, etymologically related to *ts'ang* 藏 meaning "to store," also designates a "storage bin," in Latin: *horreum*.
[9]*Fu* 腑, related to *fu* 府, "the official residence of a higher official" where he transacts public affairs, may be approximated to the Latin term *aula*.
[10]See the commentary of Ma Shih in the *Su-wen* 11/128 as well as pp. 179–180 below.
[11]所謂五臟者藏精氣而不瀉也, 故滿而不能實. 六腑者傳化物而不藏, 故實而不能滿也. The parallel passage in *Su-wen t'ai-su* 6/34 has *ching-shen* 精神, which makes no sense here. Probably there is contamination from *Ling-shu* 47/1204, which we shall quote presently.

to a pathological nutritional condition of the organism or orb. Still more precise information is contained in the passage of the *Ling-shu* 47/1204: "The five *orbes horreales* store structive potential (*ching* 精) and configurative force (*shen* 神), *hsüeh* and *ch'i* [individually specific polarized energy], *hun* and *p'o* [individually specific configurative force]. The six *orbes aulici* assimilate liquid and solid food and transmit the active and structive fluids."

The idea that there are five yin orbs and six yang orbs goes back to the late Chou classics.[12] The numbers probably came into use because of their emblematic associations. The coupling of even numbers with yang orbs, and vice versa, points to the exchange of attributes in a hierogamy, as Granet has suggested.[13] This archaic count is already overlaid and even broken up in the *Nei-ching,* however, by empirical data and systematic ratiocination. In a crucial re-evaluation, the *orbis pericardialis* came to be considered an independent *orbis horrealis* complementary to the *orbis tricalorii.*[14] This conception is implicit in *Su-wen* 8/94 and *Ling-shu* 10/1014, 35/1161, and 71/1315, and became explicit with the expansion of sinarteriology; it was further advanced by the postulation of a number of "paraorbs" (*ch'i-heng chih fu* 奇恆之腑, *paraorbes*).[15]

The qualitative determination of the orbs by yin and yang is completed by qualification according to the Five Evolutive Phases. From this the following correspondences to the *orbes horreales* result (after the *Su-wen* 5/55f and 67/254f):

The *orbis horrealis*	is the
ligni	*orbis hepaticus*
ignis	*orbis cardialis*
humi	*orbis lienalis*
metalli	*orbis pulmonalis*
aquae	*orbis renalis*

[12]For instance, in *Lü-shih ch'un-ch'iu* 20/964.
[13]*La pensée chinoise,* p. 194.
[14]*Nan-ching* 25.
[15]*Su-wen-shih* 2/65 where Kao Shih-shih explains *ch'i-heng* 奇恆 as "different from the ordinary [yang] orbs."

The corresponding attributes for five of the six *orbes aulici* are given unequivocally but not explicitly in the *Nei-ching* (*Ling-shu* 2/926); their attributes are assigned overtly only very much later, e.g., in the *I-kuan* 醫貫 of Chao Hsien-k'o 趙獻可[16] in the Ming period:

The *orbis aulicus*	is the
ligni	*orbis felleus*
ignis	*orbis intestini tenuis*
humi	*orbis stomachi*
metalli	*orbis intestini crassi*
aquae	*orbis vesicalis*

The so-called paraorbs (*paraorbes, ch'i-heng chih fu* 奇恆之腑) which are assigned no conventional qualities, are enumerated thus in *Su-wen* 11/126: (1) brain (*nao* 腦, *cerebrum*); (2) medulla (*sui* 髓, *medulla*); (3) bones (*ku* 骨, *ossa*); (4) sinarteries (*mo* 脈, *sinarteriae*); (5) gallbladder (*tan* 膽, *paraorbis felleus*); (6) uterus (*nü-tzu-pao* 女子胞, *paraorbis uteri*). We are informed in that text only that "these six [orbs], which originate from *configuratio terrestris (ti-ch'i)* [we feel justified in interpreting: from an energetic configuration conditioning a structive polarization], without exception[17] store structive [energy] and manifest terrestrial qualities [this is tautological]. That is why they store and let nothing drain off."

GENERAL PARADIGM FOR THE DESCRIPTION OF THE INDIVIDUAL ORBS; TERMINOLOGY

What in Chinese medicine is designated as *tsang-fu* (or *tsang* in the general sense of the word) is a sphere of definite relations or functions evaluated by conventional standards of quality. The description of any orb, its "picture" (in Greek: *eikon* → *ikon*, in Chinese: *hsiang* 象, image) differs fundamentally in form and content from the apparently comparable descriptions of

[16]Quoted from the *I-pu-ch'üan-lu* 醫部全錄, Vol. IV, p. 50.
[17]A statement modified as early as Wang Ping (*Su-wen*, p. 127). See also the discussion of the individual paraorbs later in this chapter.

Western anatomy. In Chinese medical literature not all orbs are described in accordance with an identical systematic pattern. For these reasons, comprehension of the individual orbs will be greatly facilitated by an overall view of theoretically possible relations, correspondences, and qualifications of an orb and the pertinent terminology. The description of an orb (an "orbisicon") comprises

I. The three basic qualitative definitions of the orb in accordance with yin and yang and the Five Evolutive Phases, and the classifications corollary to these:

1. General determination: *orbis horrealis* or *orbis aulicus* (yin or yang)

2. Graduated determination (yin in yin, yin in yang and so on)

3. Determination by its position within the cycle of the Five E.P.s

4. Gender (*genus*): female or male (*p'in* 牝 or *mu* 牡)

5. Basic energetic character ("essential nature," *hsing* 性)

6. *Sapor* (flavor corresponding to its quality, *wei* 味)

7. Effects antagonistic to its quality (*chu* 主)

The term *chu* 主 is one of the very few for which, in addition to a normative equivalent—*dominus, dominans* (dominant, dominating)—in Western contexts we are obliged to use several distinct translations depending on the context, namely, dominant function, to dominate → to control → to regulate; antagonist, antagonist orb; to act as.

8. Injurious and noxious influences and effects (*shang* 傷)

9. Empirical manifestation of its energetic configuration

10. Sound or musical emblem or the corresponding musical instrument (*yin* 音)

11. Vocal manifestations of emotions and feelings (*sheng* 聲)

12. Characteristic color [emblem] (*se* 色)

13. Corresponding cereal (*ku* 穀)

14. Corresponding domestic animal (*ch'u* 畜)

15. Corresponding class of animals (*ch'ung* 蟲)[18]

Numbers 8 and 10 through 15 may be found in any more or less complete list of the correspondences of the Five E.P.s.[19] We have omitted them above

---

[18]This term in the narrow sense designates insects, but in a more extensive sense is used for any kind of wild animal (*bestia*).

[19]See Granet, *La pensée chinoise*, pp. 375ff.

in connection with the E.P.s, but mention them here because their practical significance can be demonstrated only within the framework of multiple concrete relationships.

II. The interaction of the orb with the macrocosm, especially its
1. Dependence on the position of sun and moon (hours of the day)
2. Correspondence to a certain planet
3. Affinity to a certain season
4. Correspondence to specific emblems of time (celestial stems and terrestrial branches)

III. Its interaction with the microcosm, especially its
1. Complementary orb (*piao* 表, *species* or *li* 裏, *intima*). Each of the orbs is linked with an orb of complementary polarity, thus forming a "functional yoke" in which the yang orb (*orbis aulicus, fu*) always represents the outward side (*species, piao* 表) and the yin orb (*orbis horrealis, tsang*) always holds the inner side (*li,* 裏 *intima*). The technical term designating this particular connection is *luo* 絡, *nectere*, to attach to.
2. Sinarteries (*ching-luo* 經絡). To each orb there corresponds a cardinal conduit (*sinarteria cardinalis, ching-mo* 經脈) and derivatively a reticular conduit (*sinarteria reticularis, luo-mo* 絡脈) and a skin zone (*cutis regio, p'i-pu* 皮部), with which we shall deal in the chapter on sinarteriology.
3. Specific unfoldment of its function (*ch'ung* 充, *perfectio*). Specific constituents of the organism and their phenomena are defined as secondary extensions of the orb. In medical terminology these specific unfoldments (*ch'ung, perfectiones*) are directly "produced" (*sheng* 生, *efficiuntur*) by the orb and always remain closely connected, "united" (*ho* 合, *coniunctae*) with it.
4. Checking orb. Each orb is subject to physiological check or counteraction (*chu* 主) by the next orb (similar to position I, 4 above), in the conquest sequence (Sequence II) of the E.P.s. This checking orb by definition can never be identical with the complementary orb (III, 1).
5. Specific radial pulse. The function of an orb may be diag-

nosed by the observation of diverse pulses, and in particular by the observation of its specific radial pulse. (This position might with equal justice have been classified under the next heading.)

IV. Sensuous and substrative projections of the orb, its

1. Outward manifestation (equivalent technical terms in Chinese: *hua* 華 and *jung* 榮, Latin term: *flos*). Each orb (explicitly only each *orbis horrealis*) has its outward manifestation in some particular region or aspect of the body surface that is always open to inspection.

2. Specific sense organ (*kuan* 官, *organum*). Each *orbis horrealis* is directly assigned, and each yang orb indirectly assigned a specific sense organ (*kuan*).[20] This sense organ coincides often but not always with the specific body opening (IV, 3).

3. Specific body opening (*k'ai ch'iao* 開竅). Each *orbis horrealis* likewise is directly assigned, and each *orbis aulicus* indirectly assigned, a specific body opening from whose response the momentary condition of the orb may be diagnosed.

4. Psychic reaction (*chih* 志, *emotio*). The Chinese word *chih* 志 in common speech means "will," but as a technical term (normative Latin equivalent: *emotio*) it points to a narrowly defined emotion or psychic reaction. The phenomenon designated in orbisiconography by *chih*, *emotio*, in pathology is named *ch'ing* 情, without the slightest difference in empirical datum.

5. Intermittently secerned fluid (*yeh* 液). This fluid, as a rule, is related to the physiological function of the orb, and its secretion frequently accompanies the corresponding psychic reaction.

6. Specific action (*pien-tung* 變動 or *tung*). Every particular mode of action or demeanor is inductively referred to a specific orb.

7. Dream motifs. The disharmonious function of the orb makes it discordant within the concert of functions of the organism, a fact that according to the *Nei-ching* may become manifest by specific dream motifs that divulge which orb is disturbed.

[20]The Chinese technical term *kuan* 官 is rendered into English, depending

8. Anatomical correspondence. This category includes the crude protoscientific anatomical observations of, and theories about, the material organs that serve as the bodily substratum of the orb, and their transformations.

V. Characteristic functions of the orb,[21] its
1. Specific function ("organ of...," chih kuan 之官)
2. Dominant function (so chu 所主). In Chapter 8 of the Su-wen each orb is ascribed a specific function metaphorically expressed. This is the essential function exercised by the orb within the organic system. The dominant function (chu) in principle designates effects emanating from the "specific unfoldment" (ch'ung, perfectio, of the orb; see III, 3 above) and consequently corresponds to a more limited aspect of the orb's functions than Position V, I. Sometimes, but not as a rule, the dominant function of an orb is identical with its specific function.
3. Constitutive function (literally: "radical function," pen 本). Some orbs are ascribed a decisive and comprehensive role in maintaining the temporal existence of the organism; the orb is supposed to contribute in a specific way to the foundation ("to found," pen) of the organism's existence. The constitutive function never coincides with the specific or dominant function of an orb.
4. Storage function (ts'ang 藏). Every orbis horrealis (tsang) stores (ts'ang) a particular form of physiological energy. Tsang means storage bin, (horreum).
5. Multiple functions. Evidently in order to accommodate certain empirical data within the correspondence system, many orbs are attributed additional functions beside those already mentioned.

In practice the same rule that holds good for grammatical

---

upon context, by "sense organ" or simply "organ," whereas its Latin equivalent (organum) is never modified.
[21]The information given in this final section very often complements theories and data of Western medicine and therefore, from our contemporary perspective, contains the most interesting information of orbisiconography.

paradigms is also valid for our orbisiconographical paradigm: in some positions logical overlaps cannot be avoided.

In the *Nei-ching* a foundation for the systematic description of all orbs in conformity with the paradigm had indeed been laid, yet information contained in this classic allows the paradigm to be completed for some orbs only. Many data can be drawn only from later authors. In the descriptions of the *orbes aulici* that may be conceived as the exterior complements of the *orbes horreales*, many positions are identical with those of their corresponding inner orbs (*intimae, li*) and, as a rule, need not be discussed separately.

Iconography of the Yin Orbs (Orbes horreales, tsang 臟)

THE *ORBIS HEPATICUS* (*KAN* 肝)

(I) The *orbis hepaticus*, as an *orbis horrealis*, is primarily yin within the system of orbs. Since within the cycle of the Five E.P.s it corresponds to the E.P. Wood (*transvectus ligni*) it may, because of this aspect, be qualified as minor yang or—what amounts to the same thing—as yang in yin (*yin chung chih yang* 陰中之陽). This latter qualification is supported by Ma Shih's commentary to the *Ling-shu* 44/1196; the former may be gleaned from the *Su-wen* 9/109, where we find the pleonastic and misleading formula: "The *orbis hepaticus* is the minor yang in yang." The passage in *Su-wen* 9/109 is an extreme example of the distortion resulting from early corruptions that have been upheld through the centuries as classical utterances out of piety or indolence. In the current text the orbs are qualified as follows:

orbis hepaticus	minor yang in yang
orbis cardialis	major yang in yang
orbis lienalis	extreme yin (*yin extremum, chih-yin* 至陰)
orbis pulmonalis	major yin in yang
orbis renalis	minor yin in yin

orbis intestini tenuis ⎫	
orbis stomachi ⎪	
orbis intestini crassi ⎬	extreme yin
orbis vesicalis ⎪	
orbis tricalorii ⎭	

Once we have a clear idea of the entire *Nei-ching* system of correspondences, it becomes evident that this table of qualifications is incompatible with it, and thus conflicts with many passages of the *Nei-ching*. As has been explained in Chapter 2, when the scientific system was taking shape, two sets of value conventions vied with one another, one based on yin and yang and by necessity generating even-numbered cycles, and another based on the cycle of the Five Evolutive Phases. Moreover, from the interaction of the yinyang cycle with calendaric and chronological emblems (celestial stems and terrestrial branches) and with data of physiological experience (sensitive points, *foramina inductoria*) a number of cyclical hybrids of restricted compatibility were produced for specialized applications in phase energetics and sinarteriology.

The copyist of the passage in the *Su-wen* 9/109, in giving the qualitative determination of the orbs, has confused the following criteria: first yinyang: the polarity of *orbes horreales/orbes aulici*; second yinyang: polarity above the diaphragm/below the diaphragm; third yinyang: the energetic polarity according to Sequence 0 of the E.P.s; fourth yinyang: special sinarteriological topology (back of the body/front of the body, inner/outward side of the limbs). The principal commentators of the *Nei-ching* (Wang Ping, Ma Shih, Chang Chih-ts'ung) do not correct the text. They either avoid taking any stand on the attributions or else try to justify them by twisted arguments. Restoration of the original text is possible, at least for the *wu-tsang* (Five Yin Orbs), by means of a parallel passage in the *Nei-ching t'ai-su* 5/21. There we have:

orbis hepaticus	minor yang in yin
orbis cardialis	major yang in yang[22]
orbis lienalis	extreme yin in yin
orbis pulmonalis	minor yin in yang
orbis renalis	major yin in yin.

These attributions agree perfectly with *Ling-shu* 44/1195f (as well as the commentary by Ma Shih). And the correct text enables us to derive with assurance the criteria that originally governed the attributions: The second part of each qualification ("... in yin, ... in yang") refers to the topological yinyang polarity above the diaphragm/below the diaphragm; the qualifiers major yang, minor yang and so on refer exclusively to the polarity of the Five.E.P.s (Sequence 0). The confusion seems to have arisen because of the yinyang polarity predominating in sinarteriology.

Because of preponderantly active polarity, the *orbis hepaticus* is called a male *orbis horrealis* (*mu-tsang* 牡臟).[23]

Since the *orbis hepaticus* is qualified by the evolutive phase Wood, in turn there corresponds to it, among the five mani-

[22]The only attribution correctly given in the *Su-wen* passage.
[23]*Ling-shu* 44/1195.

festations of energy, mildly rising warmth (*hsüan* 暄);[24] among
the five *sapores* (flavors), the sour *sapor* (*suan* 酸);[25] among
colors, the green color (*ts'ang* 蒼 or *ch'ing* 青);[26] among tones
(*yin* 音), the tone *chüeh* 角 (or, if *yin* is taken to mean the sound
of musical instruments, the sound of *ch'in* 琴, lute);[27] among
vocal manifestations, the calling voice (*hu* 呼); among domestic
animals, the chicken;[28] among cereals, wheat; and among classes of animals, those having a hairy coat (*mao* 毛)[29] correspond
to the *orbis hepaticus*. The smell associated with the *orbis hepaticus*
is that of urine or sour sweat (*sao* 臊).[30] The *orbis hepaticus* is
checked physiologically by the *orbis pulmonalis*.[31]

For defining the influences injurious (*shang* 傷) to the *orbis
hepaticus* the rule is that all influences with a systematic affinity
to the orb are beneficial to its function in moderate doses and
injurious in strong doses. Thus the normal function of the *orbis
hepaticus* requires sour *sapores* (food and drugs of sour flavor);[32]
yet sour *sapores* also drain off the energy of the *orbis hepaticus*
and thus tend to exhaust it.[33] Similar reasoning applies to the
wind (*feng*) and to spring, influences that stimulate the energies
of the *orbis hepaticus* yet when defined as climatic or seasonal
excesses (*yin* 淫) may also overstimulate and thus impair the
function of this orb.[34] Quite clearly this is also true of anger
(*nu* 怒, *ira*), the specific emotion of the *orbis hepaticus*.[35]

(II) In the macrocosm the planet Jupiter (*sui-hsing* 歲星)[36]
corresponds to the *orbis hepaticus*. At the beginning of the year,
during the first and second Chinese months (approximately

[24]*Su-wen* 67/604 *et passim*.
[25]*Ibid.* 5/55, 23/244 *et passim*.
[26]*Ibid.* 5/55, 67/604, 22/234; *Ling-shu* 44/1165.
[27]*Su-wen* 5/55; *Ling-shu* 44/1165; *Ch'ien-chin yao-fang* (quoted from the
I-pu ch'üan-lu, Vol. IV, p. 83).
[28]*Su-wen* 5/55.
[29]*Ibid.* 4/40, 67/604.
[30]*Ibid.* 4/40.
[31]*Ibid.* 10/114.
[32]*Ibid.* 10/116.
[33]*Ibid.* 22/234.
[34]*Ibid.* 3/30, 3/33, 4/36, 5/55, 5/67, 22/234.
[35]*Ibid.* 5/55.
[36]*Ibid.* 4/40.

February and March in Western calendars), the physiological energy of man (*jen-ch'i, ch'i humanum*) is particularly effective in the *c   is hepaticus*.[37] Elsewhere in the *Su-wen* the dependence of the *orbis hepaticus* upon influences of macrocosmic dimension is chiefly related to functional disturbances. Thus in *Su-wen* 22/234 we find: "If the disease affects the *orbis hepaticus* it will heal in summer. If it does not heal in summer, it will grow worse in autumn. If [the patient] nevertheless does not die he will tide over the winter and will recover in spring. He should beware of winds!"—"Whoever gets a disease of the *orbis hepaticus* will experience a remission (*hui* 慧) in the morning, will grow worse in the afternoon, and will quiet down toward midnight." The periodicity of disease in the *orbis hepaticus* depending upon the season and the hour may be observed with relative ease, just as the periodicity of liver disorders is on record in Western medicine.[38] Still, when the text continues with a scheme involving the celestial stems, we can see a weakness similar to that noted in phase energetics: "One whose disease is in the *orbis hepaticus* will recover on a *cust* 丙 or *dust* 丁 day; one who does not recover on a *cust* or *dust* day will grow worse on *gust* 庚 and *hust* 辛. If he does not die then, he will tide over *just* 壬 and *kut* 癸 and will recover under *ust* 甲 or 乙 *bust*."

(III) The *orbis hepaticus* is united with the *orbis felleus* in a functional yoke in which it is the inner orb (*intima, li*) and the *orbis aulicus felleus* the outer orb (*species, piao*).[39] The *sinarteria cardinalis* corresponding to the *orbis hepaticus* is the *cardinalis yin flectentis pedis*.[40] The function of the *orbis hepaticus* is specifically unfolded (has its *perfectio, ch'ung* 充) in the *nervus* (*chin* 筋), i.e., in the sinews and muscles.[41] The specific radial pulse of the *orbis hepaticus* is the *pulsus clusalis mersus manus sinistrae* 左手關沈脈.[42]

[37]*Ibid.* 16/149.

[38]European physicians consider that a deterioration between 4:00 P.M. and 8:00 P.M. may indicate liver trouble.

[39]*Chung-ts'ang-ching* 中藏經, 1/11.

[40]*Ling-shu* 10/1023f. For further details see also the relevant subsection of that part of the following chapter devoted to sinarteriology.

[41]*Su-wen* 9/109, 4/40 = *Lei-ching* 3/46–48.

[42]*Mo-ching* 2/19; *Chung-i-hsüeh kai-lun*, p. 199.

(IV) The outward manifestation (*flos*) of the *orbis hepaticus* may be observed in the nails (*chao* 爪);[43] the specific body opening (*k'ai ch'iao* 開竅) of the *orbis hepaticus*, and at the same time its corresponding sense organs (*kuan* 官) are the eyes.[44] Of the intermittently secerned fluids (*yeh*) the tears (*lei* 淚) correspond to the *orbis hepaticus*.[45] From the appearance and solidity of the nails and the sharpness of sight, inferences about the functional state of the *orbis hepaticus* are possible. The "psychic reaction" corresponding to the *orbis hepaticus* is anger (*ira, nu* 怒); of the modes of action, "wrenching and pulling" (*ts'ui-la* 摧拉) is associated with it.[46]

The dream motifs which indicate a malfunction of the *orbis hepaticus* are, according to the *Nei-ching*, in good keeping with the orb's general qualifications (Wood, Spring, anger): "If the energy of the *orbis hepaticus* is exhausted, in dreaming one will see mushrooms (菌香 *cortinellus shiitake*); at the right moment one has the sensation of lying under a tree and not daring to get up."[47] "If a *flexus* deversates[48] in the *orbis hepaticus* [i.e. if the energy of the *orbis hepaticus* is deficient and the direction of its flow hence is reversed], one dreams of trees in a mountain forest."[49] In this and similar passages translated below, the "right moment" is the point when the quality of cosmic time agrees with that of the orb in question.

A crude anatomical description of the liver is given in section 42 of the *Nan-ching*: "The liver weighs four *chin* (pounds), four *liang* (ounces) and has three 'leaves' [lobes] on the left side and four on the right."[50]

In this connection an example of the the relation between empirical observation and theoretical speculation (quoted from the *I-pu ch'üan-lu*, vol. IV, p. 87) is worth recording: "If liver is plunged into water, it will sink; if [on the other hand] wood is plunged into water, it will float. If lung

---

[43]*Su-wen* 9/109, 10/114 *et passim*.
[44]*Ibid* 4/40, 5/55.
[45]*Ibid.* 23/247.
[46]*Ibid.* 5/55f, 67/604.
[47]*Ibid.* 80/871.
[48]*Ling-shu* 43/1191.
[49]*Ibid.* 43/1192.
[50]*Nan-ching* 4/108. One *chin* is the approximate equivalent of one pound, and one *liang* the approximate equivalent of one ounce. For the functional changes associated with certain anatomical data see *Ling-shu* 47/1206.

is plunged into water, it will float; if [however] metal is plunged into water, it will sink. What is the meaning of this? Liver does not correspond to pure Wood, for when *bust* 乙 and *gust* 庚 unite, it [liver] absorbs a weak yin energy which makes its adhesiveness [literally its "thoughts" (*i* 意)] tend toward [lit. "take pleasure in" (*hsi* 喜)] Metal. This is the reason why liver, plunged into water, sinks. Lung does not correspond to pure Metal, for since *hust* 辛 and *cust* 丙 together follow Fire, its adhesiveness tends toward Fire. For this reason lung, plunged into water, stays afloat. Yet why then does cooked lung sink and cooked liver float? This is precisely because *hust* 辛 (*aqua yin*, yin Water) and *gust* 庚 (*metallum yang*, yang Metal) on the one hand and *bust* 乙 (*metallum yin*, yin Metal) and *ust* 甲 (*humus yang*, yang Earth) on the other hand come together."

(V) Within the integral organism the *orbis hepaticus* is compared to the general (*chiang-chün* 將軍), who is the source of plans and reflections.[51] In other words, the *orbis hepaticus*, as the seat of the active aspect of the individually specific configurative force (*hun* 魂)[52] is responsible for actively projecting the qualities of the integral personality. This faculty is only indirectly associated with the *orbis hepaticus*. Its "storage function," according to the *Ling-shu*,[53] bears on *hsüeh* 血, i.e., on the individually specific *structive* energy, which is essentially but not exclusively substantiatied in blood. *Hsüeh* in turn is the residence of *hun*: "If the configurational[54] energy of the *orbis hepaticus* is exhausted, one is overcome by fear; if it is replete, by anger."

In the *Nei-ching* the *orbis hepaticus* still is called simply a "depository" of individually specific structive energy (*hsüeh*), but Wang Ping's commentary offers a more precise interpretation of this function which is developed further by later authors. He explains:[55] "The *orbis hepaticus* stores *hsüeh*, and the *orbis cardialis* moves it. What is the meaning of the sentence: 'When a man moves, the *hsüeh* circulates in the sinarteries; when a man is in repose, the *hsüeh* returns to the *orbis horrealis hepaticus*'? The dominant function (*chu* 主) of the *orbis hepaticus* is to constitute an (equalizing) reservoir (*mare, hai* 海) of *hsüeh*."

[51]*Su-wen* 8/94.
[52]*Su-wen* 9/109; *Nei-ching t'ai-su* 6/33; concerning the term *hun* see pp. 184–185 below and also *Su-wen-shih* 2/59.
[53]*Ling-shu* 8/968. This book very frequently gives a more "modern" and better differentiated interpretation of classical postulates and theories.
[54]For this term see p. 168 below.
[55]In his commentary to the *Su-wen* 10/119.

Mare, in Chinese *hai* [literally "sea"], is a technical term defined to mean an equalizing reservoir. In the chapter of the *Ling-shu* especially dedicated to the reservoir function[56] all twelve *sinarteriae cardinales* are designated in a very vague and equivocal way as "*hsüeh* reservoirs" (*mare hsüeh, hsüeh-hai*), but this thesis was not upheld later on. At any rate Wang Ping seems to have been the first explicitly to postulate a function of the *orbis hepaticus* that today is accepted as a matter of course.[57]

Wang Ping's comment refers to the classical utterance "If man is supine the *hsüeh* returns into the *orbis hepaticus.*"[58] Let us compare to this what" Li Ch'an 李梃 expounds in his *I-hsüeh ju-men* 醫學入門 (1575):[59] "The *orbis hepaticus* stores individually specific structive energy (*hsüeh*) and for this reason is called "reservoir of *hsüeh.*" If the *hsüeh* reservoir is filled abundantly one always imagines that one's body[60] is large; if its supply is reduced one imagines that one's body is slim. During the day [the *hsüeh*] circulates [in the body]. The eyes, by receiving individually specific structive energy, can see;[61] the feet, by receiving individually specific structive energy, may walk...."—"When one is supine at night, the *hsüeh* returns into the *orbis hepaticus*. If one is irresolute in making plans, then the *orbis hepaticus*, exhausted, communicates [its] heat to other orbs. If the fluids of the mouth and nose or the urine cannot be controlled [this indicates] that the *orbis hepaticus* no longer stores any *hsüeh.*"

The *orbis hepaticus* regulates (controls) the functions of sinews and muscles (*chin* 筋, *nervus*) and thus is of decisive importance for the development of physical force. It is the basis (*pen*) of all symptoms of fatigue.[62]

[56]Chapter 33, entitled *Hai-lun* 海論 ("Treatise on the *maria* [= equalizing reservoirs]"), pp. 1156ff.
[57]See also the *I-hsüeh ju-men* 醫學入門 of the Ming era, quoted in the *I-pu ch'üan-lu*, Vol. IV, p 87.
[58]*Su-wen* 10/119.
[59]Quoted from the *I-pu ch'üan-lu*, Vol. IV, p. 87.
[60]*Shen* 身. Conceivably the term here points to the "body" [*corpus*] of the organ, the physical liver.
[61]This is an echo of *Su-wen* 10/119.
[62]See *Su-wen* 9/109, to which should be compared the notes in the *Su-wen i-shih*, p.79 and the parallel texts of the *Lei-ching* 3/49 and the *Nei-ching t'ai-su* 6/33.

THE *ORBIS CARDIALIS*(*HSIN* 心)

(I) The *orbis cardialis*, as one of the *orbes horreales*, is primarily yin. Yet because in the cycle of the Five Evolutive Phases it corresponds to Fire (*transvectus ignis*) it may in this aspect be qualified as yang or yang in yang or even, pleonastically, as major yang in yang.[63] As a consequence of this preponderantly active polarization, the *orbis cardialis* is, like the *orbis hepaticus*, called a "male orb" (*mu-tsang* 牡臟).[64]

Many correspondences of the *orbis cardialis* are due to its determination by the E.P. Fire. Among these we may enumerate sudden damp heat (*shu* 暑)[65] as its specific manifestation of energy, bitter (*k'u* 苦) as its *sapor* (flavor),[66] scarlet (*ch'ih* 赤) as its corresponding color, the tone *chih* 徵[67] or the sound of the thirty-six-reed mouth organ (*yü* 竽)[68] as its corresponding sounds (*yin* 音), and laughter (*hsiao* 笑) as its corresponding vocal manifestation.[69] A special affinity to the *orbis cardialis* is ascribed among domestic animals to the sheep, among cereals to glutinous millet (*shu* 黍), and among classes of animals to the plumed animals (*yü* 羽).[70] Among smells, the scorched aroma (*chiao* 焦) points to the *orbis cardialis*.[71] The physiological check (*chu*) of the *orbis cardialis* is the *orbis renalis*.[72]

As for the influences injurious to the *orbis cardialis* (*shang*) the same rule applies as to other orbs: related effects in moderate doses are beneficial, but in excessive doses detrimental to the normal functions of the orb. Still, experience has led to a modification to the effect that excessive energy should be drained off not by the corresponding bitter *sapor* (which in reducing tonus also has a narcotic and paralyzing effect) but

[63]See *Su-wen* 9/109 and the commentary to the *Ling-shu* 44/1196, and especially p. 118 above.
[64]*Ling-shu* 44/1195.
[65]*Su-wen* 67/604.
[66]*Ibid*. 5/57, 67/604.
[67]*Ibid*. 5/57; *Ling-shu* 44/1195.
[68]Quoted from the *I-pu ch'üan-lu*, Vol. IV, p. 121.
[69]*Su-wen* 5/57.
[70]*Ibid*. 4/41. 67/604.
[71]*Ibid*. 4/41.
[72]*Ibid*. 10/114.

by the sweet flavor.[73] Damp heat (*shu*), heat as such (*calor, je* 熱), and summer stimulate the energy of the *orbis cardialis* yet also tend to exhaust it under the aspect of a climatic or seasonal excess (*yin* 淫). The same is true for pleasure (*hsi* 喜, *voluptas*) the emotion corresponding to the *orbis cardialis*.[74]

(II) In the macrocosm the planet Mars (*ying-huo-hsing* 熒惑星) corresponds to the *orbis cardialis*.[75] In the course of the year the energy of man (*ch'i humanum*) chiefly flows in the *orbis cardialis* during the ninth and tenth Chinese months (approximately October and November) when the "structive configuration brings on the first ice and when Earth starts to withhold [literally: to lock in] its force."[76]

Concerning the influence of hours and seasons on disturbances of the *orbis cardialis*, we are told in the *Su-wen* 22/235: "If the disease affects the *orbis cardialis*, it will heal during the Indian summer (*ch'ang-hsia* 長憂). If it does not heal during the Indian summer it will grow worse in winter. If [the patient still] does not die in winter he will tide over spring and will get up in summer. He should beware of hot food and hot clothing"—"Whoever gets a disease of the *orbis cardialis* will have a remission at noon, grow worse toward midnight, and quiet down in the morning."

Here, as before, the periodicity is, on the whole, based on experience, but again we find excessively a priori correspondences between the celestial stems and the stages of cardial disease: "Someone whose disease lies in the *orbis cardialis* will recover on an *esut* 戊 or *fust* 己 day; one who does not recover on an *esut* or *fust* day will grow worse on *just* 壬 and *kut* 癸. One who does not die on *just* and *kut* will tide over *ust* 甲 and *bust* 乙 and will get up under *cust* 丙 or *dust* 丁" (*Ibid.*).

(III) The *orbis cardialis* is united with the *orbis intestini tenuis* in a functional yoke in which as an *orbis horrealis* the former represents the inner side (*li, intima*), the latter as *orbis aulicus* represents the outer side (*piao, species*).[77] The *sinarteria cardinalis*

---

[73]*Ibid.* 22/235, as well as the commentary of Ma Shih on p. 236. See also pages 148–152 below. The *orbis lienalis* function is similarly modified.
[74]*Su-wen* 5/57.
[75]*Ibid.* 4/41.
[76]*Ibid.* 16/149.
[77]*Ling-shu* 47/1209; *Chung-ts'ang-ching* 1/13.

corresponding to the *orbis cardialis* is the *cardinalis yin minoris manus*.[78]

The *orbis cardialis* has its specific unfoldment (*perfectio, ch'ung*) in the sinarteries by which the major part of the individually specific structive energy (*hsüeh*)[79] is distributed throughout the system (*hsüeh-mo* 血脈). These *hsüeh-mo* conduits[80] and the vascular system described by Western anatomy are superficially similar, but there remain fundamental material and theoretical differences which are only partly accounted for by the long lapse of time between the formation of the theories in Europe and China.[81] The specific radial pulse of the *orbis cardialis* is the *pulsus pollicaris mersus manus sinistrae* 左手寸沈脈.[82]

(IV) The *orbis cardialis* has its outward manifestation (*flos*) in the face (*mien* 面) or complexion (*se* 色);[83] its corresponding body opening (*k'ai ch'iao*) is the ears;[84] its corresponding sense organ (*kuan*) is the tongue.[85]

In the *Su-wen* there is a contradiction concerning the "body opening" corresponding to the *orbis cardialis*; the commentators (Wang Ping, Ma Shih, Chang Ching-yüeh) acknowledge and acquiesce in it. For in *Su-wen* 5/57 the tongue also is counted among the body openings, which is not only absurd but also contradicts the passage quoted from *Su-wen* 4/41. This contradiction may be resolved if one pays attention to the distinction between "body opening" (*ch'iao*) and "sense organ" (*kuan*). That of all sensitive parts ("sense organs") the tongue has a particular affinity to the *orbis cardialis*—which encompasses all that Western medicine describes as the function of the heart and circulatory system—will make sense to any doctor aware that anomalous stress on these organs causes a change in the tongue's appearance. It is also correct from an empirical as well as from a speculative viewpoint to designate the ears as the openings corresponding to the *orbis cardialis*. For not only can it be shown (an argument neglected by the authors of the *Nei-ching*) that a physiological connection exists between acoustic stimuli and the tonus of the *orbis cardialis;* of even greater significance is the fact that the *orbis cardialis* in the polar diagram (Sequence 0) of the evolutive phases is situated on the same axis with the *orbis renalis* to which

---

[78]*Ling-shu* 10/1030.
[79]See pp. 185–187.
[80]*Su-wen* 9/109 and *Lei-ching* 3/46.
[81]See the remarks in Chapter 4 of this volume.
[82]*Mo-ching* 2/18; *Chung-i-hsüeh kai-lun*, p. 199.
[83]*Su-wen* 9/109, 10/114.
[84]*Ibid.* 4/41 and *Lei-ching* 3/48.
[85]*Ling-shu* 17/1074.

the ears primarily correspond. Thus we expect interference phenomena involving the two orbs.

Chinese medicine systematically studies the appearance and color of the face and tongue and the acuteness of the acoustic and olfactory senses in order to draw inferences about the functional condition of the *orbis cardialis*.

Of the intermittently secerned fluids sweat (*han* 汗) corresponds to the *orbis cardialis*.[86] The psychic reaction (*emotio, chih*) corresponding to the *orbis cardialis* is pleasure (*hsi* 喜, *voluptas*);[87] of the modes of action, sorrowful demeanor[88] or blazing and flaming[89] are associated with it.

On dream motifs that are supposed to indicate a disturbance in the *orbis cardialis*, the *Nei-ching* says: If the energy in the *orbis cardialis* is exhausted, in dreams one will look for fire and yang things; at the right moments one [even] dreams of fire and blazes."[90]—"If in the *orbis cardialis* energy is abundant, one easily laughs in dreams or is afraid."[91]— "If a *flexus* deversates in the *orbis cardialis* [i.e., if there is acute deficiency of energy], in one's dreams there appear hills and mountains or blazing flames."[92]

The authors of the *Nan-ching* 42[93] provide a speculative description of the *orbis cardialis*: "The heart weighs 12 *liang* (ounces), has 12 apertures and 3 bristles, and has a capacity of three *ko*[94] of clear fluid."

(V) Within the integral organism the *orbis cardialis* fills the role of "sovereign ruler" (*chün-chu* 君主) from whom emanate directing influence (literally *shen*, configurative force) and clear insight (*ming* 明).[95] As the seat or depository of configurative force,[96] the *orbis cardialis* maintains the individuality and

[86]*Su-wen* 23/247.
[87]*Ibid.* 5/57, 67/604.
[88]*Ibid.* 5/57. See also the *emotio* of the *orbis renalis*.
[89]*Ibid.* 67/604.
[90]*Ibid.* 80/871.
[91]*Ling-shu* 43/1191.
[92]*Ibid.* 43/1192.
[93]*Nan-ching* 4/108.
[94]One *ko* corresponds to approximately one deciliter.
[95]*Su-wen* 8/94.
[96]*Su-wen* 23/250 and the parallel in *Nei-ching t'ai-su* 6/33; also *Ling-shu* 71/1315. On the term *ching-shen* used in the latter text, see pp. 000–000 below.

integrity of the person (*shen* 身) against foreign influences.[97] For this reason it may be considered the foundation of all vital functions.[98] The fact that the dominant function (*chu*) of the *orbis cardialis* is to direct the working of the sinarteries and pulses has already been touched upon.

There is an osmosis between the function of the *orbis cardialis* as an integrating factor of the organism and of the personality, and psychological senses of the term *hsin* ("heart"). This is evident from passages such as that in *Su-wen* 1/3: "Men today incessantly exert their configurative force (*shen*), striving to satisfy their *hsin* (their individual consciousness, their conscious individuality). By this they thwart the development of [true] pleasure." Ma Shih's commentary on *Ling-shu* 8/965 leads from a narrow technical usage to a broad philosophical interpretation of the word *hsin*: "What is called *hsin* (*orbis cardialis*, heart), *i* 意 (imagination), *chih* 知 (psychic movements, *emotiones*), *szu* 思 (cogitation), *chih* 志 (knowledge), *lü* 慮 (reflection) does not, it seems to me, reach beyond what is expressed by the concept of *hsin*." The second word *hsin* 心 in this sentence is perhaps best rendered by "centered consciousness" or by "substance of consciousness."

THE *ORBIS LIENALIS* (*P'I* 脾)

(I) The *orbis lienalis*, as one of the *orbes horreales*, is primarily yin. Of the Five Evolutive Phases, Earth represents the conventional quality of the *orbis lienalis*. Earth (*transvectus humi*), it will be recalled, marks the central position of transition and neutral balance between the polarities, and it may constitute a polar complement to any of the peripheral E.P.s. Its boundless faculty of neutralization and integration can be defined in the yinyang system as an extreme structive disposition. That is why the *orbis lienalis* is assigned the qualification of extreme yin (*chih-yin* 至陰, *yin extremum sive ultimum*).[99] This quality lies completely outside the graduated cycle of yin values, just as the central E.P. Earth appears to be segregated from the cycle of the peripheral E.P.s. If, in addition, the topological criterion is taken into consideration, the *orbis lienalis* may even be

---

Su-wen 9/109 is also relevant; we accept the emendation suggested in the *Su-wen-shih* 2/57, first line: "...is the abode (處) of *shen*."

[97]*Ling-shu* 8/965: "That by which one is a match for [other] beings is called *hsin*" 所以任物者謂之心.

[98]*Su-wen* 9/109.

[99]*Ibid.*

qualified as extreme yin in yin (*yin chung chih chih-yin* 陰中之至
陰).[100] Because of this pronounced yin polarity the *orbis lienalis*
metaphorically is called a female orb (*p'in-tsang*).[101] A number
of secondary qualifications of the *orbis lienalis* are the direct
consequence of its qualitative homology with the E.P. Earth.

Energy corresponding to the quality of the *orbis lienalis*
exercises a universally neutralizing and calming influence
(*chien-ching* 兼靜).[102]

The expression *chien-ching* 兼靜 in the pertinent texts is ambiguous and
therefore has been subject to divergent interpretations. *Chien* 兼 commonly
may be rendered by "to collect," "to coalesce," "combined," or "altogether," and as a philosophical term of the Mohists, by "universal."[103]
Ching 靜 means "still," "in repose" and as a Taoist term is sometimes used
to designate the ataraxy of the adept. The ancient technical connotations
apparently have influenced later commentators, such as Chang Ching-yüeh
and the authors of the *Su-wen i-shih*[104] and yet their interpretations seem
far-fetched and even erroneous if we consider the systematic background of
the quotation together with Wang Ping's commentary. Wang Ping explains:
" '*Chien*' means to combine 兼 the configurative forces of cold and heat,
warmth and coolness."[105] In other words, they must be combined in keeping
with the quality of the Earth, the neutral point of transition. When all polar
opposites have been integrated and neutralized, stillness (*ching* 靜) will
prevail. In sum, the two words *chien* and *ching* were originally understood as
synonyms.

The *sapor* ("flavor") corresponding to the *orbis lienalis* is sweet
(*kan*).[106] Other correspondences of the *orbis lienalis* are the
yellow color (*huang*);[107] the tone *kung* 宮[108] or the sound of the
drum (*ku*);[109] among the vocal manifestations, singing (*ko*
歌)[110]; among domestic animals, the ox (water buffalo, *niu*);

[100]See the commentary in the *Ling-shu* 44/1196.
[101]*Ling-shu* 44/1195.
[102]*Su-wen* 67/604 and the parallels to this passage in the *Lei-ching* 3/53 and
Su-wen i-shih 67/437.
[103]Especially in the expression *chien-ai* 兼愛, universal love.
[104]See note 102.
[105]See p. 56 above. Wang Ping's interpretation can certainly be questioned,
but it carries weight because it was probably he who incorporated these
passages into the *Su-wen* (see *Su-wen* 67/607).
[106]*Su-wen* 5/58, 23/244.
[107]*Ibid* 5/58 and 67/604.
[108]*Ibid.* 5/58; *Ling-shu* 44/1195 *et passim.*
[109]*Ch'ien-chin yao-fang,* cited from the *I-pu ch'üan-lu,* Vol. IV, p. 158.
[110]*Su-wen* 5/58.

among cereals, yellow nonglutinous millet (*chi* 稷); among the classes of animals, the naked ones (i.e., man);[111] and among smells, the aromatic, agreeable ones (*hsiang* 香).[112] The *orbis lienalis* has its physiological check in the *orbis hepaticus*.[113] As for the injurious influences (*shang*), the rule is as usual that related effects are beneficial in moderation and noxious in excess. As with the *orbis cardialis*, this general formula is amended to the effect that an excess of energy is not drained off by the *sapores* [drugs and foods] of the corresponding sweet flavor (which has a comforting and warming but also a tonifying effect) but rather by bitter *sapores*. The sweet *sapor*, on the other hand, is used to replenish the energy of the *orbis lienalis*.[114] Dampness (*shih* 濕) on the one hand "damps" (moderates and neutralizes) climatic extremes; on the other hand, an excess of humidity, like overindulgence in sweets, will disturb and finally damage the function of the orb. The same is true of excessive cogitation (*szu* 思), the specific *emotio* of the *orbis lienalis*.[115]

(II) A macrocosmic correspondence of the *orbis lienalis* is the planet Saturn (*chen-hsing* 鎮星).[116] In the course of the year the *ch'i humanum* chiefly flows through the *orbis lienalis*[117] during the third and fourth Chinese months (approximately April and May), "when the energetic configuration of the Earth has stabilized and spreads."

Concerning the influence of the hours and seasons on disturbances of the *orbis lienalis* we are informed in *Su-wen* 22/236: "If the disease affects the *orbis lienalis* it will heal in autumn. If it does not heal in autumn, it will grow worse in spring. If [the patient] does not die in spring, he will tide over the summer and rise in the Indian summer. He should beware of too hot or too copious meals, of damp ground and damp

[111]*Ibid.* 4/41 and 67/604.
[112]*Ibid.* 4/42.
[113]*Ibid.* 10/114.
[114]*Ibid.* 22/236.
[115]*Ibid.* 5/58.
[116]*Ibid.* 4/41.
[117]*Ibid.* 16/149.

clothing." "Whoever gets a disease of the *orbis lienalis* will have a remission at sunset and grow worse at sunrise. He will quiet down in the afternoon." The other four *orbes horreales* (yin orbs), because of their association with the peripheral E.P., are correlated one by one with the Four Seasons,[118] but the situation is different for the *orbis lienalis,* determined by the central E.P. Earth. Just as the qualities of the peripheral evolutive phases are integrated by Earth, the *orbis lienalis* neutralizes and integrates the polar energies of the other four orbs. This function is reflected in the system of orbs by the fact that the third terrestrial branch of each direction is also called "branch of the Earth phase" (*ramus transvectus humi*).[119] The obvious consequence—that the last 18 days of each season correspond to the E.P. Earth— is of more symbolic than practical significance.[120]

We again record the speculative correspondences between the stages of disease in the *orbis lienalis* and the celestial stems: "One whose disease is in the *orbis lienalis* will recover on a *gust* 庚 or *hust* 辛 day. One who does not recover on a *gust* or *hust* day will grow worse under *ust* 甲 and *bust* 乙. One who does not die under *ust* or *bust* will tide over *cust* 丙 and *dust* 丁 and will get up under *esut* 戊 or *fust* 己."[121]

(III) The *orbis lienalis* is united with the *orbis stomachi* in a functional yoke in which as *orbis horrealis* it represents the inner side (*li, intima*).[122] The *sinarteria cardinalis* corresponding to the *orbis lienalis* is the *cardinalis yin maioris pedis.*[123] The specific unfoldment (*ch'ung, perfectio*) of the *orbis lienalis* is the flesh (*chi-jou* 肌肉).[124]

Chi-jou 肌肉 or simply *jou* 肉 designates the flesh of the muscles, connoting not so much its motor function as the somatic element which gives the body its characteristic shape and which, by its changes, permits inferences to be drawn about the individual's nutrition and reserve capacities. In contra-

---

[118]See p. 47 above.
[119]See Fig. 15 and the accompanying explanation.
[120]*Su-wen* 29/294 and *Lei-ching* 3/54. A contrary opinion (*Ling-shu* 44/1195) that the *orbis lienalis* corresponds to Indian summer represents a less consistent and less influential tradition.
[121]*Su-wen* 22/236.
[122]*Ling-shu* 47/1209; *Chung-ts'ang-ching* 1/15.
[123]*Ling-shu* 10/997.
[124]*Su-wen* 9/109, 10/114 and 5/58 *et passim*.

distinction *chin* 筋 (*nervus*, muscles and sinews) points to the mechanical elements, sometimes concealed, of the locomotive system.

The specific radial pulse of the *orbis lienalis* is the *pulsus clusalis mersus manus dextrae* 右手關沈脈.[125]

(IV) The outward manifestation (*flos*) of the *orbis lienalis* is the lips (*ch'un* 脣);[126] its specific body opening (*ch'iao*) is the mouth.[127]

The tongue has already been attributed to the *orbis cardialis*[128] as its sense organ; since the mouth can hardly be considered a sense organ in its own right, it is natural to incorporate the lips into the sensorium of the *orbis lienalis*. Even so, the sense of taste residing in the tongue[129] probably must also tacitly be included among the functions corresponding to the *orbis lienalis*. The *Ling-shu* makes a hair-splitting and unsatisfying distinction: ".... If the *orbis cardialis* is in harmony, the tongue may perceive distinctly the five *sapores*.... If the *orbis lienalis* is in harmony, the mouth may perceive distinctly the Five Cereals...."[130]

Of the intermittently secerned fluids (*yeh*) the *saliva lienalis* (*hsien* 涎) corresponds to the *orbis lienalis*.[131]

The specific psychic reaction (*emotio, chih* 志) of the *orbis lienalis* is "cogitation" (*szu* 思, *cogitatio*).[132] Of the modes of behavior and action (*pien-tung*) "retching" (*yüeh* 噦)[133] and moistening (*chu* 注)[134] are associated with the *orbis lienalis*.

On dream motifs which indicate disturbances in the *orbis lienalis*, the *Nei-ching* has: "If the energy of the *orbis lienalis* is exhausted, one dreams that one lacks food and drink. At right moments one dreams of erecting walls and buildings."[135]— "If the energy is abundant in the *orbis lienalis*, one dreams that one chants and plays music; yet one's body is heavy and one

[125]*Mo-ching* 2/21; *Chung-i-hsüeh kai-lun*, p. 199.
[126]*Su-wen* 9/109, 10/114.
[127]*Su-wen* 4/41; *Ling-shu* 17/1074.
[128]See pp. 146–147 above.
[129]But not the tongue's tactile sensitivity nor its part in linguistic articulation.
[130]*Ling-shu* 17/1074.
[131]*Su-wen* 23/247 and its parallel in the *Ling-shu* 78/1368.
[132]*Su-wen* 5/58, 67/604.
[133]*Ibid.* 5/58.
[134]*Ibid.* 67/604. The Chinese word *chu* 注 means "to pour," "to water"; our translation "to moisten" is justified by the context as well as by the commentary of Wang Ping (on. p. 607).
[135]*Su-wen* 80/871.

cannot rise.[136] "If a *flexus* deversates in the *orbis lienalis*, in one's dreams there appear hills and marshes, ruined buildings, and storms."[137]

The anatomical substratum of the *orbis lienalis*, the spleen, is described in the *Nan-ching* 42[138] as an organ "weighing two *chin* (pounds), 3 *liang* (ounces), large and flat in shape, 3 inches wide, 5 inches long, with half a *liang* of fatty appendages."[139]

(V) Within the integral organism the *orbis lienalis*—together with its outer orb (*species*), the *orbis stomachi*—holds the role of depository organ or temporary depot (*ts'ang-lin chih kuan* 倉廩 之官) from which are distributed the five *sapores*[140] (its specific function). Its "fundamental function" is to serve as the foundation of depositing and distribution and in its "storage function" it is the seat of "constructive energy" (*ying* 營, *ch'i constructivum*).[141]

These classical definitions must be explained, because they are in part, if not interpolated, at least open to misinterpretation because the *orbis lienalis*, in the course of the interpretation and continued development of orbisiconography since the Han period, has acquired so many additional aspects.

The functional distinction between *orbes horreales* (*tsang*, yin orbs) and *orbes aulici* (*fu*, yang orbs) is said to be that the former "store structive potential (*ching-ch'i*) without letting it drain off," whereas the latter "move and assimilate nutritive matter but do not store it."[142] Now in the notoriously dubious context[143] under discussion, the *orbis lienalis* is aligned with five[144] of the six *orbes aulici* as constituting the foundation (*pen*) of temporary storage. One may be inclined to suppose that here again the text is vitiated, but such a suspicion cannot be upheld on mere impressions; at any rate in later medical literature hardly any fuss is made over the congruent functions of the *orbis lienalis* and of five of the *orbes aulici*. The problem may

---

[136]*Ling-shu* 43/1191.

[137]*Ibid.* 43/1192.

[138]*Nan-ching* 4/108.

[139]In comparison, European anatomy, e.g. Braus, *Anatomie des. Menschen*, Vol. II, p. 560, gives the average size of the spleen as length 12 cm, width 7 cm, thickness 4 cm, and its weight as ca. 150 g.

[140]*Su-wen* 8/94.

[141]*Su-wen* 9/109 and its parallels in the *Nei-ching t'ai-su* 6/28 and the *Lei-ching* 3/46f.

[142]See p. 110 above.

[143]See p. 117 above.

[144]The *orbes stomachi, intestini crassi et tenuis, tricalorii, et vesicalis*.

be solved if we examine the wording of the definitions more closely and compare it with the consensus of medical writers on the subject.

The expressions used here to characterize the fundamental functions (*pen*) are *ts'ang* 倉 and *lin* 廩. In spite of phonetic similarity to the term designating the storage function and the "storing" considered an essential trait of all *orbes horreales* (藏, written with radical 131, read *tsang* as a noun and *ts'ang* as a verb), *ts'ang* 倉 is distinct semantically, etymologically, and graphically. Written with radical 9 and rendered here by "depository," it primarily designates a grain depository or silo in which supplies are stored between harvests for short periods only. *Lin* designates a magazine in which supplies destined for distribution were temporarily stored; a derived sense of the word is "scholarships granted in the form of food allotments" taken from such magazines. *Ts'ang* 倉 and *lin* in nonmedical usage thus suggest the idea of limited short-term storage of food destined for consumption—which, *mutatis mutandis*, may also be considered as the function of the *orbes aulici*. The term *ts'ang* or *tsang* 藏 on the contrary indicates a storehouse or treasure house in which precious goods and reserves are stored for an indefinite time. The *orbes horreales* store certain forms of qualitatively determinate energy— "configurational energy" (*ch'i*)—for an undefined period, in theory the life span of the individual. These stores are broached and consumed only in exceptional circumstances, for if they are exhausted death ensues. Similarly, in the *Tao-tsang*, the "Taoist Canon," and the *Fo-tsang*, the "Buddhist Canon," the quintessence of the respective teachings is meant to be conserved eternally.

As an *orbis horrealis* the *orbis lienalis*, unlike the *orbes aulici*, stores a particular form of configurational energy, called "constructive energy" (*ch'i constructivum, ying-[ch'i]*). Yet because it corresponds to the E.P. Earth (*transvectus humi*), it resembles the *orbes aulici* in being a sphere of incessant exchange and transition, although in the latter this function is differentiated. Thus is resolved the apparent contradiction implied by the passage quoted from *Su-wen* 9/109.

The central position of the *orbis lienalis* and its resulting polyvalence and flexibility have prompted a gradual expansion of its functions. The majority of these added functions have proven to be in harmony with empirical data and so rapidly became integral parts of the conventional iconography of the *orbis lienalis*.

In the *Nan-ching* 42[145] it is asserted that the dominant function of the *orbis lienalis* consists in enveloping the individually specific structive energy. This passage may alternately be

[145]*Nan-ching* 4/108, after the crude anatomical description of the spleen.

translated to say that the *orbis lienalis* represents a "parcel of *hsüeh*." It is also attributed an essential role in the storage (*ts'ang*) of ideas, and it extends its warmth to all *orbes horreales*.

The authors of the *Chung-ts'ang-ching* 中藏經[146] advance still further in this direction. They call the *orbis lienalis* the "organ of critical distinction and of reflection," as essential to imagination and insight as to the digestion of the Five Cereals (i. e., of food in general). This interpretation was confirmed in principle during the T'ang by Sun Szu-mo: "The *orbis lienalis* controls imagination. The *orbis lienalis* is the abode of imagination [i.e., of ideas]."[147]

The functional conception of the *orbis lienalis* (and of the *orbis stomachi*) was greatly influenced in the Sung by Li Tung-yüan 李東垣, founder of the "strengthening the Earth school" (*pu-t'u-p'ai* 補土派) of Chinese medicine. For reasons just explained, Li taught that the harmonious function of the *orbes lienalis et stomachi*, the representatives of the central E.P. Earth, is crucial to the health of the entire organism, and he adapted therapy to this theory. From this context a definition evolved that became explicit in the Ming and today is part of China's universal medical tradition: "The roots of the acquired constitution are in the *orbis lienalis*. . . . [The E.P.] Earth is the mother of the Myriad Beings."[148] Chang Ching-yüeh, renowned as author of the *Lei-ching*, writes in an essay "On the *orbes lienalis et stomachi*:[149] "The guardian of the [native] structive potential is [in] the 'Gate of Destiny' (*porta fortunae*);[150] the guardians of food are the *orbes lienalis et stomachi*. For this

---

[146]"Treasury Classic," a book that, at least in its extant form, is wrongly ascribed to the famous Han physician Hua T'uo. It contains medical theories expounded in a remarkably lucid style (See the *I-chi-k'ao*, p. 629). *Chung-ts'ang-ching*, 1/15f.

[147]Quoted from the *I-pu ch'üan-lu*, Vol. IV, p. 157.

[148]*I-tsung pi-tu* 醫宗必讀 (Compulsory reading for physicians; first printed 1637), by the physician Li Chung-tzu 李中梓, cited from the *I-pu ch'üan-lu*, Vol. IV, p. 176.

[149]In his collected writings, *Ching-yüeh ch'üan-shu* 景岳全書, cited from the *I-pu ch'üan-lu*, Vol. IV, p. 187.

[150]See the relevant paragraph on pp. 142–146 below.

reason the 'Gate of Destiny' receives the configurational energies of the native constitution (*ch'i nativum*), and the *orbes lienalis et stomachi* receive the configurational energies of the acquired constitution (*ch'i ascitum*)." And he goes on in a section "On the treatment of the *orbes lienalis et stomachi*": "If a disease develops in the *orbes lienalis et stomachi* treatment must of course be given to the *orbis lienalis*. For the *orbis lienalis* is the *orbis horrealis* [corresponding to] the E.P. Earth. [Consequently its energy] moistens and irrigates [what corresponds to all] Four Directions. If all the orbs participate in the energy of the *orbis lienalis*, and the *orbis lienalis* in turn participates in the energy of all the other orbs, this is because they all communicate with one another. . . . Thus one who knows how to treat the *orbis lienalis* is capable of harmonizing all the orbs."[151]

The account just given of the functions of the *orbis lienalis* has provided ample evidence that the concept of an orb (*tsang*) in Chinese medicine can never be made completely congruent with the description which Western medicine gives of an organ and its functions. Thus the *orbis lienalis* comprises some functions that in Western medical theory belong not only to the spleen but also to the pancreas, the stomach, and the duodenum—and some that Europeans describe only vaguely if at all.

THE *ORBIS PULMONALIS* (*FEI* 肺)

(I) The *orbis pulmonalis*, as one of the *orbes horreales*, is primarily yin within the total orb system. Within the cycle of the Five E.P.s it corresponds to Metal (*transvectus metalli*) and thus may also be qualified as minor yin, yin in yang (or even minor yin in yang).[152] Because of its preponderantly structive polarity, the *orbis pulmonalis* is counted among the female *orbes horreales* (*p'in-tsang*).[153]

A number of secondary correspondences proceed from the correspondence of the *orbis pulmonalis* to the E.P. Metal.

[151]*Ching-yüeh ch'üan-shu*, cited from the *I-pu ch'üan-lu*, Vol. IV, p. 190.
[152]*Su-wen* 9/109 and the commentary in the *Ling-shu* 44/1196. See especially pp. 118ff above.
[153]*Ling-shu* 44/1195.

Energy adapted to the character of the *orbis pulmonalis* has a cooling effect (*liang* 凉).[154] Also to the *orbis pulmonalis* there correspond the pungent *sapor* (flavor) (*hsin* 辛), the color white,[155] the tone *shang* 商[156] or the sound of the resonant stones (*ch'ing* 磬),[157] the crying voice (*k'u* 哭) among vocal manifestations,[158] the horse among domestic animals, rice among cereals, animals with a carapace (shell, *chieh* 介) among the classes of animals.[159] Among smells, the smell of raw meat (or fish) (*hsing* 腥) points to the *orbis pulmonalis*.[160]

The *orbis pulmonalis* is physiologically checked (*chu*) by the *orbis cardialis*.[161] As for the influences injurious (*shang*) to the *orbis pulmonalis*, since related effects are beneficial in moderate strength and detrimental in excessive doses, an excess of energy in the *orbis pulmonalis* is drained off by its corresponding pungent *sapor* and a deficiency is replenished by its antithetical sour *sapor*.[162] Dry weather of moderate duration and at the right time is beneficial to the *orbis pulmonalis;* yet it becomes injurious to it and especially to its unfoldment, the skin, if it is too intense and persists too long. The specific emotion of the *orbis pulmonalis*, sorrow (*yu* 憂, *aegrimonia*) tones down its functions.[163]

(II) A macrocosmic correspondence of the *orbis pulmonalis* is the planet Venus (*t'ai-pai-hsing* 太白星).[164] During the seventh and eighth Chinese months (approximately August and September), "when structive energy commences its task of destruction,"[165] the physiological energy of man (*ch'i humanum*) chiefly flows through the *orbis pulmonalis*.[166]

The influence of hours and seasons on disturbances of the

[154]*Su-wen* 67/605.
[155]*Ibid.* 5/59, 23/244 *et passim.*
[156]*Su-wen* 5/59; *Ling-shu* 44/1195 *et passim.*
[157]*Ch'ien-chin yao-fang* 17/304.
[158]*Su-wen* 5/59.
[159]*Ibid.* 4/42, 67/605.
[160]*Ibid.* 4/42.
[161]*Ibid.* 10/114.
[162]*Ibid.* 22/237.
[163]See also pp. 148ff.
[164]*Su-wen* 4/42.
[165]The "destructive" effects of structive energy have been explained on pp. 28–29.
[166]*Su-wen* 16/149.

orbis pulmonalis is described in *Su-wen* 22/237: "If the disease affects the *orbis pulmonalis* it will heal in winter; if it does not heal in winter, it will grow worse in summer. If [the patient] does not die in summer, he will tide over the Indian summer and will get up in autumn. He should beware of cold food and drink and of cool clothing."—"Whoever gets a disease of the *orbis pulmonalis* will have a remission in the afternoon and grow worse at noon. He will quiet down toward midnight."

The correspondences between the stages of disease in the *orbis pulmonalis* and the celestial stems may also be quoted from the same source: "One whose disease is in the *orbis pulmonalis* will recover on a *just* 壬 or *kut* 癸 day. One who does not recover on a *just* or *kut* day will grow worse under *cust* 丙 and *dust* 丁. One who does not die under *cust* and *dust* will tide over *esut* 戊 and *fust* 己 and will get up under *gust* 庚 or *hust* 辛."

(III) The *orbis pulmonalis* is united with the *orbis intestini crassi* in a functional yoke in which, as an *orbis horrealis*, it takes the inner side (*intima, li*).[167] The *sinarteria cardinalis* corresponding to the *orbis pulmonalis* is the *cardinalis yin maioris manus*.[168] The specific unfoldment (*ch'ung, perfectio*) of the *orbis pulmonalis* is the skin (*p'i* 皮) and body hair (*mao* 毛).[169] Their appearance permits inferences to be drawn on the general constitution of the *orbis pulmonalis*. The specific radial pulse of the *orbis pulmonalis* is the *pulsus pollicaris mersus manus dextrae* 右手寸沈脈.[170]

(IV) The outward manifestation (*flos*) of the *orbis pulmonalis* is hair (*mao* 毛)—according to the classics,[171] hair in general; according to the T'ang author Sun Szu-mo, the hair of the head (*fa* 髮) only.[172] The specific body opening (*ch'iao*) of the *orbis pulmonalis,* here identical with its corresponding sense organ (*kuan*), is the nose.[173] Consequently, of the intermittently secerned fluids the *orbis pulmonalis* is assigned to the nasal

[167] *Ling-shu* 47/1209.
[168] *Ibid.* 10/984.
[169] *Su-wen* 5/59, 9/109.
[170] *Mo-ching* 2/20; *Chung-i-hsüeh kai-lun*, p. 199.
[171] *Su-wen* 9/109, 10/114.
[172] *Ch'ien-chin yao-fang*, quoted from the *I-pu ch'üan-lu,* Vol. IV, p. 223. According to classical theory, the hair on the head (*fa*) is associated with the *orbis renalis* (cf. below, p. 143).
[173] *Su-wen* 4/42, 5/59; *Ling-shu* 17/1074 *et passim.*

secretions (*t'i* 涕).[174] The particular psychic reaction (*emotio, chih*) associated with this orb is sorrow (*yu* 憂, *aegrimonia*). Of the modes of behavior and action (*pien-tung*), coughing (*k'o*)[175] and destruction by severe and harsh effects of weather (*su-sha* 肅殺)[176] correspond to the *orbis pulmonalis*.

Dream motifs thought to indicate disturbances in the *orbis pulmonalis* are enumerated in the *Nei-ching:* "If the energy of the *orbis pulmonalis* is exhausted, this causes white objects to appear in dreams,[177] or the cruel killing of people."[178]—"If there is abundance of energy in the *orbis pulmonalis*, one will be frightened in dreams, cry, or soar through the air."[179]—"If a *flexus* deversates in the *orbis pulmonalis*, one dreams of soaring through the air or sees strange objects made of metal."[180]

The anatomical substratum of the *orbis pulmonalis*, the lungs, are defined in the *Nan-ching* 42:[181] "The lungs weigh 3 *chin* (pounds), 3 *liang* (ounces), have 6 leaves [lobes] (*yeh*) and 2 ears—a total of 8 leaves."

(V) Within the integral organism the orbis pulmonalis holds the office of "(prime) minister" (*hsiang-fu* 相傅) on whom rhythmic order (= specific function) depends.[182]

The *orbis pulmonalis* essentially represents what Western medicine defines as the sphere of respiratory function: today it appears that respiration has repercussions not only upon the rhythm of the pulse but on all energetic processes in the body. This is reflected in Chinese terminology, where "breath" is one of several incidental meanings of the term *ch'i* (energetic configuration or configurational energy). Chang Ching-yüeh explains: "The *orbis pulmonalis* controls the *ch'i* [the energetic configuration manifesting itself in respiration]. If the *ch'i*

---

[174]*Su-wen* 23/247 and its parallel in the *Ling-shu* 78/1368.
[175]*Su-wen* 5/59.
[176]*Su-wen* 67/605.
[177]White is the emblematic color of the West, of Metal, and is therefore associated with weapons; at the same time it is the color of mourning.
[178]*Su-wen* 80/871.
[179]*Ling-shu* 43/1191.
[180]*Ibid.* 43/1192.
[181]*Nan-ching* 4/108.
[182]*Su-wen* 8/94.

is in rhythmic harmony, of course all constructive and defensive energy (*ying-wei*) and all orbs are in good order."[183]

The *orbis pulmonalis* controls the function of the skin (=dominant function) which, as Wang Ping explains, "envelops sinews and muscles and wards off all heteropathies (*heteropathica, hsieh*)."[184] The *orbis pulmonalis* is the foundation of configurational energy distributed rhythmically by breathing (=fundamental function [*pen*]).[185] The *orbis pulmonalis* stores the individually specific structive configurative forces (*p'o* 魄),[186] in other words the structive components of the forces maintaining the individuality and even the existence of a being (=storage function).

THE *ORBIS RENALIS* (*SHEN* 腎)

(I) The *orbis renalis* is one of the *orbes horreales* and is primarily yin within the orb system. It corresponds to the E.P. Water (*transvectus aquae*) and thus is doubly qualified as yin; it represents major yin or yin in yin.[187] This entirely structive polarization explains why the *orbis renalis* is considered female in gender (*p'in-tsang*).[188]

A number of secondary correspondences are the direct consequence of the qualification of the *orbis renalis* by the E.P. Water. The corresponding meteorological phenomenon is bitter cold (*lin* 凛).[189] To the *orbis renalis* also correspond the salty (*hsien* 鹹) *sapores* (flavors),[190] the color black, the tone *yü* 羽[191] or the sound of the twenty-five stringed lute (*seh* 瑟);[192] among vocal manifestations, the moaning voice (*shen* 呻);[193]

---

[183]無所不治. Commentary in the *Lei-ching* 3/44.
[184]*Su-wen* 23/251.
[185]*Ibid.* 9/109.
[186]*Ibid.* 23/250 and 9/109 as well as pp. 184–185 and Table 14 below.
[187]See p. 118 above and the commentary in the *Ling-shu* 44/1196.
[188]*Ling-shu* 44/1195.
[189]*Su-wen* 67/605.
[190]*Ibid.* 5/60, 23/244; 4/42 *et passim.*
[191]*Ibid.* 5/60 and *Ling-shu* 44/1195 *et passim.*
[192]*Ch'ien-chin yao-fang* 19/341.
[193]*Su-wen* 5/60.

among domestic animals, the pig; among edible plants the soybean; among the classes of animals, the scaly animals (*lin* 鱗) (=fishes).[194] Among smells, a decaying odor (*fu* 腐) is associated with the *orbis renalis*.[195]

The *orbis renalis* is physiologically checked (*chu*) by the *orbis lienalis*.[196] As for the influences injurious (*shang*) to the *orbis renalis*, since related effects in moderate strength are beneficial and in excessive strength are injurious, an excess of energy in the *orbis renalis* is drained off by its corresponding salty *sapor*, whereas its energy is replenished by the complementary bitter *sapor* (*k'u* 苦).[197] Too much of the latter will injure its *perfectio*, the bones and marrow (medulla). Analogously, bitter cold, corresponding to the *orbis renalis*, injures the *hsüeh*.[198] The *orbis renalis* is harmed by its corresponding emotion, fear (*k'ung* 恐).[199]

(II) A macrocosmic correspondence of the *orbis renalis* is the planet Mercury (*ch'en-hsing* 辰星).[200] During the tenth and eleventh Chinese months (approximately November and December), "when ice covers the ground and the energetic configuration of the earth [yin and yang] unite" the physiological energy of man (*ch'i humanum*) chiefly flows in the *orbis renalis*.[201] The influence of hours and seasons on the disturbances of the *orbis renalis* is described in the *Su-wen* 22/237: "If the disease affects the *orbis renalis* it will heal in spring. If it does not heal in spring it will grow worse in the Indian summer. If [the patient] does not die during Indian summer he will tide over the autumn and will get up in winter. He should beware of scalding food and heated clothing."— "Whoever gets a disease of the *orbis renalis* will have a remission toward midnight and will grow worse during the hours of the

[194]*Ibid*. 4/42, 67/605.
[195]*Ibid*. 4/42.
[196]*Ibid*. 10/114.
[197]*Ibid*. 22/237.
[198]*Ibid*. 23/248 and 5/60, as well as pp. 185–186 below.
[199]*Ibid*. 5/60.
[200]*Ibid*. 4/42.
[201]*Ibid*. 16/249.

E.P. Earth[202] [i.e., from 1:00 to 3:00 and from 7:00 to 9:00, both A.M. and P.M.]; he will quiet down in the afternoon."
The correspondences between celestial stems and the stages of disease in the *orbis renalis* are also given: "One whose disease is in the *orbis renalis* will recover on an *ust* 甲 or *bust* 乙 day. One who does not recover on an *ust* or *bust* day will grow worse under *esut* 戊 and *fust* 己. One who does not die under *esut* and *fust* will tide over *gust* 庚 and *hust* 辛 and will get up under *just* 壬 or 癸 *kut*."

(III) The *orbis renalis* is united with the *orbis vesicalis* in a functional yoke in which, as *orbis horrealis,* the former takes the inward side (*intima, li*).[203] Two partly contradictory theories about the spatial extension and the material substratum of the *orbis renalis* compete in the *Nei-ching.* Western anatomy describes the kidneys as a double organ. According to one tradition represented in the *Nei-ching,*[204] probably the more ancient one, both kidneys constitute the substrate of the integral *orbis renalis* and, inversely, the functions of the *orbis renalis* are supported equally by both kidneys (holistic theory). According to another, perhaps somewhat more recent, tradition also represented in the *Nei-ching* and more fully in the *Nan-ching,*[205] the designation *shen* (*orbis renalis*) applies only to the left organ, whereas the right organ is named *ming-men* (命門, Gate of Destiny, *porta fortunae*). The latter has relative functional independence, and performs some of the functions that the holistic theory attributes to the complete *orbis renalis* (dualistic theory). In later centuries, although champions of the holistic theory have been more numerous and influential, the dualistic theory has managed to survive up to our time. Advocates of the dualistic theory sometimes postulate duplicate *orbes horreales,* the *orbis renalis* and the *orbis portae fortunae.* That is why in *Ling-shu* 47/1209 two regular *orbes aulici,* the *orbis vesicalis* and the *orbis tricalorii,* are assigned as complements to the *orbis renalis.*[206]

The *sinarteria cardinalis* corresponding to the *orbis renalis* is

---

[202]See the note on p. 170 of the *Su-wen i-shih* as well as p. 81 above.
[203]*Chung-ts'ang-ching,* 2/21.
[204]See, for example, *Su-wen* 5/60 *et passim.*
[205]*Nan* 36 = *Nan-ching* 3/100.
[206]See the paragraphs devoted to these orbs below.

the *cardinalis yin minoris pedis*.[207] The boncs (*ku*) and the marrow (*sui*) constitute the specific unfoldments (*ch'ung, perfectiones*) of the *orbis renalis*.[208] The specific radial pulse of the *orbis renalis* is the *pulsus pedalis mersus manus sinistrae* 左手尺沈脈.[209] A number of authors (Wang Shu-ho 王叔和, Li Tung-yüan 李東垣, Li Shih-chen 李時珍, Yü Chia-yen 喩嘉言, Li Shih-ts'ai 李士材, and Chang Ching-yüeh likewise relate the pulse *pulsus pedalis mersus manus dextrae* to the *orbis renalis*, or at least to the *porta fortunae*.

In order to decide whether this twofold correspondence is justified, precise and stringent empirical data would be required which seem not to be available as yet. At any rate, by purely logical and systematic criteria the attribution may (with some reservations) be justified. The *pulsus pedalis* (*ch'ih-mo* 尺脈) of the right hand in a way serves as a reserve position (not to say makeshift position) for the accomodation of vague or contradictory correspondences. In this way three authors[210] align with the *pulsus mersus* [*pedalis manus dextrae*] the *porta fortunae*, three authors the *orbis renalis*, two the *orbis tricalorii* and one even the *orbis intestini crassi*. The range of attributions is even greater for the *pulsus superficialis* of the same position: it is three times attributed to the *orbis tricalorii*, twice to the *orbis intestini tenuis*, twice to the *orbis intestini crassi* and once each to the *orbis vesicalis, orbis pericardialis,* and *orbis renalis*. As will be explained shortly, the *orbis renalis* comprises two distinct functional complexes; thus not only the distinction of *orbis renalis* and *porta fortunae* but also the assignment of two different pulses seems justified in principle.

In 1963 the Commission on Textbooks of the Chinese Academy of Medicine approved a course of lectures in diagnostics (*Chung-kuo chen-tuan-hsüeh chiang-i* 中國診斷學講義). The authors took an essentially pragmatic attitude when on pp. 68f. they assigned both *pulsus pedales mersi* to the *orbis renalis* and both *pulsus pedales superficiales* to the abdomen (*hsiao-fu* 小腹), i.e., equally to the *orbes intestini tenuis et crassi*.

(IV) The outward manifestation (*flos*) of the *orbis renalis* is the hair of the head (*fa* 髮).[211] Among the body openings (*ch'iao*) the urethra and the anus (*liang-yin* 兩陰) are associated with the *orbis renalis*.[212] Among the sense organs (*kuan*) the ears corres-

---

[207]*Ling-shu* 10/1010.

[208]*Su-wen* 5/60, 18/185; 9/109, 10/114.

[209]*Mo-ching* 2/19; *Chung-i-hsüeh kai-lun*, p. 199.

[210]See the table on p. 199 of the *Chung-i-hsüeh kai-lun*.

[211]*Su-wen* 9/109, 10/114.

[212]*Ibid.* 4/42; See also the *Ch'ien-chin yao-fang*, quoted from the *I-pu ch'üan-lu*, Vol. IV, p. 263.

pond to the *orbis renalis*.[213] (We have already mentioned that the ears considered as body openings [*ch'iao*] are also attributed to the *orbis cardialis*.[214] Chang Ching-yüeh states[215] that "the ears are simultaneously [attributed to] the *orbes cardialis et renalis*.")

Of intermittently secerned fluids (*yeh*), the *orbis renalis* is assigned the saliva produced at the base of the tongue (*t'uo* 唾, *saliva renalis*).[216] In the medical classics there is a distinction between two kinds of saliva, depending upon their different functional and organic origins. There is the *saliva lienalis* (*hsien* 涎) which, according to Wang Ping and Ma Shih,[217] is secreted in the mouth and at the lips; and there is the *saliva renalis* (*t'uo*) which in the opinion of the same authors originates on the teeth. The teeth are considered a bony substance, related to the bones and thus to the *orbis renalis*.

The particular psychic reaction associated with the *orbis renalis* is fear (*k'ung* 恐, *pavor*).[218] Among the modes of behavior and action (*pien-tung*), trembling and quivering (*li* 慄)[219] as well as freezing and congealing (*ning-li* 凝冽)[220] correspond to the *orbis renalis*.

About dream motifs that may indicate disturbances in the *orbis renalis* we find in the *Nei-ching*: "If the energy of the *orbis renalis* is exhausted, this causes ships and boats and drowning men to appear in one's dreams. At the right time one dreams of lying in the water and becomes frightened."[221]—"If there is abundance of energy in the *orbis renalis*, in dreaming one has the sensation that the back and the waist are split apart and

[213]*Su-wen* 5/60. In this text the ears are designated only as the "openings" (*ch'iao*) of the *orbis renalis*; cf. the text and commentary in the *Lei-ching* 3/51, *Ling-shu* 17/1074 *et passim*.
[214]See pp. 126f above.
[215]Commentary to the *Lei-ching* 3/48.
[216]*Su-wen* 23/247; text and commentary cf the *Ling-shu* 78/1368; see also p. 132 above.
[217]Commentaries in the *Su-wen* 23/247f.
[218]*Su-wen* 5/60, 67/605.
[219]*Ibid.* 5/60.
[220]*Ibid.* 67/605.
[221]*Ibid.* 80/871.

can no longer be stretched."[222]—"If a *flexus* deversates in the *orbis renalis* one dreams of approaching a ravine, plunging into water, or being in the water."[223]

Concerning the anatomical substratum of the *orbis renalis*, the kidneys, we are informed in the *Nan-ching*:[224] "To each orb there belongs but one [substratum]; only for the *orbis renalis* are there two. What does this mean? Now the two kidneys do not both constitute [the substratum of] the *orbis renalis*. Only the left kidney is the [substratum of] the *orbis renalis*; the right one is the *porta fortunae* (*ming-men*)." "The kidneys are two. They weigh one *chin* (pound), one *liang* (ounce)."[225]

(V) Within the organism two groups of complementary functions correspond to the *orbis renalis*. The *orbis renalis* constitutes the "foundation of the [hibernal] retreat and suspension of communication" (*feng-ts'ang* 封藏, first fundamental function),[226] "the organ for the concentration of [energetic] forces" (*tso-ch'iang chih kuan* 作强之官) which influences the technical skills (first specific function),[227] and which stores the [directed] emotions or will power (*chih* 志, *emotiones*, first storage function).[228] The *orbis renalis* "regulates" hibernation and similar stages of latency[229] (first dominant function). At the same time the *orbis renalis* is the seat and foundation of the structive potential (*ching* 精)[230] (second fundamental function), and the root of life (*hsing-ming chih ken* 性命之根).[231]

Whereas in the *Chung-ts'ang-ching* 中藏經 the *orbis renalis* is called the abode of the configurative force combined with its structive potential (*ching-shen*),[232] in the *Nan-ching* this function is expressly attributed to the *porta fortunae* ("Gate of Destiny"):

[222]*Ling-shu* 43/1191.
[223]*Ibid.* 43/1192.
[224]*Nan-ching* 3/100 (question 36).
[225]*Nan-ching* 4/109 (question 42). Neither the text nor the commentary say whether this is the weight of each or of both together. The scrotum, which Chinese doctors today call *wai-shen* 外腎 (renal exterior), should also be considered part of the substratum of the *orbis renalis*.
[226]*Su-wen* 9/109.
[227]*Ibid.* 8/94.
[228]*Ibid.* 23/250.
[229]*Ibid.* 9/109.
[230]See pp. 176–177 and Table 19 below, *Su-wen* 9/109, and particularly the *Ch'ien-chin yao-fang*, quoted from the *I-pu ch'üan-lu*, Vol. IV, p. 263.
[231]*Chung-ts'ang-ching*, 2/21.
[232]See pp. 193–195 below.

"The *porta fortunae* is the place in which all configurative forces combined with [their] structive potentials (*ching-shen*) have their abode, the place in which the basic vital energy (*yüan-ch'i, ch'i originale*)[233] is fixed."

The explicit distinction of *orbis renalis* and *porta fortunae*, by the way, goes back to this passage, the first half of which is quoted at the end of the preceding section. In the *I-hsüeh cheng-chuan* 醫學正傳 (Canonical tradition of medicine, Ming) we are informed: "According to the *Nei-ching*, the *orbis pericardialis* is the complement of the *orbis ignis ministri tricalorii*, a correspondence which also holds for the cardinal sinarteries (*sinarteriae cardinales*). Thus both kidneys originally [were the substratum of] one single orb. The distinction of left and right first introduced by Yüeh-jen [the presumptive author of the *Nan-ching*] did not exist at the beginning, but even he does not maintain that the *orbis renalis* corresponds to the *ignis ministri*. And yet the thesis of [Wang] Shu-ho,[234] that the *orbis tricalorii* and the *porta fortunae* correspond to one another in the relation of outer (*piao, species*) and inner (*li, intima*) has a deeper significance...." We shall come back to this question in the discussion of the *orbis tricalorii*.

The *orbis renalis* has been described as the foundation or seat of the structive potential (and even of the configurative force) at least since the T'ang period.[235] On the basis of this description—which is only an explicit, more elegant, and more general formulation of what is implicit in several passages of the *Nei-ching*[236]—a third fundamental function of the *orbis renalis* was defined and explicitly stated in the *I-tsung pi-tu* 醫宗必讀[237] of the Ming: "The *orbis renalis* is the foundation of the native constitution (*hsien-t'ien chih pen* 先天之本)." This third fundamental function of the *orbis renalis* constitutes an essential element of modern Chinese medical theory.[238]

We shall return later to a theory postulating a connection between the *orbis renalis* and the brain (*nao* 腦), which attained great significance in the writings of Didactic Taoism[239] and is reflected in the *Nei-ching*.[240]

[233]*Nan-ching* 3/100.
[234]Wang Shu-ho is the author of the *Mo-ching*, the "Classic of the Pulse."
[235]Concerning the dating of the *Chung-ts'ang-ching*, see *I-chi-k'ao*, p. 629 and pp. 633ff.
[236]*Su-wen* 1/5; 9/109.
[237]*I-tsung pi-tu*, quoted from the *I-pu ch'üan-lu*, Vol. IV, p. 273.
[238]*Chung-i-hsüeh kai-lun*, p. 63.
[239]One source, the *Nei-ching-t'u* 內經圖, has been interpreted by Erwin Rousselle in "Seelische Führung im lebenden Taoismus II. Ne Ging Tu, 'Die Tafel des inneren Gewebes,'" *Eranos Jahrbuch*, 1933 *1*: 153–173.
[240]See pp. 162–163.

THE *ORBIS PERICARDIALIS* (*HSIN-PAO-LUO* 心包絡)

(I) The *orbis pericardialis*, at least in the system of sinarteriology,[241] is counted as a sixth *orbis horrealis*[242] although all the medical classics, and even more so nonmedical texts, speak of "The five *tsang* (*orbes horreales*)" as a stereotype. Hence, it is likely that the concept of an *orbis pericardialis* primarily arose from a desire for symmetry in sinarteriology, and that this orb then was only incidentally and summarily assigned correspondences to fill out the orbisiconographic pattern.

This hypothesis receives additional support from the fact that in the *Su-wen* the *orbis pericardialis* is not once mentioned by its technical name, *hsin-pao-luo*, and that in the *Ling-shu* this name occurs only in passages that refer to sinarteriology or to acupuncture. On the other hand, the commentators are unanimous in identifying the *atrium pectoris* (*tan-chung* 膻中),[243] repeatedly mentioned in the *Nei-ching*,[244] with the *orbis pericardialis*. Another synonym for both terms is *dominus cardialis* (*hsin-chu* 心主). In the *Ling-shu*, for example, one finds the equation: "The *atrium pectoris* is the walled palace of the *dominus cardialis*."[245] From the context of this passage it seems very doubtful whether the authors and commentators really had a clear idea of an organic substratum and its corresponding orb. Nevertheless, the term is also taken up in other chapters of the *Ling-shu* (10/1014 and 71/1315).

(III) The *orbis pericardialis* is united with the *orbis tricalorii* in a functional yoke in which, as an *orbis horrealis*, the former takes the inner side (*li, intima*).[246] The *sinarteria cardinalis* corresponding to the *orbis pericardialis* is the *cardinalis yin flectentis manus*.[247] As specific radial pulse there is attributed to the *orbis pericardialis* (or to the *atrium pectoris*), only in post-Sung medical texts, the *pulsus pedalis superficialis manus dextrae* (Hua Po-jen 滑伯仁) or, since Li Shih-chen, usually one of the *pulsus pollicares* [*mersus sive superficialis*] *manus sinistrae* 左手寸脈.[248]

(V) Within the organism the *orbis pericardialis* holds the office of an "official ambassador" (*ch'en-shih chih kuan* 臣使之官)

---

[241]See chapter 4.

[242]According to the commentary of Ma Shih in *Su-wen* 8/95.

[243]This is chiefly a sinarteriological term, designating a sensitive point (foramen) situated on the *sinarteria respondens* at its intersection with an ideal line drawn between the breasts. The substrate organ is situated sagittally behind this foramen within the thorax.

[244]*Su-wen* 8/94; *Ling-shu* 33/1157, 35/1161.

[245]*Ling-shu* 35/1161.

[246]*Nan-ching* 25:3/83.

[247]*Ling-shu* 10/1014.

[248]*Ching-i-hsüeh kai-lun*, p. 199.

(specific function) who is the origin of joy and pleasure.[249] The *orbis pericardialis* is the reservoir (*hai, mare*) of the energy put at the disposition of the individual at birth (*ch'i genuinum*).[250] From the definitions of the *orbis pericardialis* given in the texts just quoted and their commentaries, and from its roles in sinarteriology and pathology, one has the impression that its functions are distributed by Western medicine among the heart, lungs, and circulatory system (especially the aorta).

CRITICAL COMPARISON OF THE BENEFICIAL AND INJURIOUS INFLUENCES ON THE *ORBES HORREALES*, AS POSTULATED IN THE *NEI-CHING*

We have already briefly discussed the effects injurious to each orb as postulated in the *Nei-ching*. In that treatise we find not only exceptions to the rules that may be explained by the accommodation of empirical data, but also inner contradictions. A critical examination of classic inconsistencies is in order. The following passages require scrutiny:

1. *Su-wen* 5/55–60: At the end of passages devoted to the correspondences of the Five Evolutive Phases, the injurious effects (*shang, laesiones*) caused by *sapores* (flavors, *wei*) and meteorological configurations (*t'ien-ch'i*) are related to the unfoldments (*perfectiones, ch'ung*) of the *orbes horreales*. Each sentence may be summarized by the formula: "To evolutive phase *A* there corresponds the *orbis horrealis B*, the *sapor X*, and the meteorological configuration *Y*; *X* and *Y* injure the *perfectio C* of orb *B*." According to the rule, all five positions (*A,B,C, X,* and *Y*) must correspond to the same conventional quality. In fact the rule is perfectly observed only for the E.P. Wood (*orbis hepaticus*) and the E.P. Earth (*orbis lienalis*). The departures from the rule bear on the *perfectiones* (*C*) in the case of the E.P.s Fire and Water and on the meteorological configuration (*Y*) in the case of the E.P. Metal.

2. *Su-wen* 23/234–237: At the end of passages devoted essentially to the reactions of the five *orbes horreales* under changing macrocosmic conditions, it is explained which *sapores* replenish

[249] *Su-wen* 8/94 and the parallel in the *Lei-ching* 3/44.
[250] *Ling-shu* 33/1157; also the commentary in the *Su-wen* 8/94–96; cf. also the entry "*ch'i genuinum*" in the following section.

an energetic deficiency of an orb, and which drain off excessive energy. As a formula, the prescription is: "The energy of the *orbis A* is replenished (*pu* 補) by means of *sapor R* and is drained off (*hsieh* 泄) by means of *sapor S*." According to the rule, an influence qualitatively similar to the orb will drain off and finally exhaust its energy. An influence that according to the polar scheme of the E.P.s (= Sequence 0) is qualitatively complementary to the orb will replenish its energy. Here the E.P.s Wood (*orbis hepaticus*), Metal (*orbis pulmonalis*) and Water (*orbis renalis*) agree with this rule. The E.P. Fire (*orbis cardialis*) departs from it because a draining effect is postulated for the sweet *sapor*; the E.P. Earth (*orbis lienalis*) is replenished by energy of similar quality (sweet *sapores*) and is drained by the bitter *sapores*, which it conquers (Sequence II).

3. *Su-wen* 23/247: The meteorological influences injurious to each of the orbs are enumerated under the heading "What the *orbes horreales* abhor." According to the rule, an excessively intense effect (*yin* 淫) qualitatively similar to the respective orb must be "abhorred" (*wu* 惡). Only the orbs corresponding to the first three evolutive phases (*orbes hepaticus, cardialis, et lienalis*) comply with this rule. The *orbis pulmonalis* abhors cold (which it conquers according to Sequence II of the E.P.s) and the *orbis renalis* abhors drought (which it produces according to the Sequence I of the E.P.s).

4. *Su-wen* 23/248 and the parallel text of *Ling-shu* 63/1268ff.: Under the heading "Which of the five *sapores* must be avoided," the familiar affinity between the specific unfoldment (*perfectio, ch'ung*) of an orb and its corresponding *sapor* is referred to by the formula: "*Sapor A* moves [literally "runs," *tsou*] to the unfoldment *B*. If *B* is ill, one should not eat too much of *sapor A*." According to the rule, *A* and *B* must be of similar conventional quality. In reality, only the orbs corresponding to the E.P.s Wood, Earth, and Metal (*orbes hepaticus, lienalis, et pulmonalis*) comply with the rule. The bitter and salty *sapores* (E.P.s Fire and Water) instead are paired with the complementary unfoldments.

5. *Ling-shu* 78/1368: Two consecutive paragraphs deal with exactly the same relationships discussed under 4, but in this passage all statements are in accord with the rule.

6. *Ling-shu* 56/1244: Finally we have to mention a category of relations entitled "The Five Restrictions" (*wu-chin* 五禁) which in reality deals with the same correspondences as in 4 and 5. The formula is: "If the disease is in orb *A*, [food corresponding to] *sapor B* should be restricted."[251] The rule is that *A* and *B* are of identical or of complementary quality or else that *B* checks *A* in accordance with the conquest sequence (Sequence II) of the E.P.s. If the last of the three possibilities is adopted, all positions are in perfect agreement with the systematic rule.

After close examination of these eight excerpts from the *Nei-ching,* our conclusions concerning exceptions to the rules may be formulated.

First it is worth noting that departures from the rule occur in all four excerpts from the *Su-wen* but only in one of the four excerpts from the *Ling-shu.* This once more seems to confirm the suspicion voiced earlier that within the classical tradition the *Ling-shu* corresponds to a more recent and more consistent textual layer.

The two passages under 4 very likely represent parallel traditions of the same text. The inversion of the *perfectiones* of the *orbes cardialis et renalis* takes place on a single axis and has evidently been determined by the accommodation of empirical data. Later commentators[252] have argued stringently that the inversion conforms to the system.

Of the departures within group 1,[253] the one bearing on the meteorological configuration (*t'ien-ch'i*) of the E.P. Metal is

---

[251]In translating *chin* 禁 by "restriction," "to restrict," we have chosen the rendition best adapted to the context, but we do not want to obscure the ambiguity inherent in the Chinese term, which in administrative context usually must be rendered by "to prohibit," "prohibition." The question remains whether the consumption of *B* should only be restricted or if it should be completely prohibited.

[252]See *Su-wen-shih* 3/119 and the *Ling-shu-shih* 靈樞識 5/64f.

[253]*Su-wen* 5/55–60.

certainly due to a corruption of the text: the character *je* 熱 (heat) must be corrected to *tsao* 燥 (drought).[254] The two other variants in this group may be explained as interpolations undertaken to accommodate the two aspects of physiological energy, *hsüeh* and *ch'i*, within the correspondence scheme. It is also remarkable that the E.P.Metal is twice represented in the column of the *perfectiones* (once by "skin" and "body hair" [*mao*] and once by *ch'i*, which is primarily assigned to the *orbis pulmonalis*) whereas the E.P. Water is not represented at all. By reference to the *Huang-ti nei-ching t'ai-su*,[255] both suspect passages may be corrected, replacing *ch'i* by *mo* (sinarteries) and *hsüeh* by *ku* (bones).

The departures within group 2 are limited to the *orbes lienalis et cardialis*. As has been pointed out, the E.P. Earth (and thus the *orbis lienalis*) is without a direct polar complement in the cycle of conventional value standards. Since this theoretical assertion has empirical support,[256] the exceptional correspondence of the central orb (*orbis lienalis*) can be accepted as being in agreement with the system as well as with experience. There remains only the verbal contradiction that the sweet *sapor* on the one hand replenishes the energy in the *orbis lienalis* and on the other hand[257] may be characterized as being injurious to its *perfectio*. The disciples of Li Tung-yüan's "strengthening the Earth" school (*pu-t'u-p'ai*) have resolved this far from fundamental tension.

They argue that the draining off of energy of the *orbis cardialis* by means of the sweet *sapor* instead of the bitter *sapor* corresponding to Fire results primarily from the shift in the system caused by the exceptional attribution of the *orbis lienalis*; but it is corroborated by empirical data.

This finally leaves only the departures in group 3 as problematical. Here the meteorological configurations corresponding to the *orbes pulmonalis et renalis* have been interchanged. The most likely hypothesis is that this exchange was prompted by

[254]This emendation is also proposed in the *Su-wen-shih* 1/33.
[255]As quoted by Tamba Motohiro in his *Su-wen-shih* 1/33; we have been unable to find this citation in our text of the *T'ai-su*.
[256]See pp. 131, 133f above.
[257]See items 2–6 in the enumeration of contradictory passages in the *Nei-ching*.

empirical findings. No interference of theories contemporary with the text can be ascertained, so these two departures very likely were in the original version of the *Su-wen*,[258] and the remaining correspondences in this group comply with the rule.

The Iconography of the Yang Orbs (Orbes aulici, fu 腑)

The paradigm used for the description of the *orbes horreales* will also be used for the *orbes aulici* (*fu*). But Chinese sources are less informative on the functions of the *orbes aulici* than on those of the *orbes horreales*.[259] The disproportion is less considerable than it appears, for much of the paradigm's content is implicit. The majority of data given for an *orbis horrealis* also applies to the *orbis aulicus* which is united to it in a functional yoke (*piao li*).

Thus data on the *orbis hepaticus* indirectly apply to the *orbis felleus*, data on the *orbis cardialis* indirectly apply to the *orbis intestini tenuis*, and so on. To find out which is the complementary yin orb, the reader should look at the beginning of Section III of the respective paradigm. Macrocosmic correspondences (Section II of our paradigm) need not be given in this section.

THE *ORBIS FELLEUS* (*TAN* 膽)

(I) The *orbis felleus*, as one of the *orbes aulici*, is primarily yang. At the same time, in accordance with an ancient and never-abolished tradition fixed in the *Su-wen*,[260] it is considered one of the Six Paraorbs (*ch'i-heng chih fu* 奇恆之腑). These are the organs that according to the same passage "were produced by a terrestrial configuration, store [structive energy], and imitate the Earth; because of this they store and do not permit [energy] to drain off (*ts'ang erh pu hsieh* 藏而不泄)." From this twofold correspondence the *orbis felleus* derives a double determination of its functions and a privileged position as compared to the other *orbes aulici*.[261]

[258]The parallel text of the *Nei-ching t'ai-su* 6/33 and its commentary also confirm these two departures from the rule. The arguments set forth on p. 71 of the *Su-wen shao-shih* completely pass over the chronological problem and do not convince us.

[259]A significant reason for this lack of balance has been indicated on p. 18 above.

[260]*Su-wen* 11/126, as well as the text and commentary of the *Lei-ching* 4/76.

[261]Cf. Chang Ching-yüeh's commentary in the *Lei-ching* 3/47

This qualification seems justified insofar as the *orbis felleus* is the only *orbis aulicus* that participates in the assimilation of food but not in its ingestion and transportation.

It is only consistent that the *orbis felleus* does not figure in the enumeration given in the *Su-wen* 9/109 in which the *orbis lienalis* is mentioned in the company of the remaining five *orbes aulici*.[262]

It is also called "*orbis aulicus* with refined [i.e., qualitatively homogeneous] contents" 中精之腑,[263] as distinct from the other *orbes aulici*, which carry only "murky" (*chuo* 濁), i.e., qualitatively heterogeneous contents. The Evolutive Phase of the orb is Wood.

(III) The *orbis felleus* is united with the *orbis hepaticus* in a functional yoke in which as *orbis aulicus* it takes the outward side (*piao*, species).[264] The *sinarteria cardinalis* corresponding to the *orbis felleus* is the *cardinalis yang minoris pedis*.[265] Its corresponding radial pulse is almost unanimously given as the *pulsus clusalis superficialis manus sinistrae* 左手關浮脈.[266]

(IV) On dream motifs indicating a disturbance in the *orbis felleus* we find in the *Nei-ching*: "If a *flexus* deversates in the *orbis felleus*, one dreams that one is engaged in fights and battles or that one cuts open one's own body."[267]

On the anatomical substratum of the *orbis felleus*, the gallbladder, we are informed in the *Nan-ching* 42:[268] "The gallbladder is situated between the short leaves (flaps) of the liver, weighs 3 *liang* (ounces), 3 *chu* (ca. 3 × 100 grains) and is filled with three *ko* (deciliters) of refined ("clear") fluid (*ching-chih* 精汁)."

(V) Within the organism the *orbis felleus* exercises the function of an "orienting organ [lit. 中正之官: organ of central straightness] from which the power of decision issues" (specific function).[269] The *orbis felleus*, so to speak, steers the impulses of all other orbs: "All eleven orbs take their cue from the *orbis felleus*."[270]

[262]See p. 117 above.
[263]*Ling-shu* 2/926.
[264]*Ibid.* 47/1209; *Chung-ts'ang-ching*, 1/12.
[265]*Ling-shu* 10/1019.
[266]*Mo-ching* 2/19; *Chung-i-hsüeh kai-lun*, p. 199.
[267]*Ling-shu* 43/1192.
[268]*Nan-ching* 4/109.
[269]*Su-wen* 8/94.
[270]*Ibid.* 9/109.

According to the classical theory, cues issued by the *orbis felleus* directly affect only the other orbs, whereas the circulation of the different kinds of energy throughout the organism depends directly on the *orbis cardialis* and above all on the *orbis pulmonalis*. Not later than the Ming period, however, the *orbis felleus* was ascribed a direct influence at least on the circulation of the constructive and defensive energies (*ying-wei*): "The *orbis felleus* moves the constructive and defensive energies." Commentary: "Although the constructive and defensive energies are controlled by the *orbis pulmonalis*, their flow is also controlled (*chu* 主) by the *orbis felleus*."[271]

THE *ORBIS INTESTINI TENUIS* (*HSIAO-CH'ANG* 小腸)

(I) The *orbis intestini tenuis* is an *orbis aulicus* and because of this is primarily yang. The Evolutive Phase of this orb is Fire. (III) It is united with the *orbis cardialis* in a functional yoke in which, as *orbis aulicus*, it takes the outward side (*piao, species*).[272] The *sinarteria cardinalis* corresponding to the *orbis intestini tenuis* is the *cardinalis yang maioris manus*;[273] its corresponding radial pulse by classical consensus is the *pulsus pollicaris superficialis manus sinistrae* 左手寸浮脈.[274] (IV) On dream motifs indicating a disturbance in the *orbis intestini tenuis* we find in the *Nei-ching*: "If a *flexus* deversates in the *orbis intestini tenuis*, one will dream of populous town districts and of main thoroughfares."[275]

The anatomical substratum of the *orbis intestini tenuis*, the duodenum, is characterized in the *Nan-ching* 42:[276] "The duodenum weighs 2 *chin* (pounds), 14 *liang* (ounces), has a length of 3 *chang* (ca. 10 feet), 2 feet, and is $2\frac{1}{2}$ inches wide....It may contain 2 *tou* (bushels), 4 *sheng* (liters) of solid food and 6 *sheng*, 3 *ko* (deciliters) of liquid food."

(V) Within the integral organism the *orbis intestini tenuis* has the role of the "organ that receives and assimilates (*hua*)" the bulk of food.[277] In other terms, in it the fine and the crude, the clear and the murky elements of food are separated and redistributed.[278]

[271]*I-hsüeh ju-men*, quoted from the *I-pu ch'üan-lu*, Vol. IV, p. 102.
[272]*Ling-shu* 47/1209 and *Chung-ts'ang-ching*, 1/14 f.
[273]*Ling-shu* 10/1004.
[274]*Mo-ching* 2/18; *Chung-i-hsüeh kai-lun*, p. 199.
[275]*Ling-shu* 43/1192.
[276]*Nan-ching* 4/109; *Ling-shu* 31/1155.
[277]*Su-wen* 8/94 and the parallel in *Ling-shu* 2/926.
[278]See the quotation from the *I-hsüeh ju-men* in *I-pu ch'üan-lu*, Vol. IV, p. 140.

THE *ORBIS STOMACHI (WEI* 胃)

(I) As an *orbis aulicus* the *orbis stomachi* is primarily yang. The Evolutive Phase of this orb is Earth.

(III) It is united with the *orbis lienalis* in a functional yoke in, which, as *orbis aulicus*, it takes the outward side (*piao, species*).[279] The *sinarteria cardinalis* corresponding to the *orbis stomachi* is the *cardinalis splendoris yang pedis*;[280] its corresponding radial pulse is the *pulsus clusalis superficialis manus dextrae* 右手關浮脈.[281]

(IV) On dream motifs which indicate a disturbance in the *orbis stomachi* we find in the *Ling-shu* 43/1192: "If a *flexus* deversates in the *orbis stomachi* one dreams of eating and drinking."

Concerning the anatomical substratum of the *orbis stomachi*, the stomach, we are informed in the *Nan-ching* 42:[282] "The stomach weighs 2 *chin* (pounds), two *liang* (ounces), is of contorted, elongate shape, 2 feet 6 inches long, 2 feet 5 inches thick, and 5 inches in diameter. It can lodge 2 *tou* (bushels) of solid food and 1 *tou*, 5 *sheng* (liters) of liquid food."

(V) Within the organism thē *orbis stomachi* exercises the function of an "intermediate depository" (*ts'ang-lin* 倉廩)[283] serving as the distribution center for food of the five *sapores* (specific function).[284] Like its yin complement, the *orbis lienalis*, the *orbis stomachi* holds a central position of mediation and exchange (E.P. Earth). It is the equalizing reservoir (*hai, mare*) for the energy drawn from food and distributed throughout the system of orbs.[285] If its function collapses completely—as diagnosed by complete disappearance of the corresponding pulse (*pulsus stomachi*)—this is interpreted as a sure sign of imminent death.[286] "Once the energetic configuration [and thus the function] of the *orbis stomachi* has run down, it is hardly feasible to apply any other medicine."[287]

[279]*Ling-shu* 2/926, 47/1209, *et passim*.
[280]*Ibid.* 10/993.
[281]*Mo-ching* 2/21f; *Chung-i-hsüeh kai-lun*, p. 199.
[282]*Nan-ching* 4/109; cf. *Ling-shu* 31/1155.
[283]The meaning of this technical term was discussed on pp. 133f above.
[284]*Su-wen* 8/94.
[285]*Ibid.* 11/129, 29/294; *Ling-shu* 33/1156, 56/1242f.
[286]*Su-wen* 18/181ff, and the parallel in the *Lei-ching* 4/111 (text and commentary).
[287]*I-tsung pi-tu* quoted in *I-pu ch'üan-lu*, Vol. IV, p. 176.

THE *ORBIS INTESTINI CRASSI* (*TA-CH'ANG* 大腸)

(I) The *orbis intestini crassi* as an *orbis aulicus* is primarily yang. Its Evolutive Phase is Metal.

(III) It is united with the *orbis pulmonalis* in a functional yoke in which, as *orbis aulicus*, it takes the outward side (*piao, species*).[288] The *sinarteria cardinalis* corresponding to the *orbis intestini crassi* is the *cardinalis splendoris yang manus*.[289] In the classics the radial pulse of the *orbis intestini crassi* is the *pulsus pollicaris superficialis manus dextrae* 右手寸浮脈.[290] Authors beginning with Li Shih-chen (died 1593) associate the *pulsus pollicaris manus dextrae* with the inner thorax in general and assign to the *orbis intestini crassi* any one of the four *pedalis* pulses (*ch'ih-mo*): the *pulsus pedalis superficialis sive mersus manus dextrae sive sinistrae*.[291]

(IV) A disturbance of the *orbis intestini crassi* may be detected, according to the *Ling-shu*, by dream motifs: "If a *flexus* deversates in the *orbis intestini crassi*, one dreams of fields and rural landscapes."[292]

Concerning the anatomical substratum of the *orbis intestini crassi*, the large intestine, here called "curved intestine" (*hui-ch'ang* 廻腸), we learn from *Nan-ching* 42: "The curved intestine is four inches wide, 1½ inches in diameter, 2 *chang* (about 2 × 10 feet), 1 foot in length. It receives 1 *tou* (bushel) of solid and 7½ *sheng* (liters) of liquid food."[293]

(V) In the organism the *orbis intestini crassi* exercises the function of a conduit in which the assimilation and temporary storage of food take place.[294]

THE *ORBIS VESICALIS* (*P'ANG-KUANG* 膀胱)

(I) The *orbis vesicalis* as an *orbis aulicus* is primarily yang. Its Evolutive Phase is Water.

(III) It is united with the *orbis renalis* in a functional yoke in which, as an *orbis aulicus*, it takes the outward side (*piao,*

[288]*Ling-shu* 47/1209, *Chung-ts'ang-ching* 1/19.
[289]*Ling-shu* 10/990, 12/1048 *et passim*.
[290]*Mo-ching* 2/20f.
[291]*Chung-i-hsüeh kai-lun*, p. 199.
[292]*Ling-shu* 43/1192.
[293]*Nan-ching* 4/107; *Ling-shu* 31/1155.
[294]*Su-wen* 8/94; *Ling-shu* 2/926; *Lei-ching* 3/47; cf. *Chung-ts'ang-ching*, in *I-pu ch'üan-lu*, Vol. IV, p. 242.

species).[295] The *sinarteria cardinalis* corresponding to the *orbis vesicalis* is the *cardinalis yang minoris pedis*.[296] The classics and the majority of later writers assign this orb the radial pulse *pedalis superficialis manus sinistrae*.[297]

(IV) How an acute deficiency of energy in the *orbis vesicalis* and the accompanying reversal of functions affect dreams is indicated in the *Ling-shu* 43/1192: "If a *flexus* deversates in the *orbis vesicalis*, in dreams one takes walks and excursions." Concerning the anatomical substratum of the *orbis vesicalis*, the urinary bladder, we find in *Nan-ching* 42:[298] "The bladder weighs 2 *liang* (ounces), 2 *chu* (200 grains) and is 9 inches in height and width. It may contain 9 *sheng* (liters), 9 *ko* (deciliters) of urine."

(V) Within the organism the function of the *orbis vesicalis* may be compared to that of a regional capital (*chou-tu* 州都), for in this orb all the active and structive fluids convene and are stored[299] (specific function). It is only after having been assimilated, in part during their course through the *orbis vesicalis*, that some of the fluids are excreted.

Chinese medicine gives the *orbis vesicalis* functions essentially different in character and extent from those attributed to the bladder by Western medicine. In particular Chinese medicine assigns it a considerable portion of the functions that Europeans ascribe to the kidneys. Consequently, the *cardinalis vesicalis*, the conduit assembling the largest number of sensitive points (foramina), shows a considerably wider variety of correspondences to various bodily disorders than would be justified by the mere accessory role that Western medicine assigns to the bladder.

Diagrams of the *orbis vesicalis* show an organ in the form of a bladder but with only one orifice,[300] or with two orifices at most. In the latter case the upper orifice connects to the lower opening of the *orbis intestini tenuis* (Fig. 18).[301]

[295]*Ling-shu* 2/926; *Chung-ts'ang-ching*, 2/22. According to the *Ling-shu* 47/1209, the *orbis vesicalis* together with the *orbis tricalorii* constitute the outer orb and complement of the *orbis renalis*. The function of the latter, as we have seen in connection with its paradigm, is sometimes divided between an *orbis renalis* and a *porta fortunae*.

[296]*Ling-shu* 10/1006.

[297]*Mo-ching* 2/20 (22f.); *Chung-i-hsüeh kai-lun*, p. 199.

[298]*Nan-ching* 4/110.

[299]*Su-wen* 8/94, text and commentary; *Lei-ching* 3/45, text and commentary.

[300]See the figures in the *Lei-ching t'u-i* 3/80 and in the *I-tsung chin-chien* 82/154.

[301]See the figure, text and commentary in *Ling-shu* 10/1008.

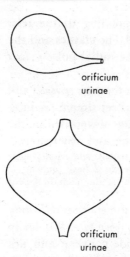

orificium
urinae

orificium
urinae

Fig. 18

THE *ORBIS TRICALORII* (*SAN-CHIAO* 三焦)

(I) The *orbis tricalorii*, as one of the *orbes aulici*, is primarily yang.
(III) United in a functional yoke with the *orbis pericardialis*,
as an *orbis aulicus* the *orbis tricalorii* takes the outer side (*piao,
species*) in this combination.

This match is implied for sinarteriology in the *Ling-shu*[302] and has been
generally accepted as standard. The theory described in another passage,
postulating that the *orbis tricalorii* together with the *orbis vesicalis* constitutes
the outer orb and complement of the *orbis renalis*, has not survived in later
theory.[303]

The *sinarteria cardinalis* corresponding to the *orbis tricalorii* is the
cardinalis yang minoris manus.[304] The *orbis tricalorii* is attributed
the radial pulse *pulsus pedalis superficialis* (*sive mersus*) *manus
dextrae* 右手尺脈 by most authors.[305]

(IV) The problem of the anatomical substratum of the *orbis
tricalorii*, the *tricalorium* ("three heated spaces") puzzled Chinese
doctors long before Western authors confronted it. As with

[302]*Ling-shu* 10/1014ff., 12/1048.
[303]*Ibid.* 47/1209.
[304]*Ibid.* 10/1017.
[305]*Mo-ching* 2/23; *Chung-i-hsüeh kai-lun*, p. 199.

practically all orbisiconographic concepts, three stages in the development of the notion may be distinguished. In the process of separating them, the logical links binding together seemingly contradictory statements will become evident.

During the first stage, from the germination of protoscientific speculations to the compilation of the most ancient parts of the *Su-wen* (end of the Chou and early Han), a consistent medical theory was attempted on the basis of available empirical data. At that time, because of the dominance of the inductive and synthetic mode of cognition, hypotheses of surprising precision bearing on the physiological functions were evolved. But compared to these, ideas on the anatomical substrates remained crude and rudimentary. At that early stage an organ (*kuan*) called *tricalorium* (*san-chiao*) was given a small number of functions without any effort to define their spatial location or the anatomical extent of their substratum.

During a second stage, which covered the first three centuries of our era, in which extensive parts of the *Ling-shu* and probably of the *Nan-ching* were compiled, efforts were made to verify and to perfect the traditional teachings in every respect. Even analytical means were brought to this task. This era is distinguished in philosophy by Wang Ch'ung 王充 and in medicine by the great systematic theorists Chang Chung-ching 張仲景, Wang Shu-ho 王叔和, and whoever did the work credited to the legendary surgeon Hua T'uo 華佗 (whose anatomical knowledge may have gone considerably beyond what was set down in medical literature for centuries to come). During this period, attempts were made on the basis of the crude anatomical knowledge then available to define the substrates of each orb, including the *tricalorium*—which at this stage can be called the "three caloria" (*chiao* 焦), for they had come to be viewed as entities distinct in space.

The results of these efforts, ignored since the T'ang period and today mere historical curiosities, were recorded in the *Ling-shu* and *Nan-ching*.[306] In order to give an idea of these theories, we quote from the *Ling-shu*: "The 'upper calorium' (*calorium superius*, *shang-chiao* 上焦) extends upward from the upper (cardiac) orifice of the stomach (胃上口) and ascends together

---

[306]*Ling-shu* 18/1081ff.; *Nan-ching* 3/91ff.

with the esophagus (*yen* 咽), piercing (*kuan* 貫) the diaphragm (*ko* 膈) and spreading within the thorax (*hsiung-chung* 胸中)...."— "The 'medial calorium' (*calorium medium, chung-chiao* 中焦) likewise originates in the stomach, behind the *calorium superius*. . . ."—The 'lower calorium' (*calorium inferius, hsia-chiao* 下焦) branches out of the large intestine and sheds [its energy] into the bladder."[307]

These descriptions suggest that the *tricalorium* was conceived as a network of energetic conduits, somewhat similar to the sinarteries, yet participating in the metabolic functions—not only transmitting energy but also assimilating it.

The third stage extends to the beginning of the twentieth century. Very precise and subtle rules for the description of functional relationships were formulated. Once these rules had been checked against experience, the meager analytical data collected at the second stage were completely abandoned. The third stage is intimated in the extant version of the *Nan-ching* 38,[308] and is set forth with assurance by Sun Szu-mo in his *Ch'ien-chin yao-fang*: "The tricalorium has a name, yet no bodily shape (有名無形)."[309]

(V) Within the organism, the *orbis tricalorii* may be compared to water communications (*chüeh-tu chih kuan* 決瀆之官)[310] (specific function). In other words, it is the foundation and controller[311] of the entire circulation of body fluids: "It is the commander-in-chief (*tsung-ling* 總領) of the energies (*ch'i*) of all orbs, whether effective as constructive and defensive energies, inside and outside the sinarteries, to the left or to the right, above or below. If [the energy of] the *orbis tricalorii* is unimpeded (*t'ung* 通), inside and outside, left and right, above and below are all in communication (*t'ung*). Among [the functions] affecting the whole personality (*chou-shen* 周身), pervading

[307]A diagram of the *tricalorium* is given, among others, in the *Lei-ching t'u-i* 3/81.
[308]*Nan-ching* 3/102; *Chung-ts'ang-ching*, 2/23. Whether this and similar critical passages have been interpolated into the *Nan-ching* is worth investigating.
[309]Quoted from the *I-pu ch'üan-lu*, Vol. IV, p. 300.
[310]*Su-wen* 8/94. *Chüeh* 決 means "to burst through" the confines of the other orbs; *tu* 瀆, "a connecting channel." Chang Ching-yüeh (commenting on *Lei-ching* 3/45) also subscribes to this explanation.
[311]See the sections devoted to the *orbes cardialis, pericardialis, et felleus* earlier in this chapter.

(*kuan* 灌) the body, harmonizing the interior and calming the exterior, developing on the left and sustaining on the right, conducting upward and communicating downward, none is more important than this.''[312]

The *orbis tricalorii* is the source both of the constructive energy (*ying* 營, *ch'i constructivum*) that moves through the conduits of energy (*ching* 經) and nourishes all the orbs,[313] and of the defensive energy (*wei* 衞, *ch'i defensivum*), which moves outside the conduits, permeating the surface of the body and warding off exogenous heteropathies.[314]

A modern metaphor that comes to mind for the various Chinese theories on the functions of the *orbis tricalorii* is that of a radio relay station in which incoming signals are not only boosted but may also be transformed (*hua* 化), that is, frequency-modulated, emitted on a different wavelength, focused in a certain direction, and so on.

The fact that the ancient Chinese associated the physiological boosting function of the *orbis tricalorii* with the release of heat (*chiao* 焦) is no surprise. But we should now, on the basis of our more thorough understanding, be wary of the customary yet misleading translations of *chiao* by *Erwärmer*, *rechauffeur*, "heater," and so forth.

Some characteristics of the *orbis tricalorii* have led the modern physicians Bachmann and Schmitt to the hypothesis that the *tricalorium* can be identified with the endocrine system. Although several factors seem to justify this identification, it would never have been tried except for the fallacious assumption that congruence may be achieved between the description of a Chinese orb and the characteristics that Western medicine postulates for its substratum. Close and serious study never supports this assumption; for instance, numerous among the symptoms associated with the *cardinalis yang minoris manus* (which is the

---

[312]*Chung-ts'ang-ching* 2/23 and similarly *Lei-ching t'u-i* 3/81. By the way, the sentence preceding the quotation "The *tricalorium* has the cognomen '*orbis aulicus* of central clarity 中清之腑'" is certainly a corruption of the text, due to interference of the descriptive formula of the *orbis felleus*, given in the same context: "中瀆之腑, 'of the central channel [*incilis medii*]'" (see above, p. 153).

[313]This is a form of energy that according to *Ling-shu* 18/1080 and 1082 issues from the *calorium medium*, but according to *Chung-ts'ang-ching* 2/23 proceeds from the *calorium superius*.

[314]*Ling-shu* 18/1080, 1083; *Chung-ts'ang-ching* 2/23. This form of energy originates in the *calorium inferius*.

energetic conduit associated with the *tricalorium*) are neuralgic or neuralgiform affections of the head and thorax;[315] these disturbances cannot simply be attributed to malfunctions of the endocrine system.

In the *Ling-shu* 2/926 and similarly in the *Chung-ts'ang-ching* 2/23 the *orbis tricalorii* is called an "orphaned" orb. In Ming times, centuries later, Chang Ching-yüeh explains this statement in the sense that the substrate of the *orbis tricalorii* (the *tricalorium*) differs from those of the other orbs in regard to extension within the body.[316] The context of the original statement, at any rate, suggests that it belongs to the early textual tradition in which the functional yoke tying together the *orbis tricalorii* and the *orbis pericardialis* had not yet been defined, and the *orbis tricalorii* along with the *orbis vesicalis* were opposed to the *orbis renalis*.

The Paraorbs (ch'i-heng chih fu 奇恆之腑)

In a repeatedly quoted passage of the *Su-wen* 11/126 six so-called *paraorbes* (*ch'i-heng chih fu*) are enumerated.[317] With the exception of the *orbis felleus* (which, as we saw, simultaneously has the status of an *orbis aulicus*), none of them has any elaborate iconography. We shall now briefly deal with those paraorbs that are not discussed elsewhere.

THE *PARAORBES CEREBRI ET MEDULLAE* (*NAO* 腦, *SUI* 髓)

In the "Treatise on the [Equalizing] Reservoirs" (*hai-lun*),[318] the *paraorbis cerebri* is called reservoir of the medulla (*sui-hai, mare medullae*). If there is redundancy of energy in the *paraorbis cerebri*, "one moves nimbly and expands great energies, becoming overstrained"; if there is deficiency of energy "the brains will [seem to] gyrate, the ears will ring, the muscles will shrink, one will have fits of dizziness and unconsciousness and lie in numbness and torpor."[319] And from another passage of the *Ling-shu*[320] we learn that no qualitative distinction is to be made between bones and the medulla: "When the refined fluids of

---

[315]*Chen-chiu-hsüeh chiang-i*, pp. 136–144.
[316]Commentary in the *Lei-ching* 3/47.
[317]See p. 112 and p. 152 above.
[318]*Ling-shu* 33.
[319]*Ibid.* 33/1158.
[320]*Ibid.* 36/1166.

the Five Cereals blend harmoniously, they constitute a grease (*kao* 膏) that is washed into the empty spaces of the bones and that [likewise] replenishes (*pu* 補) the brain and the medulla." These meager indications tend to show that the *paraorbes cerebri et medullae* are little more than accessories to the *orbis renalis*, of which the brain and the marrow (and/or *medulla*) [321] are considered the specific unfoldment (*ch'ung, perfectio*). In the brain and medulla the inborn vital potential (*ch'i nativum*) [322] is stored and conserved; it manifests itself and is spent in the psychic reactions (*chih, emotiones*) in general and in the psychic reaction *par excellence*, the directed will. But this storage function is also expressly attributed to the *orbis renalis*.

This example of interlaced correspondences reveals why the iconography of the Chinese *paraorbes cerebri et medullae* is so sparse compared with the multifarious functions that Western physiology and neurology ascribe to the brain and medulla. At a time when neurology and histology could be no more than vaporous speculation, those functions were incorporated into the iconography of the orbs (especially the *orbes cardialis, lienalis, felleus, et renalis*) to whose qualitative manifestations they showed an affinity. By this expedient for long centuries the logical and systematic requirements of a rational science were better served than by some strikingly "modern" hypothesis that could not have been proven.

PARAORBIS UTERI (*NÜ-TZU-PAO* 女子胞)

The *paraorbis uteri* (like the uterus in Western medicine) has essential significance for menstruation and pregnancy. In the *paraorbis uteri* originate (*ch'i* 起) two cardinal conduits—although there is no assertion that they are attached (*luo* 絡) to it or pertain to it (*shu* 屬)—the *cardinales impares respondens et impedimentalis*,[323] by the symptoms of which diagnosis and therapy of disturbances of menstruation and pregnancy may be guided.

Moreover, in *Su-wen* 33/321 a *"sinarteria uteri"* (*pao-mo* 胞脈) is mentioned—at least that is the way all commentators under-

---

[321]The Chinese term *sui* 髓 applies both to the contents of the large bones and of the dorsal spine. It is rendered in accordance with the context either by "marrow" or by "medulla."

[322]See. p. 145 above as well as the entry *"ch'i nativum"* in the following section.

[323]See below, pp. 278f and pp. 283f.

Table 18. Comparative Synopsis of the Principal Functions of the Orbs

	Orbis or Pararbis	Specific Function	Fundamental (or Dominant) Function	Storage Function
	hepaticus	"General": seat of the individually specific configurative force (hun); planning and reflection	"Nervus": expansion of physical force	Hsüeh (individually specific structive energy which in turn is the basis of hun
	cardialis	"Sovereign": seat of the configurative force (shen), conditions the character and the cohesion of the personality	Mo: Sinarteries and pulses	Shen
	pericardialis	"Ambassador": the source of enjoyment and pleasure	Equalizing reservoir of physiological energy (ch'i)	
Yin orbs (Orbes horreales) store structive potential	lienalis	"Depository": temporary storage and distribution; critical faculty and reflection	Root of the acquired constitution	Ying (constructive energy)
	pulmonalis	"Minister": rhythmic order.	Root of ch'i, i.e., of the initial point of the energetic circulation	P'o (structure aspect of the individually specific configurative force)
	renalis	"Potentialization of energy": stages of latency	Root of the inborn constitution	Chih (willpower); vital fluids; medulla
	tricalorii	"Water communications": central command of the movements of the energy of all orbs: foundation and controlling authority over the circulation of all fluids		

	Orbis or Paraorbis	Specific Function	Fundamental (or Dominant) Function	Storage Function
Yang orbs (*Orbes aulici*) move and assimilate food in the widest sense	*stomachi*	"Intermediate, temporary depot": equalizing reservior of all orbs for the energy derived from food		
	intestini crassi	"Organ of transportation": transformation and temporary storage; evacuation of dregs		
	vesicalis	"Regional capital": temporary storage and distribution of active and structive energy		
	felleus	"Organ of orientation": resoluteness; movement of physiological energies: *ying* and *wei*		
Paraorbes store different forms of energy	*cerebri*	Completes the functions of the *orbis renalis*		Structive potential; *ch'i nativum—mare medullae*
	medullae	Sustains the mobility of the joints; nourishes the *cerebrum*		
	ossum sinarteriarum	"Stem": framework of the body; moves active and structive physiological energies (*ch'i* and *hsüeh*)		*Aula medullae* *Aula hsüeh*
	uteri			Pregnancy

stand the term[324] without reflecting on the isolation of this postulate. This *sinarteria uteri* pertains to (*shu* 屬) the *orbis cardialis* and attaches to the *paraorbis uteri*. Thus a systematic link is established between the functions of the uterus and the *orbis cardialis*. Besides, the *paraorbis uteri* is indirectly connected with other orbs, in particular with the *orbis lienalis* and the *orbis hepaticus*.[325]

Comparative Synopsis of the Principal Functions of the Orbs

While examining in detail the multiform aspects and functions of each orb we risk losing sight of their rational concurrence within the organic system of orbisiconography. A synoptic table of their essential functions (Table 18) may prove helpful.

The Forms of Energy (Energetics)

Passing the functional orbs of the microcosm in review is of little use unless we also have a clear idea of the forms and designations of the energies flowing in them. For this reason since ancient times in Chinese medical literature the discussion of energetics is closely related to orbisiconography.[326] In dealing with energetics in this chapter we continue a historical tradition.

During the past decade we have investigated the problems and terminology of Chinese energetics from diverse angles and have published the results of our research in three articles. Here we concentrate on a synthesis of the subject, but for the convenience of readers to whom these German publications are not accessible we summarize their most important findings.[327]

The energetic terms that will be examined all occur in philosophical treatises, and most of them have uses in everyday language. Because their

---

[324]For the term *pao* 胞, it should be noted, is also used as a synonym of the *orbis vesicalis* (*p'ang-kuang*). See *Su-wen* 43/393.

[325]*Su-wen* 7/84 and likewise 40/366; see also *Su-wen* 27/271 and the *Ling-shu* 57/1247.

[326]*Su-wen* 1, 5, 9, 13, 23, 43, 62, 77, and others; *Ling-shu* 8, 10, 16, 18, 30, 32, 54, 56, 71, 75, 80; *Lei-ching* 3 and 4; *Tung-i pao-chien* 東醫寶鑑 1; *Chung-i-hsüeh kai-lun*, pp. 73–81.

[327]Author's articles "Untersuchungen," "Wissenschaftliches Denken," "Farbemblematik in China," and "Die energetische Terminologie." Much of the last paper is incorporated below.

meanings are conditioned by these non-medical senses, it is well to bear in mind the distinction between the practical and theoretical meanings of terms. Philosophers and theorists usually give their fundamental concepts a logically precise yet at the same time flexible and inclusive meaning; practical scientists appreciate terms with sharp and clear logical contours, yet prefer them narrowly and inflexibly defined. As a rule, in a philosophical context the stress is on the general meaning, and in a technical context such as Chinese medicine (which is an applied science) the emphasis is on the specific meaning of the term.

In Chinese medicine more than a dozen basic forms of energy, and well over two dozen accessory forms, are described. It would be misleading to propose a parallel between this family of terms, at first sight disconcertingly prolific, and the simple, clear, and universal concept of energy in modern physics. The latter corresponds to a speculative and theoretical generic term, whereas the Chinese names of energy almost invariably represent specific designations for energetic phenomena that in a given empirical setting occur regularly with invariant quality. A legitimate—and from an epistemological point of view instructive—comparison is between the multiform terminology of Chinese energetics and the no less diversified terminology of electrical engineering in which expressions such as direct current, alternating current, light current, heavy current, high tension, low tension, anode current, collector current, grid tension, high frequency, low frequency, and so on, always designate one basic phenomenon, electrical energy, which each term describes in regard to only one single, narrowly defined, empirical (technical) aspect which in ordinary usage is not specified. Exactly the same principle applies to the qualitatively rather than quantitatively differentiated energetic terminology in Chinese practical medicine.

CH'I 氣 (ENERGETIC CONFIGURATION, CONFIGURATIONAL ENERGY)

Within the framework of Chinese thought no notion may attain to such a degree of abstraction from empirical data as to correspond perfectly to one of our modern universal concepts. Nevertheless the term *ch'i* comes as close as possible to constituting a generic designation equivalent to our word "energy." When Chinese thinkers are unwilling or unable to fix the quality of an energetic phenomenon, the character *ch'i* 氣 inevitably flows from their brushes. And yet unlike our concept of energy, *ch'i*, whatever the context and absolutely without exception, always implies a qualitative determination of energy. In other words *ch'i* means energy of definite (or defineable) quality. For this reason we use for the technical term *ch'i* the standard definitions[328] "configurational energy"[329]—i.e., energy of a definite direction in space, of a definite arrangement, quality, or structure—and "energetic configuration."[330] In addition, we make very limited use (in phase energetics) of the normative equivalent *configuratio*.

The specific quality of a certain *ch'i* may remain implicit, specifiable only from the technical context or else it may as likely as not be indicated by an explicit qualifier.

Of all energetic terms *ch'i* is the only one that without further justification may serve as a normative expression in combination with a qualifier.

By first considering those epithets of *ch'i* that are of the greatest medical importance, we shall get an idea of the wide scale of technical distinctions of energy and become acquainted with the technical meanings, fields of application, and normative equivalents of terms that otherwise could be rendered only imperfectly or not at all. The following list might easily have been longer, but we have omitted qualifiers that any sinologist could explain with ease.

(1) *Ch'i alienatum* ("Alienated *ch'i*," *tsa-ch'i* 雜氣);[331] internal medicine, pathology: An exogenous pathological factor that infringes upon the rules of macrocosmic (rarely social) processes. Because it is "estranged" from these processes and because of its irregular origin in the microcosm, it does not move in the normal conduits of orthopathic (as well as other heteropathic) stimuli. For this reason diseases arising from a *ch'i alienatum* can be diagnosed only with difficulty. Antonym: *ch'i orthopathicum*; conditional synonym: *ch'i heteropathicum*.

[328]See the introduction to this volume.
[329]In German, *konstellierte Energie*.
[330]In German, *energetische Konstellation*.
[331]In common speech *tsa* 雜 means "mixed," "heterogeneous," "variegated"; the choice of Latin equivalent is justified by the technical sense.

(2) *Ch'i alienum* ("heterogeneous *ch'i*," *i-ch'i* 異氣); internal medicine, pathology, common speech: This term is less precisely defined than the former and as a rule designates an exogenous pathogenic influence.

(3) *Ch'i articulatum* or *configuratio articulata* ("nodal *ch'i*," *chieh-ch'i* 節氣); phase energetics, astronomy, calendar: The general situation in the macrocosmos over one of the 24 equal divisions of the solar year (*articulationes anni*). Sometimes the term *chieh-ch'i* (*ch'i articulatum*), rather than *chieh* alone, directly designates this "fortnightly period."[332]

(4) *Ch'i ascitum*[333] ("acquired *ch'i*," *hou-t'ien chih ch'i* 後天之氣); all medical disciplines: Previously restricted to cosmology and mantics, this term has been used since the Yuan in medicine as a metaphorical name for the acquired constitution or momentary condition of the body.[334] Antonym: *ch'i nativum*.

(5) *Ch'i cardinale* ("cardinal conduit *ch'i*," *ching-ch'i* 經氣); sinarteriology, acupuncture, and related disciplines: 1. Narrow meaning: The *ch'i* moving in the conduits (sinarteries). 2. Wide meaning: All energy integrated into ("circulating," *ching*) a physiological cycle.[335]

(6) *Ching-ch'i* (精氣); all medical disciplines and common speech: This double term, explained more closely on pp. 179–180 below, may have one of three meanings depending upon context: 1. Free ("unattached") structive potential. 2. Potentialized configurational energy of undefined quality. 3. Structive and active energy; in this sense the term constitutes a loose combination of semantically independent antonyms, "unattached structive energy" and "an active[336] energetic configuration."

(7) *Ch'i caeleste* ("celestial *ch'i*," *t'ien-ch'i* 天氣); all medical disciplines: This term designates: 1. Macrocosmic influences; effects of the momentary energetic situation in the macrocos-

---

[332]See pp. 72–73 above.
[333]Latin: *ascisco*, "to take over," "to contract."
[334]*I-sheng* 醫勝, p. 2.
[335]*Chen-chiu-hsüeh chiang-i*, p. 41.
[336]See the explanation below on p. 175 and p. 176.

mos (in this connotation sometimes synonymous with *ch'i magnum* [q.v.]. 2. Since *t'ien* ("Heaven") stands for the active, dynamic pole of the Cosmos, an active, dynamizing influence or an active polarization.

(8) *Ch'i constructivum* ("constructive *ch'i*," *ying-ch'i* 營氣); sinarteriology and related disciplines: Composite synonym of *ying* 營, "constructive energy."

(9) *Ch'i contravehens* ("countercurrent *ch'i*," *ni-ch'i* 逆氣); internal medicine, sinarteriology, and pathology: Energy running counter to and counteracting the normal movement or circulation, with pathological consequences. Antonyms: *ch'i secundovehens* (very rarely); *ch'i orthopathicum, ch'i merum.*

(10) *Ch'i defensivum* ("defensive *ch'i*," *wei-ch'i* 衛氣); sinarteriology and related disciplines: Composite synonym of *wei,* "defensive energy."

(11) *Ch'i deversans* or *configuratio deversans* ("deversant *ch'i* or configuration," *k'o-ch'i* 客氣); 1. pathology, internal medicine: Extraneous or supernumerary energy that has penetrated into a certain orb and there "deversates" (i.e., dwells as an uninvited guest). 2. phase energetics: The mutable component of the meteorological or immunological situation, linked to the alternation of the terrestrial branches.

(12) *Ch'i dominans* or *configuratio dominans* ("dominant *ch'i* or configuration," *chu-ch'i* 主氣); phase energetics: The immutable component of the meteorological and immunological situation during a definite period called a step (*gradus, pu* 步).

(13) *Ch'i flectens* ("shrinking *ch'i*," *chüeh-ch'i* 厥氣); internal medicine: Composite synonym of *chüeh* 厥, the reversal of the normal direction of flow or expansion of physiological energy and simultaneous secondary manifestations of this disturbance (weakness, numbness, coldness, paresthesias in the affected extremities and organs). The meaning of this term is much wider than that of *ch'i contravehens.*

(14) *Ch'i frumentarium* ("alimentary *ch'i*," *ku-ch'i* 穀氣); orbisiconography, sinarteriology, and related disciplines: 1. The energy available in food. 2. That part of physiological energy that has been assimilated from food.

(15) *Ch'i genuinum*[337] ("genetic *ch'i*," *tsung-ch'i* 宗氣); orbisicono-graphy, sinarteriology, and related disciplines: 1.The physiologi-cal motion of the organism, resulting from the concurrence of *ch'i magnum* and *ch'i frumentarium* and manifested most typically as the respirational rhythm. 2. The inborn capacity to execute these rhythmic movements. The *ch'i genuinum* is collected in the "*ch'i* reservoir" (*mare ch'i, ch'i-hai* 氣海), which corresponds to the thorax or the *calorium superius*.[338] From there it is distribut-ed by way of the respiratory channels (*hsi-tao* 息道) and the sinarteries, beginning with the *orbis cardialis*.[339]

(16) *Ch'i heteropathicum* ("heteropathic *ch'i*," *hsieh-ch'i* 邪氣); all medical disciplines and common speech: This is the most general and most frequent technical designation (sometimes used without the graph "*ch'i*") for an exogenous or endogenous pathogenic factor.

(17) *Hsüeh-ch'i* 血氣; orbisiconography, sinarteriology, and related disciplines: A combination of antonyms: "the active and structive physiological energies."

(18) *Ch'i humanum* ("human *ch'i*," *jen-ch'i* 人氣); orbisiconog-raphy, phase energetics: The physiological energy of the microcosm resulting from the synthesis of *ch'i caeleste* and *ch'i terrestre*.

(19) *Ch'i magnum* ("great *ch'i*," *ta-ch'i* 大氣); orbisiconography: 1. Those parts of cosmic energy of which an individual partakes in breathing. 2. Cosmic energy that has been assimilated by breathing. Among the evidently very large number of qualita-tive inflections of *ch'i*, this is the only one for which the Western expression *pneuma* can be used.

(20) *Ch'i merum* ("true *ch'i*," *chen-ch'i* 眞氣); orbisiconography, sinarteriology: Generic designation of physiological energy constituted by a synthesis of *ch'i genuinum* and *ch'i originale*. This kind of energy not only sustains the integrity of an in-

---

[337]Chinese *tsung* 宗 = Latin *genus* ("ancestry," "birth").
[338]*Ling-shu* 56/1243, 71/1310.
[339]*Ibid.* 75/1345f.

dividual but protects and defends it against exogenous and endogenous attacks and disturbances.

(21) *Ch'i mersum* ("submerged *ch'i*," *ch'en-ch'i* 沈氣); 1. diagnostics: The structive aspect of physiological energy manifesting itself actively in the pulses. It may be felt deep within (yin) on firm palpation of a point of diagnostic significance (thus the synonym *pulsus mersus, ch'en-mo*). 2. pharmacology: The specific capacity of a drug, ascertained empirically and defined by conventional standards of value, to damp, draw into the interior, and structively influence disease symptoms.

(22) *Ch'i mortale* ("dying *ch'i*," *szu-ch'i* 死氣); 1. phase energetics, internal medicine, common speech: The quality of the energy during the yin hours of the sinking sun (noon to midnight), which have a damping influence on activity and liveliness. 2. diagnostics: Disease symptoms of poor prognosis, especially as determined by pulse diagnostics.

(23) *Ch'i nativum* ("inborn constitutional *ch'i*," *hsien-t'ien chih ch'i* 先天之氣); all disciplines: After a change of meaning,[340] since the Yüan period this term has been used as a metaphorical designation of the inborn constitution, the vital potential that is gradually used up in the course of life. It may be conserved by hygiene but can never be replenished.

(24) *Ch'i originale* ("original *ch'i*," *yüan-ch'i* 原氣); orbisiconography, internal medicine and related disciplines: Activated and physiologically employed *ch'i nativum*. The *ch'i originale* originates in the *orbis renalis* and combines with the *ch'i genuinum* to form the *ch'i merum*.

(25) *Ch'i orthopathicum* ("correct *ch'i*," *cheng-ch'i* 正氣); internal medicine, orbisiconography, diagnostics: The energetic resources available for the maintenance or restitution of physiological harmony by warding off or compensating for extraneous or noxious influences.

(26) *Ch'i perversum* ("perverse *ch'i*," *li-ch'i* 戾氣); common speech, internal medicine: An endogenous or exogenous pathogenous factor.

[340] *I-sheng,* p. 2

(27) *Ch'i primum* ("primordial *ch'i*," *yüan-ch'i* 元氣), not to be confused with *ch'i originale;* orbisiconography, internal medicine, common speech: 1. Still undifferentiated structive potential (in this sense synonymous with *ching-ch'i*); structive aspect of the *ch'i nativum*. 2. [rare in medical texts] Undifferentiated potential of cosmic energy, chaotic or primordial *ch'i*.

(28) *Shen-ch'i* 神氣; all disciplines: This composite synonym of *shen* 神, "configurative force," will be referred to again.

(29) *Ch'i superficiale* ("superficial *ch'i*," *fu-ch'i* 浮氣); 1. diagnostics: The active physiological energy manifesting itself actively in the pulses. It may be felt close to the surface (yang) on delicate palpation; a synonym is *pulsus superficialis, fu-mo* 浮脈. 2. pharmacology: The specific capacity of a drug (ascertained empirically and expressed in conventional standards of value) to bring symptoms to the surface of the body, to evacuate noxious factors through bodily openings, or to neutralize symptoms after they have been brought to the surface.

(30) *Ch'i terrestre* ("terrestrial *ch'i*," *ti-ch'i* 地氣); all disciplines: Since the Earth stands for the structive pole of the Cosmos, the term designates a structive, substantiative, condensing influence or a structive polarization.

(31) *Ch'i venenatum* ("toxic *ch'i*," *tu-ch'i* 毒氣); pathology, common speech: A pathogenic factor, usually exogenous, which tends to poison or pervert the physiological processes. The term is a conditional synonym of *ch'i perversum* but more restricted and intensive in connotation.

(32) *Ch'i vitale* ("enlivening *ch'i*," *sheng-ch'i* 生氣); phase energetics, internal medicine, common speech: The quality of the energy during the yang hours of the rising sun (midnight to noon). It has a quickening and invigorating influence on active enterprises.

The term *ch'i* may also receive a fairly precise implicit qualification either from its general context or from the complements to which it is opposed. The essential qualifications of this kind for the term *ch'i* in medical literature are:

(1) *Ch'i* = configurational energy of the Cosmos. This in-

flection is chiefly met in philosophical texts but also occurs in medical essays, as for example in Chang Ching-yüeh's comment on Chapter 1/29–30 of his *Lei-ching*: "Change, both inception and transformation, rests on *ch'i*, and there is no being in the Cosmos that does not originate from it. Thus *ch'i* envelops the Cosmos from without and moves the Cosmos from within. How else than by *ch'i* can the sun and the moon, the planets and the fixed stars shine, can thunder resound and rain, wind, and clouds be formed, can all beings take rise, mature, bear fruit, and withdraw in the course of the Four Seasons? Man's existence too depends entirely upon this *ch'i*."

(2) *Ch'i* = configurational energy of the Microcosm. This rather general inflection is very close to medical interests and appears in most medical writings. In the *Ling-shu* 30/1153 we have: "If one is setting out distinctions, *ching* and *ch'i*, *chin* and *yeh*, *hsüeh* and *mo*[341] are six [different phenomena]; if one summarizes [them by one designation] they are [all] called *ch'i*, 'configurational energy [of the microcosm].' " And in the *I-lin sheng-mo* 醫林繩墨[342] we find: "What lets the yin and yang rise and fall[343] is *ch'i*, what lets the *hsüeh* flow and the pulses move is *ch'i*, what lets the *orbes horreales et aulici* maintain the mutual relationships of production and sustenance is again *ch'i*. When it is vigorous [the organism] prospers; when it is decrepit [the organism] is exhausted. When it is concurring (*secundovehens*) [the organism] is at peace. When it is contrary (*contravehens*) [the organism] suffers from disease. [In sum] all these [phenomena] are as they are because of [the quality of] the *ch'i*. *Ch'i* constitutes, of course, the root and foundation of man, but it is also the origin of all disease...."

In connection with these two connotations of *ch'i* it is taken for granted or expressly stated that *ch'i* is endowed with specific qualities; yet in fact these qualities are left more or less in abeyance. In the inflections discussed below these qualities are

---

[341]All these terms are explained and defined in the present section.
[342]Compiled in the Ming era by Fang Yü 方隅. The quotation is from 3/45.
[343]This refers to the exchange of energy between polar positions within the organism (see p. 25 above).

specified; the semantic compass of the term *ch'i* thus is restricted, as is the rule in technical usage:

(3) *Ch'i* = macrocosmic configurational energy of specific quality;

(4) *Ch'i* = microcosmic configurational energy of specific quality.

The third shading is signified by the expression "four-seasonal *ch'i*," energetic configurations corresponding to the particular qualities of each of the seasons.[344] The fourth inflection occurs when *ch'i* is determined by the qualities of the orbs[345] or of the psychic reaction.[346]

(5) *Ch'i* [used with the complements *hsing* 形, "substantial body, structive substratum" or *wei* 味, *sapor*] = the active aspect of a macrocosmic energetic configuration or derivatively the dynamic aspect or the actual effect proceeding from a substratum. *Ch'i* is used with this connotation in *Su-wen* 5/48: "The yang aspect constitutes the *ch'i;* the yin aspect constitutes the *wei*," and in *Su-wen* 66/583: "*Shen* 神 [the configurative force] in the Heavens [at the active pole of the Cosmos] manifests itself as *ch'i*, 'active configurational energy'; on Earth [at the structive pole of the Cosmos] it constitutes *hsing* [substantial bodies, structive substrates]. By the interaction of *hsing* and *ch'i*, all beings come into existence and undergo transformation."

(6) *Ch'i* [used with the complement *hsüeh*, "individually specific structive energy"] = the active aspect of a microcosmic energetic configuration. Derivatively, the active aspect of physiological energy in general manifesting itself in the various rhythmic processes of the organism.

In support of this definition we may quote *Su-wen* 6/61: "Yin and yang represent the sexual quality (*nan-nü* 男女) of *hsüeh* and *ch'i*." On this, Wang Ping comments: "Yin determines (*chu* 主) the *hsüeh*, yang determines the *ch'i*."

[344]*Su-wen* 5; *Ling-shu* 44/1194 *et passim*. In the chapter title of the former the term is used with this particular inflection; *Szu-ch'i t'iao-shen ta-lun* 四氣調神大論 is best translated "Great Treatise on Harmonizing the Configurative Force [in Accord with] the Four [Seasonal] Energetic Configurations."

[345]*Ling-shu* 17/1074.

[346]*Tung-i pao-chien* 1/88b.

(7) *Ch'i* [used with the complement *shen,* configurative force] = the structive aspect of an energetic configuration, thus configurational energy substantiating, or "structing," a certain quality.

This connotation just appeared in the quotation from *Su-wen* 66/583 and will again be taken up in the discussion of the term *shen.*[347]

(8) *Ch'i* [used with the complement *te* 德, "formative force"] = the structive aspect of an energetic configuration.

(9) *Ch'i* [used with the complement *ching* 精, "structive potential"] = the active aspect of energy of specific quality, and thus active or activated energy. (This conditional connotation of *ch'i* will be discussed later.) An interesting example with the complement *te* is in *Ling-shu* 8/965: "That by which Heaven [the active pole or aspect of the Cosmos] manifests itself toward me is *te,* 'formative force,' that by which the Earth [the structive pole or aspect of the Cosmos] manifests itself toward me is *ch'i,* 'configurational energy' [enabling me to substantiate certain qualities]."

CHING 精 (UNATTACHED STRUCTIVE ENERGY)

The original meanings of *ching* are "to sift grain," "to refine," "refined"→ "to clear" ("to concentrate"), "concentrated" → "essential" → "essence"→ "quintessence." Even in medical contexts these meanings occur sporadically as in Wang Ping's explanation of the expression *chih-shen* 治神 ("to govern the configurative force") in *Su-wen* 25/259: "To govern the configurative force (*chih-shen*) means to concentrate (*chuan-ching* 專情) one's mind (*hsin* 心)." Or in Chang Chih-ts'ung's comment:[348] "'Clear' means 'quintessential,' like rain and dew." In the *Tung-i pao-chien* we find the statement: "*Ching* is a designation for optimum quality."[349]

The most general technical meanings of the term *ching* are these:

(1) *Ching* = unspecific, unattached energy derived by a concentration. What is meant by this definition appears in a passage from *Su-wen* 5/48: "*Ch'i* (configurational energy of specific quality) turns into *ching,* unspecific, unattached energy

[347]See the following section.
[348]*Su-wen-shih* 3/111.
[349]*Tung-i pao-chien* 1/81.

derived from *ch'i; ching* is absorbed by [literally "turns into"] what transforms (*hua* 化); *ching* consumes 食 *ch'i*,[350] *hsing* (the structive substratum) feeds on *wei* (the *sapores*); [inversely,] what transforms gives rise to *ching,* unspecific, unattached energy, and *ch'i* gives rise to *hsing* (the structive substrates)." The interest of these highly technical assertions lies in the fact that *ching* has two explicit complements—in other words is simultaneously defined from two viewpoints: In comparison to the *ch'i* (configurational energy of specific quality) from which it proceeds (for it is not a question of all *ch'i* turning into *ching*) and into which it may again be transformed,[351] *ching* represents an unattached, unspecific energy whose quality— if it may be said to have any—cannot be ascertained empirically and defined according to any conventional standard of value. On the other hand, in comparison to *hsing* (structive substratum of *determinate* qualities) *ching* represents a structive potential of *indeterminate* qualities.

It should be noted that the transformation (*hua*) in the course of which *ching* turns into *ch'i* or *ch'i* turns into *ching* corresponds to the process of (physiological) assimilation. This explains why the commentator Wang Ping may parallel *hua* (transformation) with *ho* (harmonization): "When *ch'i* is transformed, *ching* is produced, when the *sapores* are harmonized, the *hsing* (visible form) grows." (*Su-wen* 5/48).

(2) *Ching* = unattached structive energy → structive potential. With this principal meaning, *ching* in medical contexts exactly takes over the role played by *ling* 靈, "structive force," "structive capacity," in philosophical and Taoist technical writing; the latter term is almost unknown[352] in medical literature. This is the definition of *ching* as used throughout medical literature. In the *Ling-shu* 8/965 we have: "What life comes from is called *ching,* 'structive potential.' " The Ch'ing commentator Chang Chih-ts'ung[353] puts it more sharply: "What the first [impulse] of life comes from. . . . "[354]

[350]That is, derived from *ch'i,* at the same time diminishing its quantity.
[351]*Su-wen* 5/49: "*Ching,* after transformation, becomes *ch'i.*"
[352]One of the rare exceptions is in the title of the *Ling-shu,* "Pivot of Structive Force."
[353]*Ling-shu* 8/966.
[354]故初生之來謂之精.

This passage might easily be adduced to show that *ching* should be rendered "semen."[355] It is true that this material concept is implicit in the second definition of *ching*; "semen" as the standard translation or, worse still, standard definition of *ching*, ignores essential implications of the Chinese term.

Chang Chih-ts'ung, commenting on the *Su-wen* sentence "If the structive potential (*ching*) is insufficient, it is replenished by the *sapores*,"[356] explains: "The [term] *ching* refers to the *ching* of the five *orbes horreales*."[357] Ma Shih, elucidating *Ling-shu* 8/965, quoted above, makes the point: "If *ching* is considered in comparison with *shen*, then *ching* is of structive polarity and *shen* is of active polarity."[358] *Ching*, like *ling*,[359] is a prerequisite of life and the concrete basis of any individual existence. The *locus classicus* for this point is the *Ling-shu* 30/1153: "What always precedes the coming into existence of the personality (*shen* 身) is called structive potential"; and in the *Tung-i pao-chien* 1/74 we find: "Structive potential is the foundation (*pen* 本) of the individuality."

Like *ch'i*, *ching* may at first sight be taken for a generic designation of energy. *Ching* frequently appears as a complement of *ch'i*, in the sense that *ch'i* is always of definable quality, whereas the quality of *ching*, by definition, cannot even be postulated. Structive potential is "distilled" from a configuration of energy, from energy of a specific qualitative structure (*ch'i*). Inversely, any configuration of energy must be evolved or built up from unattached and indeterminate structive potentials.

It may here be objected that the epithet "structive" is itself a qualification of *ching*. This is logically correct but does not contradict the previous statement. "Structive" is a qualifier resulting from the polarity *ching* [= struc-

---

[355]Many scholars who have faith in their dictionaries will for a long time to come continue to translate *ching* by "essence." This is not altogether false, but it confines the imagination to a narrow rut.

[356]*Su-wen* 5/73.

[357]There is no Chinese or Western medical theory that the sperm is collected from all orbs (or organs).

[358]Concordant statements may also be found on p. 966 of the same text and in the *Su-wen-shih* 2/3.

[359]See the discussion of *ling* in "Untersuchungen," p. 429; "Wissenschaftliches Denken," pp. 538 and 541.

tive]/*ch'i* (or *shen*) [= active], and implies the capacity to render concrete, to substantiate, a given effect without regard to its quality. "Without determinate quality," on the other hand, indicates that structive potential lacks the intrinsic specific qualities that all other forms share.

CHING-CH'I 精氣

The combination *ching-ch'i* is one of the most overworked of all composite technical terms. Several kinds of logical interaction result from the syntactic relationships of its elements:

(1) *Ching* qualifies *ch'i*. The complementarity of the two components is necessarily ruled out: *ch'i* is still configurational energy,[360] but energy that is *"ching"* is

structive and/or
unattached and/or
refined and/or
potentialized,

depending on the explicit (or implicit) complement of the composite term. In *Ling-shu* 18/1083 we find these two equations: "Constructive and defensive energy = *ching-ch'i*, individually specific structure energy (*hsüeh*) = *shen-ch'i*." Now these equations are of the greatest interest. It is evident at a glance that *ching-ch'i:shen-ch'i* constitute polar complements exactly like *ching:shen*.[361] Still, *ching-ch'i* is not the same as *ching*, and *shen-ch'i* is not the same as *shen*. We know from ample testimony that the defensive energy (*wei*) and (despite its mobility) even the constructive energy (*ying*) must be classed with the active manifestations of physiological energy. We also know that *hsüeh* is a structive aspect of physiological energy. What then did the authors mean by the apparent inversion of attributes? *Ching* is by definition a structive aspect, and *shen* an active aspect. It is true that the constructive and defensive energies (*ying-wei*) may be considered structive in the special sense that they are unattached; they are not confined to any

[360]See p. 174 above.
[361]See p. 177 above, p. 189 below.

specific orb, but instead move to where they are needed. By distinction to the *ch'i genuinum*, for instance, they cause the energy assimilated through breathing and eating to substantiate. Likewise because of its individualized quality, *hsüeh* tends to maintain the specific configuration of an individual and may in this limited sense be considered a configurative force. In other words, *ching-ch'i* means "*ching*-like *ch'i*," configurational energy that is, in a sense, unattached and at the same time structive; and *shen-ch'i* means "*shen*-like *ch'i*": configurative energy that, in a sense, tends to establish and maintain a specific energetic configuration.

Of a host of similar constructions only two more are to be given. In *Ling-shu* 52/1231 we find: "Their *ch'i superficiale* not running in the conduits is the *ch'i defensivum*, their *ching-ch'i* passing through the conduits is the *ch'i constructivum*." *Ching* must be rendered by the definitions that best fit the context— in this case structive, potentialized. We proceed similarly even when there is no explicit complement to *ching*, e.g., in *Su-wen* 1/8: "... the True Man (*homo merus*) breathes *ching-ch'i* [i.e., refined structive energy which tends to sustain, to conserve[362] his individuality];" or in *Ling-shu* 30/1153, where Wu Mao-hsien 吳懋先 explains: "*Shen*[363] constitutes the *ching-ch'i* [refined] configurative energy distilled from] food."

(2) *Ching* and *ch'i* are coordinate complements. In this less frequent usage *ching* and *ch'i* are defined individually in accordance with the definitions and inflections above, *ch'i* usually in sense (6), "the active aspect of a microcosmic energetic configuration," and *ching* usually in sense (2), "a structive potential." The simplified definition "structive and active energy" often suffices. Thus Chang Chih-ts'ung comments in *Su-wen* 13/138: "This is because practitioners in this age of decay do not examine the energetic level [manifesting itself] through the complexion and the pulse as the respective levels of structive and active energies...." Throughout that chapter *ching* and *ch'i* are used as complementary terms.

[362]See p. 20 above.
[363]See next page.

SHEN 神 (CONFIGURATIVE FORCE)

Whereas *ch'i* and *ching* considered separately have no unequivocal polar determination, *shen* and the other energetic terms to be examined subsequently show a definite polarity. *Shen* is primarily the actively organizing configurative and transformative influence that determines and upholds the specific character of an individual. In other words it stands for the ultimate rationally conceivable cause of living organization (*sheng* 生). For this reason we have adopted the standard definition "configurative force,"[364] which implies capacity for active assimilation or rejection of extraneous influences. *Shen* is a speculative concept of "pure action," which by definition[365] cannot be perceived directly. *Shen* may manifest itself only to the degree that it meets with energy of complementary quality, *ching*, "structive potential" (in medicine) or *ling*, "structive force" (in Taoist and philosophical thought).[366] In medical literature two senses of *shen* appear, the first somewhat more pragmatic and inclusive than the second: (1) *shen* = a manifest configurative force, comprising the active and structive components indispensable for such a manifestation; (2) *shen* = the active aspect of configurative force, and active configurative force. A few quotations in support of each of these definitions will make the concept of *shen* clearer.

From *Su-wen* 66/583, already cited in connection with *ch'i* (5),[367] we learn: "*Shen*, 'the configurative force,' manifests itself as *ch'i*, 'active configurational energy' in Heaven [at the active pole of the Cosmos]; it constitutes *hsing*, 'structive substrates, substantial bodies' on Earth [at the structive pole of the Cosmos]." *Shen* here brings into existence both the active and the structive aspects of the Cosmos, and consequently may be said to represent both aspects implicitly.

A frequently quoted and instructive statement appears in *Ling-shu* 8/965: "When the two *ching* meet, one speaks of *shen*."

---

[364]In German *konstellierende Kraft*.
[365]See pp. 16–18 above.
[366]See p. 177 above and p. 193.
[367]On p. 175.

This translation reflects the ambiguity of *shen*. We have shown elsewhere that in nonmedical thought *shen* cannot become manifest and thus cannot be perceived without its complement *ling*, structive force or structive capacity. This logical nexus eventually leads to the systematic convertibility of *shen* and *ling*.[368] A similar situation prevails in medical literature. Whereas in general and comprehensive definitions *shen* is used in sense (1) (active + structive aspect of the configurative force), in more analytical definitions *shen*, in sense (2), the active configurative force, is always confronted with *ching* (a structive potential), again with the result that in loose discourse *shen* and *ching* may be. used interchangeably. So, depending on the viewpoint, two interpretations of the passage under discussion may be justified:

(*a*) "When the two *ching* [according to the traditional interpretation, the inborn structive potential and the structive potential made available in food] meet, *they* are called *shen*." In other words *ching* here is parallel with *shen*, as in the similar statement in *Ling-shu* 30/1153: "The two *shen* meet, and united, consitute the *hsing* [the structive substratum, the substantial body]."

(*b*) "When the two *ching* meet, *this* is called *shen*." In other words, the confrontation (*hsiang-po* 相搏) of two potentials might be considered a manifestation of *shen*, "configurative force." This latter interpretation is supported by the wider context and seconded by the commentaries. Chang Chih-ts'ung clarifies: "The *ching* of Fire is *shen*, the *ching* of Water is *ching*." We know Chang Chih-ts'ung as a man fond of concocting conciliatory formulas without bothering too much about their more subtle implications.[369] But there is no doubt that he intends to underscore that *shen* is of active polarity and *ching* of structive polarity. A more comprehensive and precise statement of the conventional postulates concerning *shen* comes from Chang Ching-yüeh:[370] "Although configurative force is

[368]Wissenschaftliches Denken," pp. 537–547.
[369]See p. 37 above. The citation from Chang is on p. 966 of the text.
[370]*Lei-ching* 1/30.

produced from unattached configurational energy (*ching-ch'i*), what has complete control of the [indeterminate] *ching-ch'i* and thus acts as the master of active and structive effort (*yün-yung* 運用) again is the configurative force (*shen*) of my consciousness."

Ch'i designates the energy constituting an individual. What determines, produces, and maintains this configuration of energy is *shen*, the configurative force. Because the influence exercised by *shen* on *ch'i* is inductive,[371] there is no temporal gap between "cause" and "effect": "When *shen* moves, the *ch'i* moves also; when *shen* stops, the *ch'i* stops also."[372]

In *Su-wen* 5/55, the correspondences of the E.P. Wood are enumerated. There we find the statement: "[The energetic configuration of the East] is in the Heavens the dark-green [color emblem]... the dark-green [color emblem] produces *shen*. *Shen* in the Heavens [at the active pole of the Cosmos] corresponds to Wind; on the Earth it corresponds to Wood ...." This qualification of *shen* by Wood means that the configurative influence of *shen* is associated with potential activity,[373] indeed a felicitous qualification.

It is to be regretted that this fine definition is not completed by similarly subtle and explicit qualifications of the other forms of energy. In fact there is hardly any doubt that this passage was interpolated during the T'ang, possibly even by Wang Ping. The whole elaborate discussion of the correspondences of the Five Evolutive Phases that concludes the first section of the fifth chapter in today's text of the *Su-wen* (5/54–61) is missing from the otherwise well-conserved *Huang-ti nei-ching t'ai-su* (3/10; this work was edited under the Sui and has come down to us in a manuscript copy of 1153–1163 preserved in Japan. It should also be pointed out that in the *Su-wen* the duplicate correspondence "in the Heavens/on the Earth" 在天 在地 is given only for the first E. P., although it is no less justified for the others, whose corresponding paragraphs are shorter by one line. On the other hand, the commentary ascribed to Wang Ping (who was in charge of the 762 edition of the *Su-wen*) explicitly refers to the words of our quotation. These indications suggest that at the beginning of the T'ang era, when a particularly intensive osmosis was in process between Didactic Taoism and medicine, the exceptionally detailed correspondences were incorporated into Chapter 5 of the *Su-wen*.

---

[371]See p. 1 above.
[372]See the commentary in *Su-wen* 13/139.
[373]See p. 49 above.

HUN 魂 *AND P'O* 魄 (INDIVIDUALLY SPECIFIC ACTIVE AND INDIVIDUALLY
SPECIFIC STRUCTIVE CONFIGURATIVE FORCE)

Shen, configurative force, is active in every phenomenon and on
every evolutive level as the influence that determines and
maintains the configuration of an individual (the term "individual" being taken, of course, in the widest possible sense).
But there is, so to speak, a generic flavor to *shen* which perhaps
explains why still more specific terms designate the force that
determines and maintains the particular qualities ("configuration") constituting the unique traits of an individual:
the individually specific configurative force *hun* and *p'o.* These
are, in a sense and to a certain degree, congruent and synonymous with *shen,* and in a sense they constitute its active and
structive aspects effective within a microcosm. The classical
definition of these terms is in *Ling-shu* 8/965: "What goes and
comes with *shen,* the active configurative force, is called *hun,*
'active aspect of the individually specific configurative force';
what leaves and enters with *ching,* the structive potential, is
called *p'o,* 'the structive aspect of the individually specific
configurative force.'"

In other words, an individually specific configurative force
(*hun*) implies the presence of the more general *shen.* In the same
manner the individually specific structive capacity (*p'o*) pre-
supposes the presence of a concrete, even though indeterminate,
structive potential (*ching*).

A somewhat more circumstantial later definition of the terms
and their interrelation is given by Chang Chih-ts'ung in his
commentary to the quoted passage[374] "[Notwithstanding the
classical relationships] *shen* corresponds to yang in yang and
hun to yin in yang, *ching* corresponds to yin in yin and *p'o* to
yang in yin." This subtle explication is based on the twofold
qualitative determination of each of *hun* and *p'o,* once relative
to each other and once in relation to their determinants. Thus
hun is yang in relation to *p'o,* yet yin (structive) in relation to its
determinant *shen. P'o* is yin in relation to *hun,* yet—because it

---

[374]*Ling-shu-shih* 2/3. The same paragraph also contains opinions of interest
by other authors.

represents the substantiative aspect or even the substantiation within the individual of *shen*, the active configurative force—is yang in relation to *ching*. *Ching* is but a kind of metaphor for the individually specific function of *p'o* within an organism. It should therefore be underscored that *hun* may under some circumstances be used synonymously with *shen*, but that *p'o* can under no circumstances be understood as a synonym of *ching*. In modern terms, *hun* stands for the constitutional forces actively fashioning the personality, and *p'o* corresponds to the structive disposition for the active accomplishments called *hun* ["psychic functions"] inscribed in the bodily substratum.

Despite their appearance in the classics,[375] the terms *hun* and *p'o*, perhaps because of the relative sophistication of the concepts they stand for, have never seen extensive use in the rather pragmatic medical literature.

HSÜEH 血 (INDIVIDUALLY SPECIFIC STRUCTIVE ENERGY)

The frequently used loose translation of *hsüeh* as blood renders the meanings of this term only approximately and partially. The explanation of the character *hsüeh* given in the early etymologic dictionary *Shuo-wen chieh-tzu* (ca. A.D. 90) 5/215 must also be taken with the reservations applying to all the etymologies of this early work. " 血 [designates] the *hsüeh* of the [animal] victim offered at a sacrifice." At the utmost we may venture the hypothesis that *hsüeh* originally designated the fluids obtained from the sacrifice of animal victims and imbibed from a cup because it was supposed to transmit the specific vital essence of the victim. In medical literature, *hsüeh* may be defined as individually specific structive energy, structive physiological energy of individual quality; it also represents the generic term for all individually specific forms of structive, physiological energy.

Hsüeh is produced and stored in the *calorium medium*—essentially the *orbes stomachi, lienalis, et hepaticus*—from where it is distributed throughout the body in accordance with demand.[376] It constitutes a fluid (*liquor, chih* 汁) that is derived by transformation (*pien-hua*) from the energy of food (*ch'i frumentarium*).[377]

[375]In addition to the passages quoted, the terms also occur in *Ling-shu* 47/1204 and 54/1238 (commentary) and in *Su-wen* 23/250.
[376]Refer to the iconography of the *orbis hepaticus*, pp. 122f above.
[377]*Ling-shu* 30/1153.

The structive polarization of *hsüeh* is expressed variously in the *Nei-ching*, for instance in *Ling-shu* 18/1083: "*Hsüeh* and *ch'i* are different in name yet similar in kind." This quotation shows its full meaning if viewed in the light of a parallel in *Ling-shu* 4/931: "Yin and yang are different in name yet similar in kind." In other words, *hsüeh* and *ch'i* are configurational energy, of which *ch'i* represents the active aspect,[378] and *hsüeh* the structive one. Chang Chih-ts'ung expressly says in his commentary on *Su-wen* 24/252: "*Ch'i* is yang, *hsüeh* is yin."

Hsüeh is but one of several forms of energy occurring in the microcosm, not simply a moving fluid. The vital functions depend not on the presence of *hsüeh* but on its particular intrinsic quality and its harmony with the other forms of energy, especially *ch'i*. This idea is clearly expressed in *Ling-shu* 47/1204: "When the *hsüeh* is in harmony, the [energy in the] conduits flows," and in *Ling-shu* 54/1238: "Once *hsüeh* and *ch'i*, the structive and the active aspects of an energetic configuration, are in harmony, once the constructive and defensive energies penetrate throughout, an individual may be constituted."

MO 脈 (PULSE; THE ACTIVE ASPECT OF THE MOVEMENT OF *HSÜEH*)

In common speech *mo* is usually rendered by "veins," which seems to be correct for diverse forms 𧖫, 𧗕, 𧗞 shown in the *Shuo-wen* dictionary (11B/575) and explained by: "That which distributes the *hsüeh* throughout the body." In medicine this meaning persists, slightly qualified, but is second in importance to these meanings:

(1) *Mo* = pulse. *Mo* designates the "movement of the *hsüeh*" that results from the reaction of the bodily substratum toward the potential (structive) energy of *hsüeh*, whose aspect it is.[379] Pertinent quotations are found in *Ling-shu* 10b/1030: "If the *mo* does not penetrate (*pu-t'ung* 不通) the *hsüeh* does not flow," annotated: "*Hsüeh* is what flows in accordance with the *mo ch'i*." We are free to give either a didactic and perhaps anach-

---

[378]See p. 175 above.
[379]To better visualize the unsymmetrical relationships between the two terms, the reader is referred to Table 19.

ronistic interpretation to this passage, or a pragmatic and simple one: "If the active reaction of the body is not generalized (i.e., if the conduits, the lines of communication, are not cleared) the individually specific structive energy cannot flow"; or; "If the pulses do not penetrate [to the surface of the body, where they can be palpated] the *hsüeh* does not circulate." The conditional complementarity of *hsüeh* and *mo* also is evident in *Ling-shu* 30/1153, already quoted,[380] in which *hsüeh* and *mo* (like *ching* and *ch'i, chin* and *yeh*) are a polar couple.

This same paragraph closes with an interesting definition: "That which hems in the *ch'i constructivum* (*ying-ch'i*), so that it can escape nowhere, is called *mo*." Since, only a few lines before, *mo* is defined as a phenomenal aspect of *ch'i*, the present explanation can only be understood in the sense that *mo* thrusts upon the constructive energy (*ying-ch'i*) an order manifested as a rhythm in time or definite paths in space.

This furnishes a perspective from which to understand the important technical term *ching-mo* 經脈 (conduits ̄of energy). *Ching* 經 originally designated the warp threads which determine the form and dimensions of a piece of fabric. Hence derives the connotation "to steer through," "to direct." In philosophy, *ching* designates a canon or a classic. In Chinese medicine the term points to the functional conduits[381] of physiological interaction. The composite word *ching-mo* 經脈 is a verb-object combination whose overall sense is verbal: "to guide the rhythmic manifestations of energy along definite conduits," or nominal: "the *mo*-guiding function." This is why the elements are never inverted.[382] Hence, *ching-mo* is never translated by "conduits *and* veins" but always by "energetic conduits" or "network of energetic conduits." Thus Chang Chih-ts'ung expressly states in *Ling-shu-shih* 4/88 that "the *ching-mo* (energetic conduits) are the paths (*tao*) of the *ch'i constructivum*."

(2) *Mo* = energetic conduits (sinarteries, the internal substratum of the pulse). This interpretation of the term *mo*, as was stated at the beginning, is supported to a certain extent by the etymology of *hsüeh*[383] as well as by the modern anatomical terms *tung-mo* 動脈 (artery) and *ching-mo* 靜脈 (vein), which have evolved from traditional elements. In the ancient

---

[380]See p. 174 above.

[381]In German *Leitbahnen*.

[382]The double term *mo-ching* 脈經 has no meaning other than that of "Classic of the Pulse."

[383]血恤脈.

medical texts this connotation remains implicit, and is brought to the fore only in commentaries on ambiguous statements. Thus we have in *Su-wen* 17/160: "*Mo* is an *aula* [temporary depository] of *hsüeh*. If [the *mo*] is long, the energetic configuration [of the body] is in order (*chih* 治); if it is short, the energetic configuration is disordered (*ping* 病)." Here the term *fu* (*aula*) suggests that *mo* is conceived as a concrete structure, such as the network of conduits. On the other hand the qualifiers *ch'ang* 長 (long, *longus*) and *tuan* 短 (short, *brevis*), used in the iconography of the pulses, leave no doubt that at the same time the authors have in view a dynamic function. This equivocality is maintained by all commentators. The Ch'ing scholar Chang Chih-ts'ung (whose comments are frequently adduced because of their apparent simplicity and precision but are often careless and ad hoc) has the support of Wang Ping as he elucidates: "*Hsüeh* moves within the *mo*. Therefore [*mo*] is the *aula* [temporary depository] of *hsüeh*." Yet one line further on he writes: "*Mo* moves in accordance with the *ch'i*." This cannot be interpreted except by "the pulse reflects the rhythmic movements of the individual's physiological energy."

YING 營:384 *WEI* 衛 (STRUCTIVE AND ACTIVE ASPECTS OF INDETERMINATE PHYSIOLOGICAL ENERGY)

Ying and *wei*, constructive and defensive energies, are complementary aspects of otherwise indeterminate physiological energies, as we are informed in *Ling-shu* 18/1083: "The *ying* and *wei* are *ching-ch'i* ("*ching*-like *ch'i*," configurational but not yet explicitly defined energy)." On p. 1077 of the same chapter

384Also *jung* 榮 and *wei* 衛. Since ancient times the characters *ying* 營 and *jung* 榮 have been interchanged freely in medical literature without the least semantic consequence. In addition to the graphical resemblance of the two characters, the convergence of independent didactic traditions may have contributed to the coexistence of two graphic forms. Thus in today's edition of the *Su-wen* (as well as in nonmedical and Taoist literature) the form *jung* predominates, whereas in the *Ling-shu* the character *ying* is used as a rule. If we recall that the terms *ying* and *wei* are most thoroughly discussed in the *Ling-shu* and that the sense of the graph *ying*, "constructive energy," best corresponds to the concept there defined, it may be readily understood that in later medical literature *ying* is given universal preference.

we learn: "Man obtains his configurational, physiological energy (*ch'i*) from food; its limpid [components] constitute the constructive energy (*ch'i constructivum*); its murky [components] constitute the defensive energy (*ch'i defensivum*). The *ying* [moves] within the conduits (*mo*); the *wei* [moves] outside the conduits." A parallel statement in *Ling-shu* 52/1231 has already been quoted.[385] In these statements, constructive energy corresponds to the structive aspect, and defensive energy corresponds to the active aspect,[386] of the structive potential. The constructive energy, thus doubly structive, moves within the conduits and so is spatially determinate. It is the neutral carrier or link by means of which the energetic circulation through the *orbes* is established and maintained.[387] In short, *ying* is at the base of what we call metabolism, for this modern term implies the structive development and sustenance of the body.[388]

The concept of individually specific structive energy (*hsüeh*) is somewhat more comprehensive in its meaning and, because of its substrate blood, is sometimes associated with the qualities "red" and "fluid"; *ying*, which is given no corresponding substrate, is without exception defined as structive energy or as indeterminate (unattached) structive potential. Still, medical literature contains no clear statement to the effect that there is an essential difference between *hsüeh* and *ying*. To the contrary, it tends to imply that both terms are designations for the same phenomenon: "The *hsüeh* moves within the *mo*"[389] (the individually specific structive energy moves within the conduits), but also: "The *ying* moves within the *mo*"[390] (the constructive energy moves within the conduits). There is also the important passage in *Ling-shu* 18/1083 examined on p. 186 above.[391]

While the structive *ch'i constructivum* circulates in spatially well-defined conduits within the body, the active *ch'i defensivum*

---

[385]See p. 180.

[386]This point has already been discussed in connection with yin and yang on p. 27 above. If the physiological rank and place are expressed by a qualitative proportion, we have

$$\frac{ching}{ying/wei} = \frac{hun/p'o}{shen} \ .$$

[387]The constructive energy is neutral, because it may be considered an aspect of *ching*.

[388]See also p. 207 below.

[389]*Su-wen* 17/160, commentary by Chang Chih-ts'ung.

[390]Comment by the same scholar in the *Ling-shu-shih* 4/88.

[391]See also pp. 207–208.

(*wei*) is diffused outside these conduits and is in particular present at the surface of the body.[392] The *ch'i defensivum* is responsible for the warmth of the flesh, the healthy complexion, the openness of the pores, the luster of the hair, the mobility of the joints and, as its name indicates, for the defensive capacity of the organism against every kind of heteropathy (*hsieh*). In other words the concept defensive energy in the last analysis covers all the physiological phenomena that we usually designate by active vital functions. The (active) maintenance and defense of the functional integrity of the organism is only one aspect of this active capacity to cope with the vicissitudes of life.

The constructive energy originates in the *calorium medium*, while the defensive energy originates in the *calorium superius*.[393] In other words, the *ying*, exactly like the *hsüeh*, is preponderantly "distilled" in the *orbes stomachi, lienalis, et hepaticus* from exogenous energies of diverse origin; the defensive energy is essentially synthetized and distributed by the *orbis pulmonalis*.

CHIN 津 AND YEH 液 (ACTIVE AND STRUCTIVE FLUIDS)

Chin designates the active, and *yeh* the structive, aspect of structive potential substantialized in the form of body fluids. These narrowly defined terms thus are close semantic parallels of *ying* and *wei*, but their aggregate state is never defined. Like the defensive energy, *chin* constitutes an active or, more precisely, an activated potential that diffuses within and from the body: "that which percolates and perspires through the pores is called *chin*."[394] Like constructive energy, the structive fluid *yeh* is what irrigates the bones "when food has been ingested and the physiological energy (*ch'i*) has been replenished (*man* 滿), and, after the bone framework has been irrigated, what completes and replenishes the [energy of] brain and medulla and causes the healthy luster of the skin." Chang

---

[392]Commentary and summary given in *Ling-shu ching pai-hua-chieh* 靈樞經白話解 18/195.

[393]*Ling-shu* 18 and the commentaries in the *Ling-shu ching pai-hua-chieh* 18/195f. In the latter text the *Ling-shu's* notion (18/1080) that the *wei* is connected with the *calorium inferius* is rejected as being inconsistent with accepted theory.

[394]*Ling-shu* 30/1153.

Chih-ts'ung elaborates in the *Ling-shu-shih* 4/34: "*Chin* is an activated fluid, and *yeh* is a structive fluid. . . . After food has entered the stomach (*orbis stomachi*) the energy of the orb is replete and by assimilation [produces] a structive fluid. This is a nutritive liquid which flows into the bones. Now when the bones are moved and flexed, contracted and extended, the [energy in the] conduits flows and their beneficial moisture (*tse* 澤) is diffused. For this reason what replenishes the [energies of] brain and medulla within, as well as what calls forth the luster of the skin on the exterior, is called structive fluid. On this I remark that *chin* and *yeh* are fundamentally of the same kind and are merely polarized into yang and yin. Thus *chin* (active fluid) may be called a limpid *yeh* (structive fluid); and [inversely] *yeh* (structive fluid) may be called a murky *chin* (active fluid')."

HSING 形 (STRUCTIVE SUBSTRATUM, CONCRETE BODY, SUBSTANTIAL FORM)

The technical use of *hsing* 形 is not limited to medical literature. It also occurs frequently in philosophical treatises beginning in the second part of the first millennium B.C. In *Shuo-wen*, p. 429, the character 形 is explained by "image" (*hsiang* 象). An important appearance outside medical literature is in the passage in the "Great Commentary" (*Hsi-tz'u*) to the *I-ching* (p. 143): "When the images [or emblems] are formed in the Heavens [at the active pole of the Cosmos] and the structive substrates are constituted on Earth [at the structive pole of the Cosmos], changes and transformations will become manifest." In this quotation, *hsing* 形 is already ambiguous. We may either accept the interpretation proposed by the *Shuo-wen* and consider *hsing* a synonym of *hsiang* 象: "In the Heavens emblems, on Earth images," or take the two terms as complementary antonyms: "In the Heavens emblems, on Earth substrates." The latter view is held by all authoritative commentators on the *Hsi-tz'u* (Wang Pi, K'ung Ying-ta, and others); and apparently the first sense predominates in Taoist compilations such as the *Chuang-tzu* 莊子 and the *Huai-nan-tzu*.

The ambiguity of the term is much less pronounced in medical texts, but still we may distinguish two meanings of *hsing*: (1) *hsing* = structive substratum, concrete form, body. Quotations in support of this sense are numerous in the classics. We had already mentioned one in *Su-wen* 5/67: "In Heaven there are *ching* (unattached structive potentials), and on Earth there are *hsing* (structive substrates, concrete forms)." We may also cite from the same chapter (p. 46): "The active aspect is transformation of the configurational energy (*ch'i*); the structive aspect is production of the concrete forms. "The same idea is developed in *Su-wen* 66/583: "The configurative force (*shen*) in Heaven [at the active pole] represents active[395] configurational energy; on Earth [at the structive pole] it produces concrete forms. In the measure that configurational energy interacts by induction with the concrete forms (of structive substrata), all beings come into existence."

A still more expressive formula is given in the *Tung-i pao-chien* 1'74: "The concrete body (*hsing*) is the abode of configurative force (*shen*); when the concrete body returns to Earth, man dies."

The second sense of *hsing* is much more abstract: (2) *hsing* = the quality of a structive substratum → constitution or qualitative configuration. Chang Chih-ts'ung, commenting on *Su-wen* 5/73, states:[396] "*Hsing* corresponds to the muscle and flesh of the body.... "—"As for [the distinction between] *hsing* and *ching* (structive potential), the *hsing* (manifest constitution) corresponds to the active aspect, and the structive potential corresponds to the structive aspect."

In sum, the term *hsing*, which in common speech may usually be rendered by "form" or "body," in technical contexts as a rule denotes a structive substratum, a concrete, substantiated energetic potential of definite structure and dimension. Only quite exceptionally may *hsing* designate the derivative abstraction, the visible manifestation or aspect of a substratum.

[395]See p. 175 above.
[396]*Su-wen-shih* 1/38.

WEI 味 (*SAPOR*)

In common speech the term *wei* 味 means "taste," "flavor," or food of a certain taste or flavor. In technical context it denotes a *sapor*, i.e., an exogenous structive potential of distinctive quality substantiated in food or drugs of definite flavor, or food or drugs of that specific quality. *Sapor* is manifest in and subject to definition by conventional taste. Since food serves to sustain the body, *wei* may be conditionally synonymous with *hsing* in the sense of an (exogenous) structive potential, the active aspect of which then is denoted by *ch'i* [active configurational energy].[397]

LING 靈 (STRUCTURE FORCE, STRUCTIVE CAPACITY)

Although the term *ling* figures in the title of the *Ling-shu* it is not properly speaking a medical term. Its principal applications are in Taoist literature, especially alchemy, and macrobiotic gymnastics. We mention it here because of the constant interplay between the medical disciplines and Didactic Taoism.

Ling, as the structive complement of configurative force (*shen*), is the capacity of a substratum to make concrete the active influences to which it is exposed.[398]

CHING-SHEN 精神 (MANIFEST CONFIGURATIVE FORCE, THE
MANIFESTATION OF CONFIGURATIVE FORCE)

The composite term *ching-shen* deserves special attention, because of its ancient currency in common speech, its widespread use in medical texts, and its employment since the nineteenth century as the Chinese equivalent for such Western concepts as spirit and psyche.

The term *ching-shen* is composed of two complementary antonyms. The second, *shen*, has been defined as "configurative force," and the first, *ching*, as "structive potential," indispensable to the manifestation of *shen*. The composite term thus designates this combination.

In *Ling-shu* 52/1231 we are told: "By means of the five *orbes horreales*, active configurative force + structive potential

[397]See the quotation from *Su-wen* 5/48 discussed earlier in connection with the term *ching* (sense 1).
[398]"Wissenschaftliches Denken," p. 544, as well as the next paragraph.

(*ching-shen*)[399] and the active and structive aspects of individually specific configurative force (*hun-p'o*) are stored." This statement is not tautological, as it may seem at first sight, for *ching-shen* stands for a generic and universal aspect of a phenomenon that, as *hun-p'o,* is restricted to an individual.

Another passage of the same text, *Ling-shu* 47/1204, has: "Man's structive and active aspects of physiological energy (*hsüeh-ch'i* 血氣) and configurative force combined with its structive potential (*ching-shen*) are that from which life is received and sustained throughout one's span of existence." Chang Chih-ts'ung, in his comparatively recent commentary on this passage, underscores the relative independence of the four juxtaposed terms: "The human personality (*jen-shen* 人身) is founded upon *hsüeh* and *ch'i,* structive and active physiological energy, whereas *ching* and *shen* represent its functions (*yung* 用). If these four [components] are united for the sustenance[400] of life, one's allotted span may indeed be lived out."[401]

Whereas in the examples just given the reader may take *ching-shen* as a composite term or as two complementary expressions, other examples suggest a closer-knit connection between *ching* and *shen.* In *Su-wen* 1/3, speaking of the ancient Exemplary Man (*sheng-jen*) we have: "... His configurative force capable of manifestation (*ching-shen*) was conserved within; where then could disease come from?" And a little farther on in the same text (3/21) we find: "Therefore the Exemplary Men concentrated[402] their configurative forces capable of manifestation (*ching-shen*), swallowed the *ch'i caeleste,*[403] and

---

[399]In this connection it should be recalled that the habitual order in which the components of antithetical couples are named is indicative of their age. As an echo of a matriarchal order in all ancient polar combinations (*yin-yang, hsüeh-ch'i, p'in-mu* . . . *ching-shen*) the structive element precedes the active element. On the other hand, in terms that are of more recent invention (approximately since the end of the Chan-kuo period for scientific expressions), the active element precedes the structive one: *hun-p'o.*

[400]Chang expressly adopts for *feng* 奉 the meaning "to sustain" (*yang* 養).

[401]*Ling-shu-shih* 4/88.

[402]傅 must of course be corrected to 專.

[403]See p. 169 above.

were in touch with[404] the cosmic manifestation of the configurative force." What the Exemplary Men concentrated within themselves was not unconnected configurative force (*shen*) and structive potential (*ching*), but the configurative force combined with the structive potential required for its enactment. This distinction, somewhat oversophisticated at first sight, becomes more obvious if we recall the ambiguity of the term *shen*.[405] From the basic definition of *shen* in the *Hsi-tz'u* (p. 149a), "Something the polarity of which cannot be fathomed is called *shen*,"[406] it is always inferred that *shen* by itself is not only inexhaustible but also unfathomable and undefinable. In spite of this, to speak of the manifestations of *shen* is to imply what elsewhere is explicitly stated: the sim-

Table 19. Comparison of Energetic Terminology

	Active Aspect of the First Polarization			Structive Aspect of the First Polarization		
	Active Aspect of the Second Polarization	Neutral	Structive Aspect of the Second Polarization	Neutral	Active Aspect of the Second Polarization	Neutral	Structive Aspect of the Second Polarization
1			[*ch'i*]	*ching* 精	[*ch'i*]		
2	*shen* 神		*ch'i* 氣			*ching* 精	[*ching*]
3	*hun* 魂	[*shen*]	*p'o* 魄				
4			*ch'i* 氣		*mo* 脈	*hsüeh* 血	
5					*wei* 衛	[*ching*]	*ying* 營
6					*chin* 津	[*ching*]	*yeh* 液
7		*ch'i* 氣					*hsing* 形
8					*ch'i* 氣		*wei* 味
9	[*shen*]					[*ling* 靈]	

Note: Implicit complements are enclosed in brackets.

[404]The Chinese term *t'ung* 通 may be rendered, depending upon the context, by "to communicate" or "to attain." Our choice of the former is motivated by the over-all sense of the sentence.

[405]This has been set forth in "Untersuchungen," p. 429, and "Wissenschaftliches Denken," pp. 538 and 541.

[406]The parallel definition of the *Nei-ching* is to be found in the *Su-wen* 66/583.

ultaneous presence of a structive complement to *shen*, either structive capacity (*ling*) or structive potential (*ching*), in combination with which *shen* may concretely manifest itself. Thus the composite term *ching-shen*, originally denoting a configurative force provided with the structive potential indispensable to its manifestation, gradually acquired the meaning "manifest configurative force," and could finally in certain contexts be used as a synonym of the word *shen*. Examples of this final stage may likewise be found in the *Nei-ching*, for instance in *Ling-shu* 71/1315: "The *orbis cardialis* is the abode of the *ching-shen* (manifest configurative force)," or in the parallels to this sentence in *Ling-shu* 54/1238 and *Su-wen* 23/250.

COMPARATIVE TABLE OF ENERGETIC TERMINOLOGY

As has become evident, the concepts centered on the idea of "physiological energy" form a network of partly intersecting, partly continuous but complementary, and partly parallel semantic lines. Some terms cannot be sharply separated from certain others but may, depending on perspective, sometimes be considered as mutually exclusive, as complementary antonyms, or as synonyms. The relative quality of each term may be grasped best in a comparative table (Table 19).

4

Standards of Value for Phenomena of Microcosmic Dimensions, II: Sinarteriology and Foraminology

General Preliminaries; Terminology

Sinarteriology, the theory of the energetic conduits (*ching-mo* 經脈, *ching-luo* 經絡, Latin *sinarteriae*) and of the sensitive points (*hsüeh, shu-hsüeh* 腧穴, Latin *foramina inductoria*) situated along the conduits, is one of the most original and most important chapters of Chinese medicine. It is important because sinarteriology is an essential element of Chinese diagnostics, pharmacotheraphy, and massage, and the sole foundation of acupuncture and moxibustion. It is original in the sense that the knowledge of hyperalgetic points or zones, found in all great civilizations, has nowhere approached the systematic perfection of Chinese sinarteriology.

The origins of the theory of the energetic conduits are lost in the darkness of ancient history. From concordant but not congruent evidence in the literature of the late Chou and early Han periods it may be inferred[1] that stone needles (*pien-shih* 砭石) were used for the treatment of disease in the second millennium B.C., and perhaps even toward the end of the Stone Age. At that stage people must have known of points at the surface of the body through which certain disease symptoms could be influenced. A systematic order of these sensitive points, however, is not documented prior to the *Nei-ching*, compiled during the third to first centuries B.C. By that time neighboring sensitive points (*foramina, hsüeh*) linked with symptoms were connected by lines, the so-called "conduits" (*ching-mo*). Some of the sensitive points coincide with pulsating points; the conduits were so named because they were thought to conduct the pulsating physiological energy about the body. Their detection by connecting the points is analogous to the

---

[1] *Shan-hai-ching* 山海經, Chapter 4; *Shuo-wen*, p. 557; *Su-wen* 12/131f *et passim*.

way a subterranean watercourse reveals itself by springs sent up through "punctures" in the earth's crust. The sensitive points provide the positive empirical and historically primary data on which the theory is based; the conduits, on the other hand, are only the result of systematic speculations.

This fact deserves to be underscored, since a considerable number of contemporary physicians in the Soviet Union, in China, and in the West, evidently ignorant of it, vainly strive either to prove that the conduits postulated by Chinese medicine do not really exist or, more frequently, to detect some kind of anatomical substratum corresponding to the conduits. Yet the sole positive phenomenon that Chinese doctors have experienced, and that can be demonstrated by means of modern research apparatus, is the functional distinction between every sensitive point and its neutral surroundings. This dissemblance is defined by measurements of electrical resistance and of thermosensitivity at the surface of the skin.[2]

Consequently the conduits must be conceived in analogy to the lines of force of a magnetic field or to the orbits of planets as defined by gravitation and mass. Like these they can never be demonstrated in the form of substratum but only as effects exercised on substrata. Also analogously, the detailed tracing of the conduits is always subject to slight modification due to new or more precise observations or to individual variations. And the only portion of the conduits that can be plotted is the part of their course that lies at the surface of the body. Their extensions within the body that are devoid of sensitive points —the sections, in other words, closest to the orbs—can be taken seriously only as essentially mnemonic aids to diagnosis and therapy.

The English term "conduit" renders the principal implications of the Chinese generic synonyms *ching-mo* 經脈 and *ching-luo* 經絡. The precise purport of *ching-mo* is "to guide the rhythmic manifestation of energy along definite paths."[3]

[2]*Chen-chiu-hsüeh chiang-i* 針灸學講義, pp. 474–494.
[3]The syntactic and etymological backgrounds of the term *ching-mo* are elucidated on p. 187 above; the elements of the word *ching-luo* will be discussed in the next paragraph.

We have therefore adopted as normative equivalents of this generic term the Latin word *sinarteria* and its English derivative "sinartery."

The Latin loan from Greek, *arteria*, signifying at the same time "pulse" and "pulsating vein," very closely approximates the meanings of the somewhat ambiguous Chinese word *mo* 脈. In order to avoid any confusion between our term and the word "artery," used in quite a different sense in modern medicine, we have added the prefix *"sin-"* (Chinese).

As early as the *Nei-ching*, various complements to the cardinal conduits (*ching-mo* or *ching-luo*) are described. Of these only the *luo-mo* 絡脈 need to be mentioned for the moment. The word *luo* 絡 means "to attach" or "a net" (Latin: *rete*);[4] the *luo-mo* are numerous netlike ramifications of the cardinal conduits. The normative equivalents of *luo-mo* therefore are *sinarteriae reticulares* in Latin, and reticular conduits in English.[5] In this way the fundamental meaning of the second generic name, *ching-luo* (*sinarteriae cardinales et reticulares*) is a combination of the senses of its components.

Just as Chinese doctors are in the habit of using the single terms *ching* 經 and *luo* 絡 in place of *ching-mo* and *luo-mo*, we likewise, as a rule, use the equivalents *cardinalis* and *reticularis* and fall back on the term *sinarteria* only in order to give a normative translation of the generic term.

The expression "sensitive point" closely corresponds to the modern Chinese definition *tz'u-chi-tien* 刺激點 (literally, "point of stimulation").[6] In ancient literature, including that of medicine, various designations of the sensitive points appear, such as *hsüeh* 穴, *k'ung* 空, *k'ung-hsüeh* 空穴, *ch'i-hsüeh* 氣穴, *shu* 俞 (or 腧); of these only *hsüeh* is, strictly speaking, a technical term. All these expressions correspond to the concepts of hole, opening, cavity—hence our choice of the normative equivalent "foramen" in both Latin and English. Its double sense, "opening" and "cavity," ideally renders that of *hsüeh*. The foramina are openings for the passage of energy (*ch'i*) which are situated in palpable concavities at the surface of the body.

In practice there are some exceptions to this definition.

[4]"To attach" (Latin *nectere*) as well as "net" (Latin *rete* and all direct derivatives, e.g. *nexorius*, *reticularis*, "reticular")" are normative equivalents of *luo* 絡.

[5]In German, *Netzbahnen*.

[6]*Chen-chiu-hsüeh chiang-i*, p. 101 *et passim*.

The technical synonym of *shu* 俞, 脈,[7] is related graphically, phonetically, and semantically to the word *shu* 輸, meaning "to transport" or "to transmit." *Shu* designates a spot at the surface of the body, but its connotation emphasizes that it communicates with a corresponding energetic configuration (an orb) and can be used to induce effects in it. As a normative equivalent of *shu* 脈 we therefore employ the term *inductorium* (as adjective and noun). Thus the normative equivalent for the Chinese generic designation of a sensitive point, *shu-hsüeh*, is *foramen inductorium*.

According to a tacit convention established in medical literature since approximately the Sung period, a graphic distinction is made between 脈 *shu* (= *foramen inductorium* in a general sense) and 俞 *shu* (*inductorium* with a specific technical connotation).[8]

The Chinese compounds *ching-luo-hsüeh* 經絡學 (literally "sinarteriology") and *shu-hsüeh-hsüeh* 脈穴學 (literally "foraminology")[9] are modern neologisms[9] on which our own designations for these disciplines are patterned. In former times the simple expression *ching-luo* or the classificatory rubric *ching-luo-lei* 經絡類 (category of sinarteriae) was applied to the discipline as well as its subject matter. We also follow this usage.

Historical and Bibliographical Preliminaries

The systematic principles and basic concepts of sinarteriology are first laid down in the *Nei-ching*. Many chapters touch upon it,[10] and chapters 58 to 63 of the *Su-wen* and Chapters 1, 2, and 10–13 of the *Ling-shu* are exclusively devoted to sinarteriology. Chapter 10 of the *Ling-shu* contains the first coherent descrip-

---

[7]The usual pronunciation (*yü*) of the basic character does not apply to the technical term, as is evident from philological as well as lexicographical evidence. See *Su-wen* 47 and 58, and *Nan-ching* 67. The pronunciation *yü* nevertheless leads an impish existence in Western literature and in nontechnical Chinese dictionaries.

[8]See pp. 335–336 below. The word *hsüeh* 穴 when used as a medical term, in contrast with the pronunciation of everyday speech, is pronounced *hsüeh* (in the second tone), probably as a consequence of a tone sandhi in its combination with *shu* (in the fourth tone).

[9]*Chen-chiu-hsüeh chiang-i, passim.*

[10]*Su-wen* 6, 16, 24; *Ling-shu* 17, 38, 41, 52, 62, 71.

tion of the cardinal conduits. During the third century A.D. Huang-fu Mi in his *Chen-chiu chia-i-ching* 鍼灸甲乙經 (Systematic classic of acu-moxi-therapy) revised the passages of the *Nei-ching* dealing with sinarteriology, systematically filling out and redefining the terminology and the correspondences between foramina and symptoms. All later authors of any consequence deal with sinarteriology as the theoretical basis of acupuncture. Under the T'ang particular contributions were made by Sun Szu-mo in his *Ch'ien-chin yao-fang* and by Wang T'ao 王濤 in his *Wai-t'ai pi-yao* 外臺秘要.

Among the large number of works on the subject appearing during the Sung period, the *T'ung-jen shu-hsüeh chen-chiu t'u-ching* 銅人腧穴針灸圖經 (Illustrated classic on acu-moxi-therapy based on the *foramina inductoria* of the bronze figure) submitted to the throne in 1026 by Wang Wei-i 王惟一 stands out. Wang played a leading role in the construction of two human bronze models to be utilized for the study of the sensitive points.

Between the Sung and the Ch'ing more than three dozen monographs or extensive sections in encyclopedias devoted to acu-moxi-therapy were added to the literature of sinarteriology.[11]

In our century, the powerfully revived interest in acupuncture in China and Japan has set off an avalanche of publications that have some bearing on sinarteriology, but even an expert has difficulty keeping track of them. Only very few attract attention by their exceptional quality or comprehensiveness.

Of these, perhaps the most valuable is *Chen-chiu ching-hsüeh t'u-k'ao* 針灸經穴圖考 (Illustrated investigations of the *foramina inductoria* of acu-moxi-therapy) by Huang Chu-chai 黃竹齋 (1957), a critical compendium exclusively devoted to sinarteriology. For every "classical" foramen (those mentioned in the classics, including the *Chia-i-ching*), all the early testimony is colligated and confronted with a selection of later commentaries up to the twentieth century. A well-balanced and up-to-date account of all aspects of acu-moxi-therapy and its theoretical foundations is given in *Chen-chiu-hsüeh chiang-i*

---

[11]Information on the titles and research value of all these books may be found in the excellent critical bibliography of the *Chen-chiu-hsüeh chiang-i*, pp. 24–27.

針灸學講議 (Textbook of acu-moxi-therapy), compiled at the Shanghai Academy of Traditional Chinese Medicine and first published in 1959. A little book which, although primarily destined for the practicing physician, recommends itself by its lucidity and thoroughness is *Shu-hsüeh-hsüeh kai-lun* 腧穴學概論 (Compendium of foraminology), compiled by Lu Shou-yen 陸瘦燕 and Chu Ju-kung 朱汝功.[12]

In the West, where acupuncture is almost the only aspect of Chinese medicine that has yet received attention, sinarteriological information may be dredged from a number of publications on this subject.[13] These works are as a rule destined for practitioners who wish to experiment in an exotic art. They are never based on a direct study of the sources but rely on data furnished by Chinese and Japanese informants or, more often, on third-hand Western sources.

General Characteristics of the Sinarteries

All sinarteries, irrespective of category, are conduits for the different forms of physiological energy. They conduct this energy between two orbs, between an orb and the extension known as its unfoldment (*perfectio*) or, more generally, between the interior of the body and its surface. Endogenous disturbances are carried to the surface by means of the sinarteries and are tracked backward along the same route in diagnosis and therapy. Inversely, exogenous heteropathies (*heteropathica, hsieh*) may break through the barrier of the skin and penetrate along the sinarteries into the orbs. "The commencement of all disease starts[14] in the skin.[15] When a heteropathy has entered, the pores open. Once the pores are opened, it may penetrate

[12]For further details see the Bibliography.
[13]Soulié de Morant, *Précis de la vraie acuponcture chinoise* (reprint; Paris, 1965); Gerhard Bachmann, *Die Aukpunktur, eine Ordnungstherapie*. The latter book contains excellent anatomical tables showing the course of the conduits. For critical evaluations of other works, see Nathan Sivin, "An Introductory Bibliography of Traditional Chinese Science: Books and Articles in Western Languages," in Shigeru Nakayama and Nathan Sivin (eds.), *Chinese Science: Explorations of an Ancient Tradition* (Cambridge, Mass., 1973), pp. 302–308.
[14]This is a pleonasm, but that is how the Chinese text puts it.
[15]A statement that the Chinese always took with a grain of salt.

deeper and deversate within the reticular conduits (*luo-mo*). If it lodges there and is not expulsed, it penetrates deeper into the cardinal conduits (*ching*). If it lodges there without being expulsed it will penetrate [still] deeper into the *orbes aulici* and [finally] take hold in the *orbes stomachi et intestini*."[16]

What is only hinted at here will become evident in the synoptic enumeration of the sinarteries: their functional imbrication, their interaction, and their hierarchic order. To start with, there is an overall distinction between

the *sinarteriae cardinales* (*ching* 經), comprising
12 (*sinarteriae*) *cardinales* ("cardinal conduits"), *ching* (*-mo*) 經脈;
12 (*sinarteriae*) *paracardinales* ("cardinal branch conduits"), *ching-pieh* 經別;
8 (*sinarteriae*) *cardinales impares* ("odd conduits"), *chi-ching pa-mo* 奇經八脈;

and the *sinarteriae reticulares* (*luo* 絡), comprising
15 (*sinarteriae*) *reticulares* ("reticular conduits"), *luo* (*-mo*) 絡脈;
an unspecified number of (*sinarteriae*) *parareticulares* ("reticular branch conduits"), *pieh-luo* 別絡;
an unspecified number of (*sinarteriae*) *reticulares parvulae* ("reticular conduits of the third generation"), *sun-luo* 孫絡.

This system of sinarteries within the body connects to the orbs, and at the surface of the body ends in
12 (*sinarteriae*) *nervocardinales* ("muscle conduits"), *ching-chin* 經筋,
12 *cutis regiones* ("skin zones"), *p'i-pu* 皮部.[17]

THE CARDINAL CONDUITS (*CARDINALES, CHING* 經)

Within the variegated fabric of the sinarteries the cardinal conduits (*ching-mo*), as their name indicates, serve the function of warp. This is true in particular of the cardinal conduits in

[16]*Su-wen* 56/479 and 63/553.
[17]See the *Chen-chiu-hsüeh chiang-i*, p. 29.

the narrow definition, the twelve energetic lines,[18] each directly connected to one of the twelve orbs. These twelve ca dinal conduits provide the supporting framework of the entire sin arteriological system.

FUNCTIONAL AND TOPOGRAPHIC COURSE

In taking an overall glance at the cour of the twelve cardinal conduits we shall first review the functional relations noted in connection with the orbisiconographic paradigms. To each *orbis aulicus* there corresponds a cardinal conduit of yang polarity (*cardinalis yang, yang ching* 陽經), and to each *orbis horrealis* there corresponds a yin cardinal conduit (*cardinalis yin, yin ching* 陰經). Each *orbis aulicus* (yang) is combined with an *orbis horrealis* (yin) to form a functional yoke. The functional cohesion between the two components of such a yoke is established by means of the cardinal conduits assigned to its outer orb (*species, piao*) and to its inner orb (*intima, li*). The rule is that each *cardinalis yang*, as an outer cardinal conduit (*cardinalis speciei, piao-ching* 表經), belongs (*shu* 屬) to an *orbis aulicus* and attaches to (*luo* 絡) a complementary *orbis horrealis*; each *cardinalis yin*, as an inner cardinal conduit (*cardinalis intimae, li-ching* 裏經) belongs to an *orbis horrealis* and attaches to (*luo*) a complementary *orbis aulicus*. In other words, every functional yoke is held together by the two functionally intertwined cardinal conduits belonging to the two orbs involved.

One example will suffice to illustrate this relationship. The *cardinalis yin maioris manus* belongs (*shu*) to the *orbis pulmonalis* (= *intima*) and attaches to (*luo*) the *orbis intestini crassi* (= *species*). Inversely, the *cardinalis splendoris yang manus* belongs to the *orbis intestini crassi* (= *species*) and attaches to the *orbis pulmonalis* (= *intima*).

For the topographical description of the cardinal conduits a number of criteria must be taken into account: (1) the triple division head/trunk/extremities, (2) the distinction above/ below, (3) the distinction dorsal/frontal, and (4) the direction of the conduit.

Within the trunk, the diaphragm (*ko* 膈) marks the border between above (yang) and below (yin). In addition, the interior or inner side corresponds to yin, and the exterior or

[18]See pp. 216ff below.

outward side corresponds to yang. This convention defines the course of the cardinal conduits on the extremities: cardinal conduits corresponding to the *orbes horreales* situated above the diaphragm (the *orbes cardialis, pericardialis et pulmonalis*) extend along the inward side of the upper extremities, and the cardinal conduits corresponding to the *orbes horreales* situated below the diaphragm (the *orbes hepaticus, lienalis, et renalis*) run along the inward side of the lower extremities. Each inner cardinal conduit meets at the tips of the fingers or toes with its complementary outer conduit (*cardinalis speciei*). Thus the cardinal conduits of the *orbes intestini crassi et tenuis atque tricalorii* (the complements of the *orbes cardialis, pericardialis, et pulmonalis*) extend along the outward side of the upper extremities, whereas the conduits corresponding to the *orbes felleus, stomachi, et vesicalis* (the complements of the *orbes hepaticus, lienalis, et renalis*) extend over the outward side of the lower extremities. (Fig. 19).

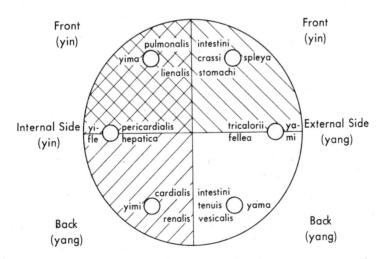

Fig. 19

The figure represents a cut through a dextral extremity viewed from above. The large, enclosing circle marks the diameter of the extremity, and the small circles correspond to the conduits. The lettering above the circles refers to conditions on an upper extremity, and the lettering below, to conditions on the lower extremity. The names of complementary orbs and cardinal conduits always show up on the same line.

For the extension of the cardinal conduits on the head, the rule is that the head, situated on top (yang), is the junction (*conventus, hui* 會) of all yang cardinal conduits. Thus the *cardinales yang manuum* (yang conduits of the hands) extend from the hands to the head, and the *cardinales yang pedum* (yang conduits of the feet) extend from the head to the feet. On the head the *cardinales yang minoris* preponderantly extend over the lateral and temporal parts, the *cardinales splendoris yang* extend mainly over the facial region, and the *cardinales yang maioris* extend generally over the occipital part and over the top of the skull (Fig. 20) regardless of their association with hands or feet.

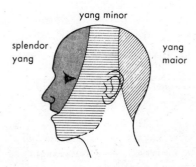

yang minor

splendor
yang

yang
maior

Fig. 20

Concerning the course of the cardinal conduits over the trunk, the rule is that the front of the trunk is yin and the back is yang. Thus the yang cardinal conduits extending from the head to the feet run over the back and the lateral regions (with the exception of the *cardinalis stomachi splendoris yang pedis*, which extends over the abdominal side). The *cardinales yin manuum* extend from the breast to the hands, and the *cardinales yin pedum* extend from the feet to the breast (*pectus, hsiung* 胸).

The directions of the cardinal conduits (*cardinales*) are shown schematically in Fig. 21. The yang cardinal conduits are rep-

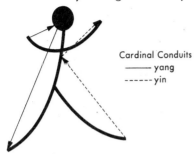

Cardinal Conduits
——— yang
- - - - - yin

Fig. 21

resented by solid lines, and the yin cardinal conduits by dotted lines. This figure already suggests that the orbs, connected by their respective cardinal conduits, constitute a closed energetic circuit, which we shall now consider in its entirety.

THE CIRCULATION OF ENERGY IN THE CARDINAL SINARTERIES

According to Chinese medical theories, several forms of energy participate in this circulation:

1. *Ch'i,* active or activated configurational energy, synthetized in the *orbis pulmonalis* from the *ch'i caeleste* (drawn in with the breath) and the *ch'i genuinum* present in the *calorium superius,* the chest. This configurational energy is communicated as a dynamic impulse to the *ch'i constructivum* (*ying*) of the *orbis pulmonalis* and thence to that of the other orbs.

2. *Mo,* the active aspect of a structive form of energy (*ch'i*). In its manifestation the pulse it dynamizes the *hsüeh* and induces its circulation.

3. *Ying,* constructive energy (*ch'i constructivum*), corresponding to the subtle components distilled from food within the *orbis stomachi.* It is conducted from the *calorium medium,* the functions of which overlay those of the *orbis stomachi,* into the *cardinalis pulmonalis,* whence it participates in the circulation of energy essentially maintained by the *ch'i constructivum.*[19]

[19]*Ling-shu* 18/1077 and the commentary in the *Ling-shu* 16/1070; *Su-wen* 18/108.

4. *Hsüeh,* individually specific structive energy, which, according to the definition given in *Ling-shu* 30/1153, coincides with *ying* at least in point of origin and principal qualities.[20] *Hsüeh* represents the most pronouncedly concrete aspect of the *ch'i constructivum* and hence to a limited extent is equivalent to blood. Its circulation and quantity are controlled by the *orbes cardialis et hepaticus.*[21] The circulation of the *ch'i constructivum* through

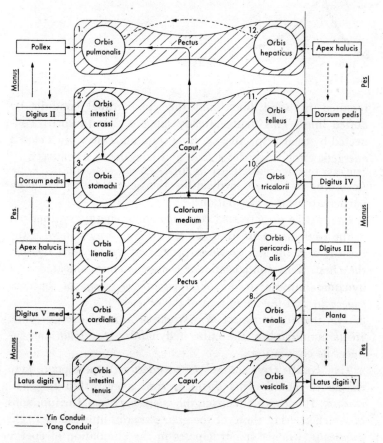

Fig. 22

[20]This problem has been discussed on p. 189 above.
[21]See the earlier description of these orbs.

the system of the orbs and their respective cardinal conduits is minutely described in *Ling-shu* 16/1070. Confining ourselves to details of immediate relevance the circulation may be represented as in Fig. 22.[22]

On the whole, the data in Fig. 22 conform perfectly to the systematic conventions. The only seams in the system calling for some clarification are the junctures between the *orbes horreales* within the chest (*pectus*) which are not referred to any conventional correspondence. Concerning the juncture of the *orbis lienalis* and the *orbis cardialis*, we are informed in the *Ling-shu*:[23] "From the *orbis lienalis* it [the *ch'i constructivum*] flows into the *orbis cardialis*." And further: "From the *orbis renalis* it flows into the outer [defensive perimeter] of the heart [i.e. the *orbis pericardialis*]"; also, "from the *orbis hepaticus* it ascends and flows into the *orbis pulmonalis*." Between the *orbes lienalis et cardialis* as well as between the *orbes renalis et pericardialis* no significant relations exist according to either the system of evolutive phases or of yinyang polarities. Between the *orbes hepaticus et pulmonalis* the relation corresponds to the "pathological" Sequence III of the E.P.s. Consequently we are here confronted with the exceedingly rare case in which gaps in the correspondence system are closed, without regard or even in contradiction to the speculative correspondences, solely on the basis of propinquity of the organs.

THE TOPOLOGY OF THE CARDINAL CONDUITS AND THEIR PHYSIOLOGICAL AND PATHOLOGICAL FUNCTIONS

Each of the twelve cardinal conduits carries the name of the orb with which it is primarily associated. Still, this designation of the cardinal conduit is only its chief emblem, a kind of physiological and pathological leitmotif, and not an absolute qualification. It is not rare that we come upon a foramen to which is attributed an important function with respect to an orb quite different from the one on whose cardinal conduit it is situated.[24]

[22]See also the *Chung-i-hsueh kai-lun*, p. 87.
[23]18/1077; see also the *Ling-shu ching pai-hua-chieh*, p. 186.
[24]To be discussed later in this chapter. Interesting examples in point are the attributions of the *conquisitoria abdominalia* to the separate *cardinales*.

If the primary qualitative determination of a *cardinalis* is its correspondence to a certain orb, a determination immediately second to this depends on the functions of the cardinal conduits. The connections between the general topology of a cardinal conduit and its physiological and pathological function may be gleaned from Table 20.

QUANTITATIVE DISTRIBUTION OF ENERGY WITHIN THE CARDINAL CONDUITS

Of no less importance than the order in which physiological energy is propagated through the system is the capacity of the orbs and their cardinal conduits for the two forms of physiological energy, *ch'i*, active configurational energy, and *hsüeh*, individually specific structive energy. According to concordant statements in several chapters of the *Nei-ching*,[25] energy is distributed among the cardinal conduits as shown in Table 21. These classical data[26] are interpreted by Chang Chih-ts'ung[27] in the sense that in complementary orbs united in a functional yoke and in their cardinal conduits the quality and quantity of the respective energies are likewise complementary.

Thus, for example, the conduits of *yin flectens hepaticus* and its associated orbis hepaticus contain little *ch'i* and much *hsüeh;* its complement, *yang minor vesicalis,* and its associated orb contain much *ch'i* and little *hsüeh.*

The only exception are the *cardinales splendoris yang* and the corresponding *orbes et cardinales stomachi et intestini crassi,* because these orbs (and especially the *orbis stomachi*) are considered to be the sphere from which *hsüeh* as well as *ch'i* originates. It is evident that not only Chang Chih-ts'ung but even the first authors of this theory of distribution were guided as much by empirical as by speculative and systematic motives. Aside from the meager correspondences just discussed, this theory is not interlinked with other parts of the correspondence system.

---

[25]*Su-wen* 24/252; *Ling-shu* 78/1370 and the parallels in the *Lei-ching* 15/312. In *Ling-shu* 65/1294 the quantities given for *yifle* and *yima* are inverted without plausible reason, and we emend in accordance with *Su-wen-shih* 3/122.

[26]In none of the editions of the *Nei-ching* consulted is there any commentary on these data by Wang Ping.

[27]Commentary in the *Su-wen* 24/252.

Table 20. The Topology and Physiological and Pathological Functions of the Cardinal Conduits

Cardinalis	Region	Pathology of the Orb	Specific Organ	Unspecific Pathology
Pulmonalis yima manus	Thorax, chest	Diseases of the *orbis pulmonalis*	Larynx	
Pericardialis yifle manus	Thorax, chest	Diseases of the *orbes cardialis et stomachi*		Psychoses
Cardialis yima manus		Diseases of the *orbis cardialis*		Psychoses
Intestini crassi spleya manus	Head, face	Diseases of the eyes, ears, nose	Teeth, mouth, larynx	Fever diseases
Tricalorii yami manus	Head, temples, chest, flanks	Diseases of the eyes, ears		Psychoses and fever diseases
Intestini tenuis yama manus	Head, neck	Diseases of the eyes, ears, nose	Larynx	Psychoses and fever diseases
Stomachi spleya pedis	Head, face	Diseases of the *orbes stomachi et intestinorum*	Larynx	Psychoses and fever diseases
Fellea yami pedis	Head, temples, chest, flanks	Diseases of the nose, ears, and eyes		Fever diseases
Vesicalis yama pedis	Head, neck, waist, back	Diseases of the nose		Psychoses and fever diseases
Lienalis yima pedis	Abdomen	Diseases of the *orbes intestinorum, stomachi et uteri*	Urogenital system	Diseases of the urogenital system
Hepatica yifle pedis	Abdomen	Diseases of the *orbes intestinorum* and of the genitals		Diseases of the urogenital system
Renalis yimi pedis	Abdomen	Diseases of the *orbes intestinorum et pulmonalis*	Larynx	Diseases of the urogenital system

Note: This table is based on *Chen-chiu-hsüeh chiang-i*, p. 106.

Table 21. Distribution of Energy among the Cardinal Conduits

Cardinalis	Conducts ch'i	Conducts hsüeh	Corresponds to the	orbis
yin flectens	little	much	pericardialis	hepaticus
yin minor	much	little	cardialis	renalis
yin maior	much	little	pulmonalis	lienalis
yang minor	much	little	tricalorii	felleus
splendor yang	much	much	intestini crassi	stomachi
yang maior	little	much	intestini tenuis	vesicalis

Medical authors from the Ming period to the present have perpetuated Chang's theory,[28] for knowledge of the normal quantities of active and structive energy in each cardinal conduit is helpful in acupuncture.

THE CARDINAL BRANCH CONDUITS (*SINARTERIAE PARACARDINALES, CHING-PIEH* 經別)

As their name indicates, the cardinal branch conduits are ramifications of the cardinal conduits, from which they branch off at the joints. Their chief function is to reinforce and to complete the circulatory framework of the twelve cardinal conduits and to multiply the functional contacts between the yin and yang cardinal conduits. Every cardinal branch conduit originates at a foramen of its cardinal conduit, situated on an extremity. From there it enters the depth of the trunk, branches into the corresponding orbs and organs, and then continues toward the outside of the head. Every yang branch conduit finally reunites with the cardinal yang conduit from which it has branched off; on the other hand, every yin branch conduit ends in a foramen situated on the complementary[29] inner conduit (*cardinalis speciei*). These rules suggest the close-knit interdependence between the functions and symptoms of the cardinal conduits and those of their corresponding branch conduits.

[28]*Chen-chiu-hsüeh chiang-i*, p. 41.
[29]Which consequently belongs (*shu*) to the complementary *orbis aulicus*, to which its own cardinal conduit is only attached (*luo*).

It is a common characteristic of all odd conduits that none of them belongs to (*shu* 屬) or is attached to (*luo* 絡) any particular orb. The designation "odd" thus derives from the fact that the odd circuits do not participate in any match of an outer (*cardinalis speciei*) with an inner cardinal conduit (*cardinalis intimae*). Some of the odd conduits are odd in another superficial sense; because they extend along an axis of symmetry of the body, unlike the cardinal conduits they have no mirrored counterpart. Within the system of conduits, the odd conduits fuction as equalizing reservoirs. Their principal role is to maintain at a constant physiological level the energy circulating in the conduit network. To achieve this, they must store surplus energy and release it into the system in the event of an energetic deficiency. Most odd conduits are equal to this task, although they have no foramina of their own (*foramina propria, ching-hsüeh* 經穴) but only foramina shared with other conduits (*foramina copulo-conventoria, chiao-hui-hsüeh*) 交會穴. They are consequently not traversed by the circulating constructive energy but only connected with it.[30] Exceptions are the two most important odd conduits, the *sinarteriae regens et respondens* (*tu-mo, jen-mo* 督脈, 任脈). Although they, too, are without direct connection to any orb, both have a number of *foramina propria*. Moreover, they are shunted into the circulation of constructive energy.[31] (Sometimes for practical purposes the *sinarteriae regens et respondens* are enumerated together with the twelve cardinal conduits, in which case a count of fourteen cardinal conduits (*shih-szu ching* 十四經) results. The course of the odd conduits is subject to no general rule.[32]

---

[30]For this reason they are aptly compared to lakes and marshes that are not affected by the current of the river which connects them, but which share its water level. See the *Chung-i-hsüeh kai-lun*, p. 105.

[31]See the sketch in the *Ling-shu ching pai-hua-chieh*, p. 187 and the *Chen-chiu-hsüeh chiang-i*, p. 35.

[32]See the descriptions of the odd conduits on pp. 273ff below.

THE RETICULAR CONDUITS (*SINARTERIAE RETICULARES, LUO-MO* 絡脈)

The fifteen reticular conduits, as their name suggests, are delicate, netlike branches that radiate from certain foramina of the twelve cardinal conduits and of the *sinarteriae regens et respondens;* in addition there is a Great Reticular Conduit of the *orbis lienalis* (*reticularis magna lienalis, p'i ta-luo* 脾大絡). The reticular conduits of the twelve cardinal conduits interlace to fill out the system of contacts between polarized cardinal conduits in the distal direction, and thus supplement the functions of the cardinal branch conduits (*paracardinales*). Whereas the latter originate from a sensitive point situated on a cardinal conduit proximal to the elbow or knee-joint, the reticular conduits originate at a sensitive point distal to these joints. The reticular conduit branching off an outer cardinal conduit (*cardinalis speciei*) extends toward the corresponding inner conduit (*cardinalis intimae*) and vice versa.

Unlike the cardinal branch conduits (*paracardinales*), the functions and symptoms of the *reticulares* are, within limits, independent of those of the corresponding *cardinales*, because of the etiological relations mentioned earlier.[33]

The "reticular branch conduits" (*parareticulares, pieh-luo* 別絡) are small irradiations that, at least in theory, issue forth from the cardinal conduits in each of the "365 joints of the body"[34] and that, in the vicinity of the joints, supply constructive energy to the flesh, bones, and skin.

Finally, the "reticular conduits of the third generation" (*reticulares parvulae, sun-luo* 孫絡) constitute an even more delicate capillary network completing that of the other reticular conduits. Although the *reticulares* and *parareticulares* are clearly distinct in their functions and their course, their designations are sometimes confused in the literature, even of recent date. Quite frequently the fifteen *reticulares*, most of which originate in the cardinal conduits, are called "reticular branch conduits" (*pieh-luo*) and, inversely, the smaller reticular branch conduits are sometimes called "reticular conduits" (*reticulares, luo*).[35]

[33]See pp. 202–203 above.
[34]*Ling-shu* 3/930; *Ling-shu ching pai-hua-chieh*, p. 34.
[35]For instance, in the *Chung-i-hsüeh kai-lun*, pp. 83, 135, *et passim*.

THE MUSCLE CONDUITS (*NERVOCARDINALES, CHING-CHIN* 經筋)

The twelve *nervocardinales* (muscle conduits, *ching-chin* 經筋) constitute conduits of energy communicating directly with the twelve *cardinales* but taking their entire course at or close to the surface of the body, without touching any orb. They originate at the tips of the extremities, skirt their joints and penetrate their muscles. The yang muscle conduits (*nervocardinales yang*) extend in the muscles covering the trunk and from there run to the head; the yin muscle conduits (*nervocardinales yin*) usually terminate in the muscles covering the trunk.

The *nervocardinales* are "knotted" (*chieh* 結) onto all the joints of the extremities. In addition, the *nervocardinales yang pedis* are knotted into the *os zygomaticum,* the *nervocardinales yin pedis* are knotted into the genitals, the *nervocardinales yang manus* meet in a knot on the lateral part of the *os frontale,* and the *nervocardinales yin manus* meet at the epigastrium approximately on the level of the diaphragm. The genitals are also the point of union between the three *nervocardinales yin pedis* and the *nervocardinalis splendoris yang pedis.* Finally, since the muscles (*"nervus"*) are conceived as the unfoldment (*perfectio*) of the *orbis hepaticus,*[36] its corresponding *nervocardinalis yin flectentis pedis* attaches (*luo*) to all other *nervocardinales.*

The chief function of the muscle conduits is the coordination and integration of the effort expended by the muscles and joints. Because of this and their indirect relationship to the orbs, they are associated with particular symptoms, amounting essentially to dysfunctions of the motive apparatus.

THE SKIN ZONES (*CUTIS REGIONES,* *P'I-PU* 皮部)

As has been explained at the beginning of this chapter, in Chinese medicine the skin is considered the foremost defense line against exogenous pathological influences (*heteropathica, hsieh*). It can assume this function because the defensive energy (*wei*) diffusing outside the conduits is active in it, and constructive energy (*ying*) is carried up to its surface by the three-level system of reticular conduits, which widely diffuse the energy

[36]See p. 120 above.

carried by the cardinal conduits at greater depths. The surface of the skin in the proximity of a cardinal conduit constitutes the so-called skin zone (*cutis regio, p'i pu* 皮部), a zone of diffusion for the functions and symptoms of the underlying *cardinalis*. The twelve skin zones corresponding to the twelve cardinal conduits have diagnostic significance for certain diseases.[37]

The Twelve Cardinal Conduits (Cardinales, ching 經) and Their Sensitive Points

It is the purpose of the following account to present in detail the systematic correspondences of Chinese medicine in the field of sinarteriology, as given in the medical classics and their interpretations. Our aim, as in the preceding chapters, is to furnish a reliable basis for further medical as well as philological research. For both purposes our account must be supplemented by drawings showing the courses of the conduits[38] and by practical guides to acupuncture.

The description of every cardinal conduit comprises four paragraphs: (1) its course according to the *Ling-shu* and the supplementary explanations given in the *Chen-chiu-hsüeh chiang-i;* (2) its symptoms (to the extent that the circulation of energy in a certain conduit is disturbed, its characteristic function comes into play; therefore general indications of symptoms also are part of the description of systematic correspondences); (3) its *foramina propria* (*ching-hsüeh* 經穴), the sensitive points (*foramina*) belonging to the cardinal conduit itself; (4) its *foramina copulo-conventoria* (*chiao-hui-hsüeh* 交會穴), the sensitive points which the cardinal conduit shares with one or more other conduits.

Each entry in the enumeration of the *foramina propria* will comprise these elements:

(*a*) The normative Latin designation of the foramen together with its mode of derivation (in parentheses)

---

[37]See *Su-wen* 56/476ff.

[38]There are quite a number of useful publications on the market: in Germany, for example, Bachmann, *Die Akupunktur, eine Ordnungstherapie* (the tables in the manual), and Busse, *Akupunkturfibel* (2d. ed.; Munich, 1954). The illustrations in this and subsequent sections are reproduced directly from the editions of the *Nei-ching chiang-i* (Figs. 23–34) and the *Chen-chiu-hsüeh chiang-i* (Figs. 25–81) which are cited in the bibliography.

The normative Latin equivalent of the Chinese name of a sensitive point may have been arrived at by one of five modes: (1) literal translation, (2) paraphrastic translation, (3) free choice of an equivalent in harmony with the system, (4) anatomical equivalent (by a Western anatomical name), (5) literal translation of a variant Chinese name of the sensitive point. Literal translation has been given preference, but if it proved impracticable for etymological, semantic, or mnemonic reasons, recourse has been taken to one of the other modes.

(*b*) The usual Chinese designation of the sensitive point, followed by a semicolon

(*c*) Variant designations used by particular authors only; variants that have been translated into Latin are asterisked.

(*d*) Latin equivalents for certain variant designations that better characterize the function of the foramen than does its usual name. Example: *prima clusarum = conquisitorium intestini tenuis*.

(*e*) An abbreviation showing the special function of the foramen. Many foramina assume a special function within the system of the cardinal conduits, as will be explained below.

(*f*) Separated by a dash from the first abbreviation, the ordinal number and abbreviated designation of the foramen according to the modern count,[39] with the classical count following in brackets[40]

Some data under (*e*) and (*f*) will be indicated by means of the following abbreviations and their combinations.

p   *foramen puteale* (*ching* 井)
e   *foramen effusorium* (*hsing* 滎)
i   *foramen inductorium* (*shu* 腧)
t   *foramen transitorium* (*ching* 經)
c   *foramen coniunctorium* (*ho* 合)

O   *foramen originalis* (*yüan* 原)
N   *foramen nexorium* (*luo* 絡)
R   *foramen rimicum* (*hsi* 郄)
I   *foramen inductorium dorsale* ([*pei-*]*shu* 背兪)
C   *foramen conquisitorium abdominale* ([*fu-*]*mu* 腹募)

cP   *cardinalis pulmonalis*
cPC *cardinalis pericardialis*

[39]As given in the *Chen-chiu-hsüeh chiang-i* and in the *Shu-hsüeh-hsüeh kai-lun*.
[40]As given in the *Chen-chiu ching-hsüeh t'u-k'ao*.

cC	*cardinalis cardialis*
cL	*cardinalis lienalis*
cH	*cardinalis hepatica*
cR	*cardinalis renalis*
cIC	*cardinalis intestini crassi*
cT	*cardinalis tricalorii*
cIT	*cardinalis intestini tenuis*
cS	*cardinalis stomachi*
cF	*cardinalis fellea*
cV	*cardinalis vesicalis*
Rg	*sinarteria regens*
Rs	*sinarteria respondens*

THE *CARDINALIS PULMONALIS YIN MAIORIS MANUS* (手太陰肺經)

COURSE

The *cardinalis pulmonalis* (Fig. 23) originates in the center of the stomach (*corpus ventriculi*), which is part of the *calorium medium*; descends in order to attach to the *orbis intestini crassi* (marked 1 in the figure), then again skirts the stomach up to the *pars cardiaca* (2); from where it penetrates the diaphragm (3) and unites with the *orbis pulmonalis* (4). From there it ascends again along the trachea, deflects into the transverse and reaches the extremity in the axilla (5). Then it runs in front of the *cardinales cardialis et pericardialis* along the inner side *(facies lateralis brachii)* of the arm (6) and down to the inner side of the elbow (7,8) into the *ostium pollicare* (*ts'un-k'ou* 寸口) (9) and from there across the thenar (10, 11) to the tip of the thumb (12). A ramification leaves the cardinal conduit proximally to the wrist and runs laterally on the inner side along the index finger to its tip (13).[41]

SYMPTOMS

Fullness and distension of the *orbis pulmonalis* [acute and chronic bronchitis, bronchiolitis],[42] cough, shortness of breath [asthma], pains in the *fossa supraclavicularis*, disturbed circulation, stiffness,

[41]*Ling-shu* 10/984.
[42]In this section *approximate* Western equivalents to the Chinese symptoms will be given in brackets.

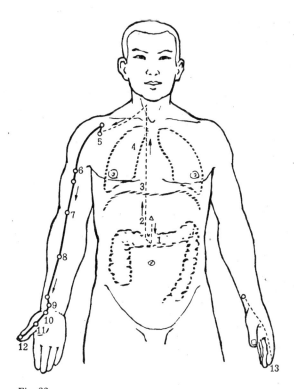

Fig. 23

pains in the forearm. Superabundant energy in the *orbis pulmonalis* entails pains in the shoulder and shoulderblade, colds in the chest with spontaneous perspiration, incontinent urination, *vento laesio* [influenza, hoarseness, blocked nasal passages, dry throat, phlegm from the bronchi], rattle in the throat, wheezing respiration through the nose and mouth. Deficiency of energy in the *orbis pulmonalis* entails pains in the shoulder and back, chills, short breath, abnormal color of the urine.[43]

Foramina propria cardinalis pulmonalis:
1 *Aula media* (1)

[43]*Chen-chiu-hsüeh chiang-i*, p. 48.

chung-fu 中府; ying chung-shu 膺中俞, fei-mu 肺募,* fu chung-
shu 府中俞, ying-shu 膺俞
Conquisitorium pulmonale
C—cP1 [cP2]

2 *Porta nubium* (1)
yün-men 雲門
cP2 [cP1]

3 *Aula caelestis* (1)
t'ien-fu 天府
cP3

4 *Candor coercitus* (1, 2)
chia-pai 俠白;[44] 夾白
cP4

5 *Lacus ulnaris* (1, 5)
ch'ih-tse 尺澤; kuei-t'ang 鬼堂, kuei-shou 鬼受
c—cP5

6 *Extremitas cavi* (1)
k'ung-tsui 孔最[45]
R—cP6

7 *Lacunae* (1, 2)
lieh-ch'üeh 列缺; t'ung-hsüan 童玄, wan-lao 腕勞
N—cP7

8 *Emissarium transitorium* (1)
ching-ch'ü[46] 經渠
t—cP8

9 *Vorago maior* (1)
t'ai-yüan 太淵; kuei-hsin 鬼心, t'ai-chüan 太泉
Oi—cP9

10 *Linea piscis* (1, 2)
yü-chi 魚際
e—cP10

11 *Metallum structivum* (2)
shao-shang[47] 少商; kuei-hsin 鬼信

[44]夾俠 means "to hem in from both sides," "to press together"; *coercere*: to squeeze together, to press.
[45]最＝極.
[46]*Ch'ü* 渠 = drain, "gutter"; *emissarium* = drain.
[47]The use of musical emblems for the notation of energetic qualities has been

p—cP11
Foramen copulo-conventorium cardinalis pulmonalis:
Aula media (chung-fu)
[cP1] = *Conventus cardinalium yin maioris manus et pedis*

THE *CARDINALIS INTESTINI CRASSI SPLENDORIS YANG MANUS* (手陽明大腸經)

COURSE
The *cardinalis intestini crassi* (Fig. 24) originates at the tip

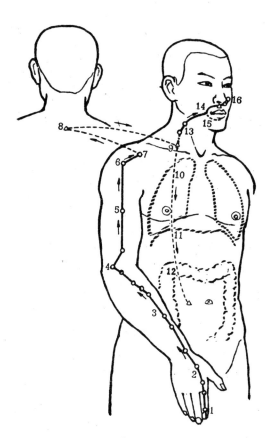

Fig. 24

of the index finger (1), then runs along the dorsal side of the index facing the thumb, traverses the *valles coniunctae* [*interstitium ossum metacarpalium I et II*] (2), continues upward in the flesh of the *flexores pollicis* (3), hence along the outward side of the forearm, skirts the elbow outside (4), extends along the outer side of the upper arm (5), runs through the cleft between acromnion and clavicula (6, 7) to the posterior border of the sternocleidomastoideus to the junction of the six yang cardinal conduits (8). From there the *cardinalis* descends again through the *fossa supraclavicularis* (9), attaches to the *orbis pulmonalis* (10), traverses the diaphragm (11), and unites with the *orbis intestini crassi* (12).

A ramification of the *cardinalis* issues forth from the *fossa supraclavicularis* (9), extends upward across the throat and posterior part of the mandible (13) and its alveoli to the maxilla (14), whence it emerges on the upper lips, meets its counterpart on the philtrum (15), and terminates laterally below the nostrils (16).[48]

SYMPTOMS

Toothache, swollen throat. This sinartery influences all dyscratic diseases,[49] such as yellow scleras, dryness in the mouth, blocked nasal passages, nosebleed, hoarseness [phthisic or luetic], pains in the shoulder and deltoid, and pains and disability of the thumb and index finger. In case of superabundance of energy the symptoms are swellings and heat in the regions touched by the conduit; in case of exhaustion of energy, shivering, inability to get warm.

Foramina propria cardinalis intestini crassi:

1 *Yang extremum* (5)

 shang-yang 商陽; *chüeh-yang* 絕陽*

 p—cICl

---

discussed on p. 70 above. The emblem *shang* 商 corresponds to the E.P. Metal.

[48]*Ling-shu* 10/990.

[49]Brought on by a disharmonious relation between yin and yang fluids (*chin* and *yeh*).

2 *Interstitium alterum* (1)
erh-chien[50] 二間; *chou-ku* 周谷, *chien-ku* 間谷
e—cIC2

3 *Interstitium tertium* (1)
san-chien 三間, *shao-ku* 少谷, *hsiao-ku* 小谷
i—cIC3

4 *Valles coniunctae* (1)
ho-ku 合谷; *hu-k'ou* 虎口, *han-k'ou* 含口, *ho-ku* 合骨
O—cIC4

5 *Rivulus yang* (1)
yang-hsi 陽谿; *chung-k'uei* 中魁
t—cIC5

6 *Pervium obliquum* (1)
p'ien-li 偏歷[51]
N—cIC6

7 *Amnis fovens* (1)
wen-liu[52] 溫溜; *she-t'ou* 蛇頭, *ni-chu* 逆注, *wen-liu* 溫留,
ti-t'ou 地頭, (*t'uo-t'ou* 沱頭), *ch'ih-t'ou* 池頭
R—cIC7

8 *Angustiae inferae manus* (1, 5)
hsia-lien[53] 下廉; *shou-chih hsia-lien* 手之下廉
cIC8

9 *Angustiae superae manus* (1, 5)
shang-lien 上廉; *shou chih shang-lien* 手之上廉*
cIC9

10 *Vicus tertius manus* (1, 5)
san-li 三里; *shou san-li* 手三里,* *shang-san-li* 上三里, *kuei-hsieh*
鬼邪
cIC10

11 *Stagnum curvum* (1)
ch'ü-ch'ih 曲池; *kuei-ch'en* 鬼臣, *yang-tse* 陽澤, *kuei-t'ui* 鬼腿
c—cIC11

---

[50]*Chien* 間 = hiatus, interstice, in Latin: *interstitium*.
[51]*Li* 歷 = *pervium* = passage-way.
[52]*Liu* 溜 = quickly flowing water; *amnis* = torrent, current, waters.
[53]In the *Shuo-wen*, p. 449, *lien* 廉 is explained as an antonym of *kuang*("wide,"
"vast"). Thus it means "narrow," "to draw together," "to collect."

12 *Cella cubiti* (1)

chou-chiao[54] 肘窌; *chou-liao* 肘髎, *chou-chien* 肘尖

cIC12

13 *Vicus quintus manus* (1)

wu-li 五里; *shou chih wu-li* 手之五里,* *ch'ih chih wu-li* 尺之五里, *ta-chin* 大禁

cIC13

14 *Latus lacerti* (2)

pi-ju[55] 臂臑; *t'ou-ch'ung* 頭衝, *ching-ch'ung* 頸衝

cIC14

15 *Promunturium humeri* (2, 5)

chien-yü[56] 肩髃; *chien-chien* 肩尖, *chien-ku* 肩骨, *chung chien-ching* 中肩井, *p'ien-ku* 偏骨, *yü-ku* 髃骨, *pien-chien* 扁肩, *pien-ku* 扁骨

cIC15 [cIC17]

16 *Os amplum* (1)

chü-ku[57] 巨骨

(*Clavicula*)

cIC16 [cIC18]

17 *Tripus caelestis* (1)

t'ien-ting 天鼎; 天頂

cIC17 [cIC19]

18 *Foramen aquaticum* (5)

fu-t'u 扶突, *shui-hsüeh* 水穴*

---

[54]The character 窌 *chiao* means "hole in the earth," "cellar" (in Latin *cella*) and in the *Chia-i-ching* is consistently used in the name of this and other *foramina*. Throughout the extant text of the *Nei-ching*, however, *chiao* 窌 is replaced by the anatomical term *liao* 髎, meaning *hiatus articulationis*, "cleft of a joint." Although this second variant at first sight appears the more plausible, only a minority of ancient and modern authors has adopted it. We likewise refrain from using it, because the foramina in the names of which the character occurs are seldom located precisely on the *hiatus articulationis*.

[55]*Ju* 臑 designates the medial or inner side of the upper arm. *Pi* 臂 designates the upper arm, the shoulder; the Latin term *lacertus* = muscle, upper arm.

[56]*Yü* 髃 designates the front side of the shoulder, or more precisely the "shoulder bone" that may be felt from the front.

[57]*Chü-ku* 巨骨 is the modern Chinese anatomical equivalent of the *nomen anatomicum* clavicula.

(*Processus adminiculans*)[58]
cIC18 [cIC20]
19 *Cella frumentaria* (1)
ho-chiao 禾窌; ho-liao 禾髎, ch'ang-p'in 長頻, ch'ang-liao 長髎,
ch'ang-yüeh 長顬, ch'ang-chuo 長顀
cIC19 [cIC22]
20 *Accipiens odores* (1)
ying-hsiang 迎香; ch'ung-yang 衝陽
(*Yang impedimentalis*)
cIC20 [cS1]

Foramina copulo-conventoria cardinalis intestini crassi:
Omnium defatigationum (*ta-chui*) [Rg14]
Canalis aquae (*shui-kou*) [Rg26]
Granarium terrestre (*ti-ts'ang*) [cS4]
Continens ventum (*ping-feng*) [cIT12]

THE *CARDINALIS STOMACHI SPLENDORIS YANG PEDIS* (足陽明經胃)

COURSE

This conduit (Fig. 25) originates at the base of the *ala nasi*
(in the *sulcus alae nasi*) (1), ascends to the *radix nasi* (2), and from
there runs laterally to a foramen situated centrally under the
eye (3), where it unites with the *cardinalis vesicalis yang maioris
pedis* (3). It then continues downward in the *sulcus naso-labialis,*
enters and again leaves the maxilla (4), skirts the corner of the
mouth (5) and the lower lip up to its middle (*foramen recipiens
liquoris,* Rs24) (6), there reverses its course and reaches the
lower border of the mandible (7), from where it ascends again
through the *interstititum articulationis mandibulae* (8), crosses the
os zygomaticum (9) and reaches the border of hair on the temple
(10). A ramification of the *cardinalis* issues forth from the
foramen magnum accipiens (cS5), extends downward over the
lateral region of the throat (12), and enters the *fossa supraclavicularis* rather medially from above (13); there it penetrates into
the trunk, traverses the diaphragm (14), unites with the *orbis*

[58] *T'u* 突 = *processus; adminiculare* = to support (on piles).

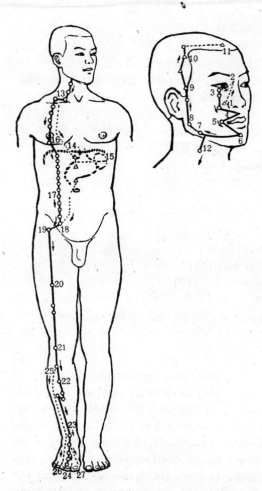

Fig. 25

stomachi, and attaches to the *orbis lienalis* (15). A direct continuation of the *cardinalis stomachi* extends from the *fossa supraclavicularis* (13) to the *linea mamillaris* (16). Shortly behind the nipple it deviates from this somewhat medially toward the *linea parasternalis* which (as well as its supposed continuation) it then follows downward (17) to the *foramen impedimentale ch'i* (cS30) (18) situated on the upper border of the inguinal region. A ramification of the continuation of this conduit originates in the pyloric part of the stomach, descends within the abdomen (18), and reaches the continuation in the *foramen impedimentale ch'i* (cS30). From there the conduit continues to the front of the upper leg (*m. rectus femoris*) (19, 20), runs through the patella (or its lateral margin (21) to the *margo tibiae* (22) from where it extends (23) across the middle dorsum of the foot and along the metatarsal of the third toe to the tip of the second toe (24). Another ramification of the continuation leaves the conduit three inches below the patella (25) and ends in the lateral commissure of the middle toe (26); still another goes out from the ramification, enters the commissure of the hallux, and ends at the tip of the hallux (27).[59]

SYMPTOMS

Severe chills, groaning, frequent sneezes, dark complexion. At the beginning of disease, aversion to people and heat; the patient starts at clapping noises and shows a tendency to withdraw from all human intercourse and shut up windows and doors tightly. During the crisis there is a desire to ascend heights, to chant, to run off without proper clothing. Sounds in the epigastrium, distended abdomen [enteritis], *flexus cruris* [*ulcera cruris*]. This sinartery influences all diseases associated with disturbances of the individually specific structive energy (*hsüeh*), such as raving madness, malaria, high fever, violent transpiration, colds with clogged nose, nosebleed, bleeding, sore lips, hoarseness [phthisic and luetic], swollen throat, abdominal hydropsy, pains and swellings of the knee, pains in the chest and breasts and in the leg, especially in the *mm. rectum*

[59]*Ling-shu* 10/993.

femoris et tibialis anterior and on the dorsum of the foot, and disability of the middle finger.

In the case of superabundant energy, the patient experiences heat effusions all over the abdomen, powerful digestive activities and frequent hunger, and yellow urine. In case of deficiency of energy there are abdominal chills, shivering, and cold in the *orbis stomachi* with ensuing plethora [gastritis, gastroenteritis].

Foramina propria cardinalis stomachi:

1 *Recipiens lacrimarum* (1)
  ch'eng-ch'i 承泣; *mien-liao* 面髎, *hsi-hsüeh* 䜌穴, 谿穴, *yang-ch'i* 羕泣, *mien-chiao* 面窌
  cS1 [cS2]

2 *Margo zygomaticus* (4)
  szu-pai 四白
  cS2 [cS3]

3 *Cella ampla* (1)
  chü-chiao 巨窌; *chü-liao* 巨髎
  cS3 [cS4]

4 *Granarium terrestre* (1)
  ti-ts'ang 地倉; *hui-wei* 會維, *wei-wei* 胃維
  cS4 [cS5]

5 *Magnum accipiens* (1)
  ta-ying 大迎; *sui-k'ung* 髓孔
  cS5 [cS7]

6 *Maxilla* (1,2)
  chia-ch'e 頰車; *chi-kuan* 機關, *ya-ch'e* 牙車, *kuei-ch'uang* 鬼牀, *ch'ü-ya* 曲牙, *chi-men* 機門, *kuei-lin* 鬼林
  cS6 [cS8]

7 *Clusa inferior* (1)
  hsia-kuan[60] 下關
  cS7 [cS8]

8 *Retinens capiti* (1)
  t'ou-wei 頭維; *t'ou-feng* 頭縫, *sang-ta* 顙大
  cS8 [cF2]

---

[60]The Latin word *clusa* (*clausa*) = defile. It etymologically approximates

9 *Accipiens hominum* (1)
  jen-ying 人迎; *t'ien wu-hui* 天五會, *wu-hui* 五會
  (*Philtrum*)
  cS9 [cS10]

10 *Porta aquae* (5)
  shui-t'u 水突; *shui-men* 水門,* *shui-t'ien* 水天
  (*Processus aquaticus*)
  cS10 [cS11]

11 *Domus ch'i* (1)
  ch'i-she 氣舍
  cS11 [cS12]

12 *Fossa supraclavicularis* (4)
  ch'üeh-p'en 缺盆; *t'ien-kai* 天蓋, *ch'ih-kai* 尺蓋
  (*Scutella egentis*)
  cS12 [cS13]

13 *Ostium ch'i* (1)
  ch'i-hu 氣戶
  cS13 [cS14]

14 *Aerarium* (2)
  k'u-fang 庫房
  cS14 [cS15]

15 *Tecti pluteus* (1)[61]
  wu-i 屋翳
  cS15 [cS16]

16 *Fenestra thoracis* (1,2)
  ying-ch'uang 膺窗
  cS16 [cS17]

17 *Medium mammae* (1,4)
  ju-chung 乳中; *tang-ju* 當乳
  cS17 [cS18]

18 *Radix mammae* (1)
  ju-ken 乳根
  cS18 [cS19]

---

the twofold meaning of the Chinese term *kuan* 關: (1) natural narrows, defile; (2) fortification, gate (often fortified) for the control of traffic.

[61]Literally "sheltering roof of an abode"; *i* 翳 designates the "feather screen of a ritual dancer" and has the derived meaning "to hide," "to screen."

19 *Non licet!* (1)
   pu-jung 不容
   cS19 [cS20]

20 *Recipiens plenitudinis* (1)
   ch'eng-man 承滿
   cS20 [cS21]

21 *Porta septi* (1)
   liang-men[62] 梁門
   cS21 [cS22]

22 *Porta clusae* (1)
   kuan-men 關門; *kuan-ming* 關明
   cS22 [cS23]

23 *Unum maius* (5)
   t'ai-i 太乙; 太一
   cS23 [cS24]

24 *Porta carnis lubrica* (1)
   hua-jou-men 滑肉門; *hua-yu-men* 滑幽門, *hua-jou* 滑肉
   cS24 [cS25]

25 *Cardo caeli* (1)
   t'ien-shu 天樞; *ch'ang-hsi* 長谿, *ku-men* 谷門, *ch'ang-ku* 長谷,
   ta-ch'ang-mu 大腸募,* *hsün-chi* 循際, *hsün-yüan* 循元, *pu-yüan*
   補元
   (*Conquisitorium intestini crassi*)
   C^cIC—cS25 [cS26]

26 *Tumulus externus* (1)
   wai-ling 外陵
   cS26 [cS27]

27 *Norma magna* (1)
   ta-chü[63] 大巨; *yeh-men* 腋門
   cS27 [cS28]

28 *Via aquae* (1)
   shui-tao 水道
   cS28 [cS29]

---

[62] *Liang* 梁 has among others the meaning of a "weir erected to facilitate fishing"; *septum* = dividing wall, partition.
[63] *Chü* 巨 is used in the place of *chü* 矩 = a carpenter's square.

29 *Vallis rivuli* (5)
   kuei-lai 歸來; *hsi-hsüeh* 谿穴, *hsi-ku* 谿谷*
   cS29 [cS30]
30 *Impedimentale ch'i* (1)
   ch'i-ch'ung[64] 氣衝, *ch'i-chieh* 氣街
   cS30 [cS31]
31 *Clusa femoralis* (1)
   pi-kuan 髀關
   cS31 [cS32]
32 *Lepus subreptus* (1)
   fu-t'u 伏兔; *wai-ch'iu* 外丘, *wai-kou* 外勾
   cS32 [cS33]
33 *Forum yin* (1)
   yin-shih 陰市; *yin-ting* 陰鼎
   cS33 [cS34]
34 *Monticulus septi* (1)
   liang-ch'iu 梁丘; *k'ua-ku* 跨骨
   R—cS34 [cS35]
35 *Nasus vituli* (1)
   tu-pi 犢鼻
   cS35 [cS36]
36 *Vicus tertius pedis* (1, 2)
   san-li 三里; *tsu san-li* 足三里,* *hsia san-li* 下三里, *hsia-ling* 下陵,
   kuei-hsieh 鬼邪
   c—cS36 [cS37]
37 *Angustiae superiores aggeri ampli* (1)
   chü-hsü shang-lien[65] 巨虛上廉; *shang chü-hsü* 上巨虛 *shang-lien* 上廉
   cS37 [cS38]

[64]The term *ch'ung* 衝 (冲) originally meant a highway. In medicine, it analogously designates a "main passage for energy" and is applied either to a foramen or a complete sinartery. As normative equivalent we have introduced the neologism *impedimentalis* (adjective and noun) derived from the Latin *impedimenta*, "baggage train."
[65]*Hsü* 虛 here is used in place of *hsü* 墟, "tumulus," "heaped-up earth," "wall," "embankment"; the Latin term *agger* = piled-up earth.

38 *Os relaxationis* (1,2)
   t'iao-k'ou[66] 條口
   cS38 [cS39]
39 *Angustiue inferiores aggeri ampli* (1)
   chü-hsü hsia-lien 巨虛下廉; *hsia chü-hsü* 下巨虛, *hsia-lien* 下廉
   cS39 [cS40]
40 *Abundantia* (1)
   feng-lung 豐隆
   N—cS40 [cS41]
41 *Rivulus liberans* (1)
   chieh-hsi 解谿
   t—cS41 [vS42]
42 *Yang impedimentalis* (1)
   ch'ung-yang 衝陽; *fu-yang* 趺陽, *hui-yüan* 會原, *hui-ku* 會骨,
   hui-ch'ü 會屈, *hui-yüan* 會源
   O—cS42 [cS43]
43 *Vallis demersum* (1)
   hsien-ku 陷谷
   i—cS43 [cS44]
44 *Vestibulum internum* (1)
   nei-t'ing 內庭
   e—cS44 [cS45]
45 *Laetitia repressa* (1)
   li-tui[67] 厲兌
   p—cS45 [cS46]

Foramina copulo-conventoria cardinalis stomachi:
Canthus nasalis (*ching-ming*) [cV1]
Clusa superior (*shang-kuan*) [cF3]
In angulo sphenoidalis (*han-yen*) [cF4]

---

[66]One of the meanings of *t'iao* 條 is "to relax," "to grow limp." The term probably points to the paretic limpness in the lower extremities that may be influenced by the treatment of this foramen.

[67]Used in the name of a sensitive point, the word *tui* 兌 always points to the ideas associated with the *I-ching* trigram or hexagram of the same name: joy, cheerfulness, merriment, in Latin: *laetitia*. (This component also occurs in the name of the foramen Rg27 below.)

Foramen medullae (*hsüan-lu*) [cF5]
Lobulus suspensus (*hsüan-li*) [cF6]
Canalis aquae (*shui-kou*) [Rg26]
Vestibulum shen (*shen-t'ing*) [Rg24]
Conventus omnium (*pai-hui*) [Rg20]
Omnium defatigationum (*ta-chui*) [Rg14]
Foramen cardiacum (*shang-kuan*) [Rs13]
Conquisitorium stomachi (*chung-kuan*) [Rs12]
Recipiens liquoris (*ch'eng-chiang*) [Rs24]
Accipiens odores (*ying-hsiang*) [cS1]

THE *CARDINALIS LIENALIS YIN MAIORIS PEDIS* (足太陰脾經)

COURSE
This conduit (Fig. 26) originates at the apex of the big toe (1) and from there tends inward medially, running along the "border of white and red flesh." After crossing the head of the first metatarsal (2) it reaches the distal rim of the *malleolus medialis* (3). From there it continues medially upward on the lower leg (4), running along the posterior border of the tibia (5), where it crosses the *cardinalis hepatica yin flectentis pedis* (6). Hence it ascends on the inner medial side of the knee and upper leg (7) and penetrates the inguinal region into the abdomen (8), where it unites with the *orbis lienalis* and attaches to the the *orbis stomachi* (9). It then traverses the diaphragm and (10), clinging to the esophagus (11), ascends to the root of the tongue (12), in which it spreads. Its ramification begins in the *orbis stomachi* (13), likewise traverses the diaphragm, and terminates in the heart (*orbis cardialis*) (14).[68]

SYMPTOMS
Swellings and pains at the root of the tongue; desire to vomit after eating; pains in the stomach; distended abdomen; puffing and eructations; evacuation of flatulence and of feces accompanied by a feeling of relief; general fatigue and asthenia. Other symptoms include inability to move about, anorexia, circulatory disorders, pains in the heart, diarrhea or obstipation, retention of urine, icterus, insomnia, swellings on the

[68]*Ling-shu* 10/997f.

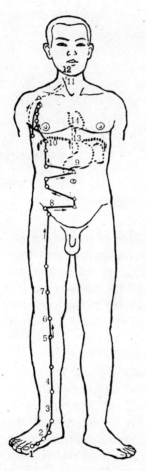

Fig. 26

medial side of the upper leg and knee, cold extremites due to *flexus*,[69] and disability of the big toe.

Foramina propria cardinalis lienalis:
1 *Candor occultus* (1)
   yin-pai 隱白; *kuei-lei* 鬼壘, *kuei-yen* 鬼眼, *yin-pai* 陰白
   p—cL1
2 *Urbs magna* (1)
   ta-tu 大都
   e—cL2
3 *Candidum maius* (1)
   t'ai-pai 太白
   Oi—cL3
4 *Caput metatarsalis hallucis* (4)
   kung-sun 公孫
   N—cL4
5 *Monticulus tali* (3)
   shang-ch'iu 商丘; 商坵
   t—cL5
6 *Copulatio trium yin* (1)
   san-yin-chiao 三陰交; *ch'eng-ming* 承命, *t'ai-yin* 太陰, *hsia chih san-li* 下之三里
   cL6
7 *Vallis percolationis* (1)
   lou-ku 漏谷; *t'ai-yin-luo* 太陰絡
   (*Nexorium yin maioris*)
   cL7
8 *Domus lienalis* (5)
   ti-chi 地機; *p'i-she* 脾舍,* *ti-chi* 地箕
   R—cL8
9 *Fons tumuli yin* (1)
   yin-ling-ch'üan[70] 陰陵泉; *yin chih ling-ch'üan* 陰之陵泉
   c—cL9
10 *Mare hsüeh* (1)
   hsüeh-hai 血海; *hsüeh-hsi* 血郗, *pai-ch'ung-wo* 百蟲窩
   cL10

[69]See above, p. 38.
[70]The foramen *yang-ling-ch'üan* is the *coniunctorium* of the *orbis felleus* [cF34].

11 *Porta sagittarii* (2)
 chi-men 箕門
 cL11

12 *Porta impedimentalis* (1)
 ch'ung-men 衝門; *tz'u-kung* 慈宮, *shang tz'u-kung* 上慈宮,
 ch'ien-chang-men 前章門
 cL12

13 *Domus aulicus* (1)
 fu-she 府舍
 cL13

14 *Nodus abdominalis* (1)
 fu-chieh 腹結; *fu-ch'ü* 腹屈, *ch'ang-k'u* 腸窟, *ch'ang-chieh* 腸結,
 yang-k'u 陽窟
 cL14

15 *Transversum magnum* (1)
 ta-heng 大橫; *shen-ch'i* 腎氣, *jen-heng* 人橫
 cL15

16 *Aegritudo abdominis* (1, 3)
 fu-ai 腹哀; *ch'ang-ai* 腸哀, *ch'ang-ch'ü* 腸屈
 cL16

17 *Clusa fortunae* (5)
 shih-tu 食竇; *ming-kuan* 命關*
 cL17

18 *Rivulus caelestis* (1)
 t'ien-hsi 天谿
 cL18

19 *Rus pectoris* (1)
 hsiung-hsiang 胸鄉
 cL19

20 *Castra angularis* (3)
 chou-ying 周營; *chou-jung* 周榮
 cL20

21 *Nexorium magnum lienalis* (2)
 ta-pao 大包
 cL21

Foramina copulo-conventoria cardinalis lienalis:
Aula media (chung-fu) [cP1]
Conquisitorium hepaticum (ch'i-men) [cH14]
Sol et luna (jih-yüeh) [cF24]
Foramen pyloricum (hsia-kuan) [Rs10]
Prima clusarum (kuan-yüan) [Rs4]
Conquisitorium vesicale (chung-chi) [Rs3]

THE *CARDINALIS CARDIALIS YIN MINORIS MANUS* (手少陰心經)

COURSE

This conduit (Fig. 27) originates in the heart (1) and, after emerging, is connected with the entire system of the *orbis cardi-*

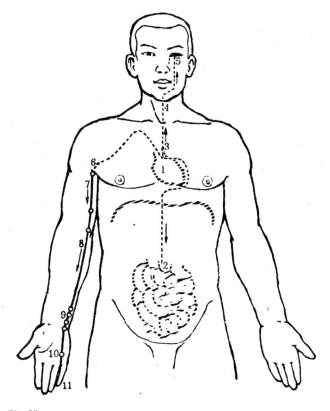

Fig. 27

alis. It traverses the diaphragm and attaches to the *orbis intestini tenuis* (2). A ramification originates in the *orbis cardialis* (3), extends upward along the esophagus (4), and links with the optical system (i.e., the eyeball and its surroundings) (5). The direct continuation of the *cardinalis* runs upward into the *orbis pulmonalis* and in the axilla (6) reaches the medial side of the arm, along which it descends behind the *cardinales pulmonalis et pericardialis* (7), crosses the elbow and forearm (8), and reaches the *caput* of the *os capitatum* (9). From there it runs through the palm (10) to the inner side of the little finger and terminates at its tip (11).[71]

SYMPTOMS

Parched throat and violent thirst, pains in the heart, contravection and *flexus* in the forearm [bad circulation, loss of feeling], pains and stiffness of the forearm, dim eyesight, pains in the chest and in the flanks, heat and pains in the palm.

Foramina propria cardinalis cardialis:

1 *Fons culminis* (1)
  chi-ch'üan 極泉
  cC1

2 *Fons caeruleus* (3)
  ch'ing-ling 青靈; *ch'ing-ling ch'üan* 青靈泉*
  cC2

3 *Mare minus* (1)
  shao-hai 少海; *ch'ü-chieh* 曲節
  c—cC3

4 *Foramen responsivum* (3)
  ling-tao 靈道
  t—cC4

5 *Vicus communicans* (1)
  t'ung-li 通里, 通理
  N—cC5

6 *Rimicum yin minoris* (2, 5)
  yin-hsi 陰郄; *shao-yin-hsi* 少陰郄,* *shih-kung* 石宮, *t'ung-kuan* 通關
  R—cC6

---

[71]*Ling-shu* 10/1001.

7 *Impedimentale laetitiae* (5)
shen-men 神門; *tui-ch'ung* 兌衝,* *chung-tu* 中都, *jui-chung* 銳中,
tui-ku 兌骨
Oi—cC7
8 *Aula minor* (1)
shao-fu 少府
e—cC8
9 *Impedimentale minus* (1)
shao-ch'ung 少衝; *ching-shih* 經始
p—cC9

THE *CARDINALIS INTESTINI TENUIS YANG MAIORIS MANUS* (手太陽小腸經)

COURSE

This conduit (Fig. 28) originates at the tip of the little finger (1) and runs along its lateral dorsal side and across the dorsum of the hand to the dorsal side of the wrist (2). There it traverses the cleft between the *os triquetum* and the *epicondylus medialis* (= *processus styloides ulnae*), in which lies the *foramen vallis yang* (cIT5). It continues through the ulnar antebrachial region to the posterior side of the elbow (3), traverses the cleft between the *olecranon* and the *epicondylus medialis humeri*. Then it ascends through the external brachial region (4) to the posterior side of the shoulder (5) and crosses the scapula (6) and the suprascapular nuchal and cervical regions (7) before penetrating through the *fossa supraclavicularis* (8) to the *orbis cardialis,* to which it attaches (9). From there it descends along the esophagus (10) and penetrates the diaphragm (11) to reach the *orbis stomachi* (12) and finally unites with the *orbis intestini tenuis* (13). A ramification runs from the *fossa supraclavicularis* (8) to the throat (14), crosses the *mandibula* (15) and the *os zygomaticum,* and reaches the *canthus lateralis* (16), from where it deviates to the ear (17). A further ramification branches off the one just described at the *mandibula* (15), extends in the direction of the nose (18), and finally ascends to the *canthus nasalis* (19, 20).[72]

SYMPTOMS

Sore throat, pains and swelling of the cervical muscles, drawing pains in the shoulders, broken feeling in the upper arm. All

[72]*Ibid.* 10/1004.

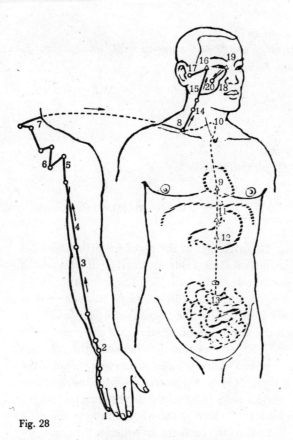

Fig. 28

symptoms associated with a dyscrasia of the structive fluids (*yeh*): hardness of hearing, dim eyesight, swellings in the mandibular regions, pains in the neck, shoulder blades, upper arms, and in the ulnar and antebrachial regions.

Foramina propria cardinalis intestini tenuis:
1 *Lacus minor* (1)
   shao-tse 少澤; *hsiao-chi* 小吉
   p—cIT1
2 *Vallis anterior* (1)
   ch'ien-ku 前谷; *shou t'ai-yang* 手太陽
   e—cIT2

3 *Rivulus posterior* (1)
  hou-hsi 後谿
  i—cIT3
4 *Foramen carpicum* (2)
  wan-ku 腕骨
  O—cIT4
5 *Vallis yang* (1)
  yang-ku 陽谷
  t—cIT5
6 *Senectus felix* (2,3)
  yang-lao 養老
  R—cIT6
7 *Adminiculans orthopathiam* (1)
  chih-cheng[73] 支正
° N—cIT7
8 *Mare parvum* (1)
  hsiao-hai 小海
  c—cIT8
9 *Rectum alae* (1)
  chien-chen 肩貞
  cIT9
10 *Inductorium lacerti* (1)
  nao-shu 臑俞
  cIT10
11 *Genus caeleste* (1)
  t'ien-tsung 天宗
  cIT11
12 *Continens ventum* (1)
  ping-feng 秉風
  cIT12
13 *Murus curvus* (1)
  ch'ü-yüan 曲垣
  cIT13
14 *Inductorium externum alae* (1)
  chien wai-shu 肩外俞
  cIT14 [cT14]

[73]*Chih* 支 = to support, to stay; *adminiculum* = stay, support.

15 *Inductorium medium alae* (1)
chien chung-shu 肩中俞
cIT15 [cT15]
16 *Fenestra caeli* (1)
t'ien-ch'uang 天窗; *ch'uang-lung* 窗籠, 窗聾, 窗龍
cIT16 [cIT13]
17 *Vultus caelestis* (1)
t'ien-jung 天容
cIT17 [cT19]
18 *Cella zygomatica* (1)
ch'üan-chiao 顴窌; *ch'üan-liao* 顴髎, *tui-ku* 兌骨
cIT18 [cIT14]
19 *Conclave auditus* (1)
t'ing-kung 聽宮; *to-so-wen* 多所聞
cIT19 [cIT15]

Foramina copulo-conventoria cardinalis intestini tenuis:
Omnium defatigationum (ta-chui) [Rg14]
Foramen cardiacum (shang-kuan) [Rs13]
Foramen pyloricum (hsia-kuan) [Rs10]
Canthus nasalis (ching-ming) [cV1]
Radius magnus (ta-chu) [cV11]
Pars addita (fu-fen) [cV41]
Cella harmoniae (ho-chiao) [cT22]
Cella pupillae (t'ung-tzu-chiao) [cF1]

THE *CARDINALIS VESICALIS YANG MAIORIS PEDIS* (足太陽膀胱經)

COURSE

This conduit (Fig. 29) originates in the *canthus medialis* (1) and first ascends across the forehead (2) to a junction on top of the skull (3). From there a branch extends to the upper tip of the ear (4). Its direct continuation penetrates the skull and attaches to the brain (5). It continues through the occipital and nuchal (6) regions to the scapula (7), descends parallel to the spine (7) along the median border of the muscles (8, 9) of the back, attaches to the *orbis renalis* (10), and unites with the

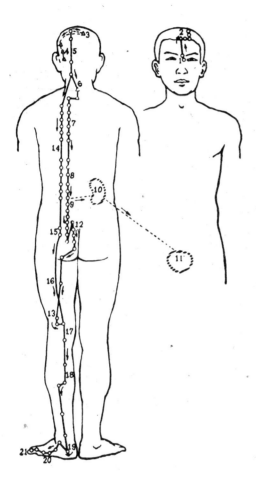

Fig. 29

orbis vesicalis (11). A ramification continues from the middle of
the back down to the *gluteus maximus,* at which it cuts back (12)
and redescends to end in the popliteal fossa (13). Another ramification leaves the cardinal conduit at the upper median part
of the scapula and first extends in an oblique lateral direction,
then reverts to the perpendicular direction and continues in
an approximate parallel to the spine (14). It crosses the waist
and the *gluteus maximus* (15) to the lateral part of the posterior

femoral region (16), deflects from the lateral posterior border of the knee into the hollow of the knee (popliteal fossa) (17), continues through the medial part of the posterior crural region down to the lower border of the calf (18), reverts to the lateral side of the lower leg, passes beside the *malleolus lateralis* to reach the heel (19), and meanders along the lateral border of the foot (20), ending at the tip of the small toe (21).[74]

SYMPTOMS

Violent headache; feeling as if the eyeballs are pressed out of their sockets; drawing pains in the occipital region; pains in the spine; broken feeling in the loins; stiffness of the hips and knees; feeling as if the calves were about to burst; stiffness and pains in the region of the *malleolus lateralis*. All symptoms associated with a dysfunction of the *nervus* [i.e. the locomotor muscles]: hemorrhoids, malaria, *chorea maniacalis*, epileptiform symptoms. Aching fontanels, dim eyesight, flowing tears, clogged nasal passages, cold in the head with acute coryza, nosebleed. Abnormal pains in the back of the head, back, loins, coccyx, hollow of the knee, calf, and foot; disability of the small toe.

Foramina propria cardinalis vesicalis:

1 *Canthus nasalis* (5,4)
   ching-ming 睛明; *lei-k'ung* 淚孔, 淚空, *ching-ming* 精明, *mu-nei-tzu* 目內眥,* *nei-tzu-wai* 內眥外
   cV1

2 *Stirps supercilii* (5)
   ts'uan-chu 攢竹; *shih-kuang* 始光, *yeh-kuang* 夜光, *ming-kuang* 明光, *yüan-chu* 員柱, *mei-chung* 眉中, *kuang-ming* 光明, *yüan-chu* 元柱, *mei-pen* 眉本,* *yüan-tsai* 員在, *mei-t'ou* 眉頭, *hsiao-chu* 小竹·
   cV2

3 *Impedimentale supercilii* (1)
   mei-ch'ung 眉衝
   cV3

4 *Impedimentale nasi* (5)

[74]*Ling-shu* 10/1006f.

ch'ü-ch'a 曲差; *pi-ch'ung* 鼻衝*
(*Deviatio curva*)
cV4

5 *Quinto loco* (1)
wu-ch'u 五處; *chü-ch'u* 巨處
(*Amplo loco*)
cV5

6 *Recipiens luminis* (1)
ch'eng-kuang 承光
cV6

7 *Caelo communicans* (1)
t'ung-t'ien 通天; *t'ien-chiu* 天臼, *t'ien-pai* 天白, *t'ien-po* 天伯
cV7

8 *Nectens recedentem* (1)
luo-ch'üeh 絡郄; *ch'iang-yang* 强陽, *nao-kai* 腦蓋, *luo-hsi* 絡郄
cV8

9 *Cervical iaspidis* (1)
yü-chen 玉枕
cV9

10 *Columna caeli* (1)
t'ien-chu 天柱
cV10

11 *Radius magnus* (1)
ta-chu[75] 大杼; *pei-shu* 背兪,* *pai-lao* 百勞
(*Inductorium dorsale*)
cV11

12 *Porta ventorum* (1)
feng-men 風門; *je-fu* 熱府*
(*Aula caloris*)
cV12

13 *Inductorium pulmonale* (1)
fei-shu 肺兪; *san-chiao chih chien* 三焦之間
cV13

14 *Inductorium yin flectentis* (1)
chüeh-yin-shu 厥陰兪; *ch'üeh-shu* 闕兪, *chüeh-shu* 厥兪
cV14

[75]*Chu* 杼 = shuttle of a loom, in Latin: *radius*.

15 *Inductorium cardiale* (1)
   hsin-shu 心兪; *pei-shu* 背兪, *wu-chiao chih chien* 五焦之間
   cV15

16 *Inductorium regentis* (1)
   tu-shu 督兪; *kao-i* 高益, *kao-kai* 高蓋
   cV16

17 *Inductorium praecordiale* (1)
   ko-shu 膈腧; *ch'i-chiao chih chien* 七焦之間
   cV17

18 *Inductorium hepaticum* (1)
   kan-shu 肝腧; *chiu-chiao chih chien* 九焦之間
   cV18

19 *Inductorium felleum* (1)
   tan-shu 膽腧
   cV19

20 *Inductorium lienale* (1)
   p'i-shu 脾腧; *shih-i chiao chih chien* 十一焦之間
   cV20

21 *Inductorium stomachi* (1)
   wei-shu 胃腧
   cV21

22 *Inductorium tricalorii* (1)
   san-chiao-shu 三焦腧
   cV22

23 *Inductorium renale* (1)
   shen-shu 腎腧; *kao-kai* 高蓋, *ching-kung* 精宮
   cV23

24 *Inductorium maris ch'i* (1)
   ch'i-hai-shu 氣海腧
   cV24

25 *Inductorium intestini crassi* (1)
   ta-ch'ang-shu 大腸腧
   cV26

26 *Inductorium prima clusarum* (1)
   kuan-yüan-shu 關元兪
   cV26

27 *Inductorium intestini tenuis* (1)

hsiao-ch'ang-shu 小腸俞
cV27

28 *Inductorium vesicale* (1)
p'ang-kuang-shu 膀胱俞
cV28

29 *Inductorium pro medio tergo* (1)
chung-lü-shu[76] 中膂俞; *chung-lü* 中膂, *chung-lü nei-shu* 內俞,
chi-nei shu 脊內俞, *hsüan-shu* 旋俞
cV29

30 *Inductorium anuli candidi* (1)
pai-huan-shu 白環俞; *yü-fang-shu* 玉房俞, *yü-huan-shu* 玉環俞
vV30

31 *Cella superior* (1)
shang-chiao 上窌; *shang-liao* 上髎
cV31

32 *Cella secunda* (1)
tz'u-chiao 次窌; *tz'u-liao* 沈髎
cV32

33 *Cella media* (1)
chung-chiao 中窌; *chung-liao* 中髎, *chung-k'ung* 中空
cV33

34 *Cella inferior* (1)
hsia-chiao 下窌; *hsia-liao* 下髎
cV34

35 *Yang conventi* (1)
hui-yang 會陽; *li-chi* 利機
cV35 [Rg3]

36 *Rima carnis* (5)
ch'eng-fu 承扶; *jou-hsi* 肉郄,* *yin-p'i-pu kuan* 陰關, *p'i-pu*
皮部, *p'i-hsi* 皮郄, *fu-ch'eng* 扶承, *ch'eng-fu p'i-pu* 承扶 皮部
cV36 [cV49]

37 *Porta femoris* (3,4)
yin-men 殷門
cV37 [cV50]

---

[76]The Chinese term *lü* 膂 designates the "flesh at both sides of the spine"
and corresponds approximately to the sacro-spinal system of the muscles of
the back, especially the longitudinal muscles.

38 *Rima superficialis* (1)
  fu-hsi 浮郄
  cV38 [cV51]

39 *Yang lacunae* (1)
  wei-yang[77] 委陽
  cV39 [cV52]

40 *Medium lacunae* (1)
  wei-chung 委中; *hsüeh-hsi* 血郄, *wei chung-yang* 委中央, *chung-hsi* 中郄, *hsi-chung* 郄中, *t'ui-wa* 腿凹, *ch'ü-ch'iu nei* 曲脉內
  c—cV40 [cV53]

41 *Pars addita* (1)
  fu-fen 附分
  cV41 [cV35]

42 *Ostium animae* (2,3)
  p'o-hu[78] 魄戶; *hun-hu* 魂戶
  cV42 [cV36]

43 *Venae et viscera* (2)
  kao-huang[79] 膏肓; *kao-huang shu* 膏肓俞
  cV43 [cV37]

44 *Atrium shen* (1)
  shen-t'ang[80] 神堂
  cV44 [cV38]

45 *Exoptatum!* (2)
  i-hsi[81] 譩譆; *wu-ch'ü-shu* 五胠俞
  cV45 [cV39]

46 *Clusa praecordialis* (1)
  ko-kuan 膈關
  cV46 [cV40]

---

[77]The term *wei* 委 applies to a place in which a course of water is dammed; *lacuna* = hollow, pond.

[78]The terms *p'o* and *hun* (in *hun-men*, no. 47) cannot be translated but only defined in technical contexts, as was explained on pp. 184–185 above. It is purely for mnemonic reasons that, on the basis of ideas suggested by authors such as C. G. Jung, the terms *animus* and *animae* are employed.

[79]*Huang* 肓 = "heart pit," vital nerve; *venae* = the very heart, marrow.

[80]Concerning the term *shen* see pp. 181–183 above.

[81]*I-hsi* 譩譆: an exclamation of pleasure and assent; *exoptatum!* = how desirable!, how agreeable!, just what could be wished for!

47 *Porta animi* (2)
   hun-men 魂門
   cV47 [cV41]
48 *Generale yang* (2)
   yang-kang[82] 陽綱
   cV48 [cV42]
49 *Domus phantasiae* (2)
   i-she 意舍
   cV49 [cV43]
50 *Granarium stomachi* (1)
   wei-ts'ang 胃倉
   cV50 [cV44]
51 *Porta viscerum* (2)
   huang-men 肓門
   cV51 [cV45]
52 *Conclave potentiae* (5,2)
   chih-shih[83] 志室; *ching-kung* 精宮*
   cV52 [cV46]
53 *Viscera involuta* (3, 2)
   p'ao-huang[84] 胞肓
   cV53 [cV47]
54 *Margo subsequens* (1)
   chih-pien 秩邊
   cV54 [cV48]
55 *Yang coniuncti* (1)
   ho-yang 合陽
   cV55 [cV54]
56 *Recipiens nervos* (1)
   ch'eng-chin 承筋, *chih-ch'ang* 直腸, *shuan-ch'ang* 腨腸, 踹腸
   cV56 [cV55]

[82]*Kang* 綱 designates the large rope of a net and has the derived meanings "essential characteristic of a situation," "principle," "salient idea in a theory," and so on (in Latin: [*foramen*] *generale*).

[83]The remarks in note 78 in regard to *hun* and *p'o* similarly apply to *ching* (p. 176 above). Since the term here certainly is not used with any emphasis, the loose "translation" by *potentia* may perhaps be justified.

[84]The word *p'ao* 胞 designates a membrane, more precisely the fetal membrane. The character 胞, however, is sometimes interchanged with 包 (to envelop), so that a participial construction is possible.

57 *Columna carnis* (5)
   ch'eng-shan 承山; *yü-fu* 魚腹, *jou-chu* 肉柱, *ch'ang-shan* 腸山,
   yü-yao 魚腰, *shang-shan* 傷山
   cV57 [cV56]
58 *Yang flectens* (5)
   fei-yang 飛揚; *chüeh-yang* 厥陽, *chüeh-yang* 厥揚, *fei-yang* 飛陽
   N—cV58 [cV57]
59 *Yang tarsi* (1)
   fu-yang 跗陽; 附陽, 付陽, 跗揚
   cV59 [cV58]
60 *Olympus* (3)
   k'un-lun 崑崙; *hsia k'un-lun* 下崑崙
   t—cV60 [cV59]
61 *Servi salutatio* (1)
   p'u-ts'an 僕參; *an-hsieh* 安邪
   cV61 [cV60]
62 *Origo ascendentis yang* (2, 5)
   shen-mo 申脈; *yang-ch'iao* 陽蹻, *kuei-lu* 鬼路
   cV62 [cV61]
63 *Porta metalli* (1)
   chin-men 金門; *kuan-liang* 關梁, *liang-kuan* 梁關
   R—cV63 [cV62]
64 *Os pyramidale* (1)
   ching-ku[85] 京骨
   O—cV64 [cV63]
65 *Os ligatum* (1)
   shu-ku 束骨; *tz'u-ku* 刺骨
   i—cV65 [cV64]
66 *Vallis communicans vesicalis* (1, 2)
   t'ung-ku 通谷
   e—cV66 [cV65]
67 *Yin supremum* (1)
   chih-yin 至陰
   p—cV67 [cV66]

[85]The word *ching* 京 primarily means tumulus or pyramid.

Foramina copulo-conventoria cardinalis vesicalis:
Curvatura coruli (ch'ü-pin) [cF7]
Apex auriculi (shuai-ku) [cF8]
Impedimentale caeleste (t'ien-ch'ung) [cF9]
Candor superficialis (fu-pai) [cF10]
Yin penetrans capitis (ch'iao-yin) [cF11]
Processus mastoideus (wan-ku) [cF12]
Lacrimarum instantium capitis (lin-ch'i) [cF15]
Cardo femoralis (huan-t'iao) [cF30]
Vestibulum shen (shen-t'ing) [Rg24]
Conventus omnium (pai-hui) [Rg20]
Ostium cerebri (nao-hu) [Rg17]
Aula venti (feng-fu) [Rg16]
Omnium defatigationum (ta-chui) [Rg14]
Via figulina (t'ao-tao) [Rg13]

THE *CARDINALIS RENALIS YIN MINORIS PEDIS* (足少陰肾經)

COURSE

This conduit (Fig. 30) originates at the plantar side of the small toe, extends obliquely to the middle of the sole (1), and appears from below on the naviculare in the *foramen fons draconis* (cR2) (2). From there it skirts from behind the *malleolus medialis* (3) and branches out into the heel (4). Then it ascends within the *m. gastrocnemius* (5) and laterally enters the hollow of the knee (6), where it changes over to the medial side, ascends the upper leg (7), penetrates into the spine, unites with the *orbis renalis* (8), and attaches to the *orbis vesicalis* (9). Its direct continuation extends upward from the *orbis renalis*, touches the *orbis hepaticus* (10), traverses the diaphragm, and penetrates into the *orbis pulmonalis* (11); thence it runs along the trachea and the larynx (12) up to the root of the tongue (13). A ramification leaves the continuation in the *orbis pulmonalis*, attaches to the *orbis cardialis* (14), and sheds energy within the thorax.[86]

SYMPTOMS

Loss of appetite in spite of hunger; dark, shiny complexion;

[86]*Ling-shu* 10/1010f.

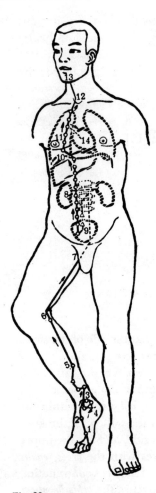

Fig. 30

cough, phlegm with bloody admixtures, gasping respiration; optical illusions and dim eyesight upon arising; nervous heart; persistent hunger. When the energy in the conduit and orb is deficient, the patient is easily startled and frightened; he complains of a hectic pulse, cold, aching, and paretic extremities resulting from of a reversal of the flow of energy (*flexus*). Hot, dry tongue; swollen, narrowed, painful fauces; oppression of the heart, pricks in the heart; icterus, diarrhea; pains in the spine and in the medial posterior region of the upper leg; pareses accompained by atrophies; cold flexus; need for much rest; hot, burning, and painful soles of the feet.

Foramina propria cardinalis renalis:
1 *Fons scatens* (1)
    yung-ch'üan 湧泉; *ti-ch'ung* 地衝, *ti-ch'ü* 地衢
    p—cR1
2 *Fons draconis* (5)
    jan-ku 然谷; *lung-ch'üan* 龍泉,* *lung-yüan* 龍淵, *jan-ku* 然骨
    e—cR2
3 *Rivulus maior* (1)
    t'ai-hsi 太谿; *lü-hsi* 呂細
    i—cR3 [cR6]
4 *Campana magna* (1)
    ta-chung 大鍾
    cR4 [cR5]
5 *Fons aquarum* (1)
    shui-ch'üan 水泉
    R—cR5 [cR4]
6 *Mare illustratum* (1)
    chao-hai 照海; *yin-ch'iao* 陰蹻
    cR6 [cR3]
7 *Amnis recurrens* (1)
    fu-liu 復溜; *ch'ang-yang* 昌陽, *wai-ming* 外命, *fu-pai* 伏白,
    fu-liu 伏留, 復留
    t—cR7

8 *Cursores copulati* (1)
 chiao-hsin[87] 交信
 cR8

9 *Ripa spissa* (5)
 chu-pin[88] 築賓, 築濱
 cR9

10 *Vallis yin* (1)
 yin-ku 陰谷
 c—cR10

11 *Os transversum* (1)
 heng-ku 橫骨; *hsia-chi* 下極, *ch'ü-chi* 屈骨, *sui-k'ung* 髓空,
 heng-ku 橫骨, *ch'ü-ku* 曲骨
 cR11

12 *Clusa yin* (5)
 ta-ho 大赫; *yin-kuan* 陰關,* *yin-wei* 陰維
 cR12

13 *Foramen ch'i* (1)
 ch'i-hsüeh 氣穴; *pao-men* 胞門, *tzu-hu* 子戶
 cR13

14 *Plenum quartum*[89] (1)
 szu-man 四滿; *sui-fu* 髓府, 隋府, *sui-chung* 髓中
 cR14

15 *Infusio media* (1)
 chung-chu 中注
 cR15

16 *Inductorium viscerum* (1, 2)
 huang-shu 肓兪
 cR16

17 *Curvatura alta* (5)
 shang-ch'u 商曲; *kao-ch'u* 高曲,* *shang-she* 商舍
 cR17

18 *Clusa lapidea* (1)

---

[87]*Hsin* 信 = *shih* 使, "messenger."
[88]*Chu* 築 = to beat down hard, to ram earth; *spissare* = to compact, to condense.
[89]Sc. the fourth foramen counted from the pubic bone upward along the *cardinalis renalis*.

shih-kuan 石關; *shih-ch'üeh* 石闕, *yu-kuan* 右關
cR18

19 *Urbs yin* (1)
yin-tu 陰都; *t'ung-kuan* 通關, *shih-kung* 食宮, 石宮, *shih-lü* 食呂
cR19

20 *Vallis communicans renalis* (1, 2)
t'ung-ku 通谷
cR20

21 *Porta pylorica* (2, 4)
yu-men[90] 幽門; *shang-men* 上門
cR21

22 *Porticus peripatetica* (1, 2)
pu-lang 步廊; 步郎
cR22

23 *Altare shen* (1)
shen-feng[91] 神封
cR23

24 *Vacuitas responsiva* (5, 3)
ling-hsü[92] 靈墟; 靈虛, *ling-ch'iang* 靈墻
cR24

25 *Horreum shen* (1)
shen-tsang 神藏
cR25

26 *In terra nostra* (5, 2)
yü-chung[93] 或中; 域中, 或中
cR26

27 *Aula inductoria* (1)

---

[90] *Yu-men* 幽門 is also the Chinese anatomical term for the pylorus (cf. Rs10).
[91] The term *feng* 封 designates an altar mound erected for religious purposes.
[92] The terms *ling* 靈 (see above, p. 193) and *hsü* 虛, "empty" [normative medical equivalent: "exhausted," *inanis*] in nonmedical technical contexts are practically synonymous; they are designations of the "neutral point" (cf. "Untersuchungen," p. 449, and p. 50 above). The "emptiness" characterizing the neutral point is a prerequisite for its inexhaustible structivity ("structive capacity," *ling*). For these reasons the departure from the normative translation is justified.
[93] We translate the variant 域中 "in our territory."

shu-fu 兪府; 輸府, 腧府
cR27

Foramina copulo-conventoria cardinalis renalis:
Copulatio trium yin (san-yin-chiao) [cL6]
Stagnum caeleste (t'ien-ch'ih) [cPC1]
Incrementum et vigor (chang-ch'iang) [Rg1]
Prima clusarum (kuan-yüan) [Rs4]
Conquisitorium felleum (chung-chi) [Rs3]

THE *CARDINALIS PERICARDIALIS YIN FLECTENTIS MANUS* (手厥陰心包經)

COURSE

This conduit (Fig. 31) originates within the thorax, where it is

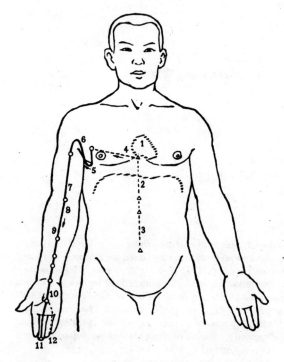

Fig. 31

united to the *orbis pericardialis* (1), descends through the diaphragm (2), and traverses the *tricalorium*, to which it attaches (3). A ramification extends transversely through the thorax (4) and to the ribs and emerges three inches below the axilla (5). It enters the axilla (6), continues on the medial (anterior) side of the arm between the *cardinales pulmonalis et cardialis* (7) into the hollow of the elbow (8), and runs between the *mm. palmaris longus et flexor carpi radialis* (9) across the wrist into the palm (10) and along the middle finger to its tip (11). A ramification leaves the one just described at the palm and runs along the ring finger to its tip (12).[94]

SYMPTOMS

Heat flushes toward the heart, twitching and convulsions of the elbow and forearm, swelling in the armpit. Feelings of tension in the thorax and the ribs, accelerated heartbeat, flushed face, darkness in front of the eyes, convulsive laughter. Symptoms specifically indicating a dysfunction of the *mo* conduits: Depressive states, pains in the heart [endocarditis and pericarditis], hot palms.

Foramina propria cardinalis pericardialis:

1 *Stagnum caeleste* (1)
   t'ien-ch'ih 天池; *t'ien-hui* 天會
   cPC1

2 *Fons caelestis* (1)
   t'ien-ch'üan 天泉; *t'ien-shih* 天濕, *t'ien-wen* 天溫
   cPC2

3 *Lacus curvus* (1)
   ch'ü-tse 曲澤
   cPC3

4 *Porta rimica* (1)
   hsi-men 郄門
   R—cPC4

5 *Foramen intermedium* (3, 2)
   chien-shih[95] 間使; *kuei-lu* 鬼路

[94]*Ling-shu* 10/1014.
[95]*Chien-shih* 間使, literally "go-between," "mediating messenger," or

cPC5

6 *Clusa interna* (1)
nei-kuan 內關
N—cPC6

7 *Tumulus magnus* (1)
ta-ling 大陵; *hsin-chu* 心主, *kuei-hsin* 鬼心
O—cPC7

8 *Medium palmae* (5, 4)
lao-kung 勞宮; *kuei-lu* 鬼路, *wu-li* 五里, *chang-chung* 掌中*
cPC8

9 *Impedimentale medium* (1)
chung-ch'ung 中衝
cPC9

Foramen copulo-conventorium cardinalis pericardialis:
Stagnum caeleste (*t'ien-ch'ih*) [cPC1]

THE *CARDINALIS TRICALORII YANG MINORIS MANUS* (手少陽三焦經) ·

COURSE

This conduit (Fig. 32) originates at the tip of the ring finger (1),
and extends between the *ossa metacarpalia IV et V* (2, 3) and
through the dorsal antebrachial region (4) to the tip of the
elbow (5). It continues through the external brachial region
(6) to the shoulder (7), where it meets the *cardinalis fellea* (8).
Then it runs to the *fossa supraclavicularis* (9) and penetrates into
the thorax, in particular its sternal region. Within the thorax
it attaches to the *orbis pericardialis* (10), traverses the diaphragm,
and unites with the complete *orbis tricalorii* (11). A ramification
issues forth from the sternal region (12), emerges in the *fossa
supraclavicularis* (9), touches the lateral cervical and nuchal
regions (13), skirts the ear from behind (14), descends in front
of the ear (15), and deflects upward medially to a point below
the eye (16). A secondary ramification issues from the primary
ramification behind the ear, penetrates into the ear (17),

"mediating emissary," applies to the foramen which "mediates" between
the *rimicum* and the *nexorium pericardialis*.

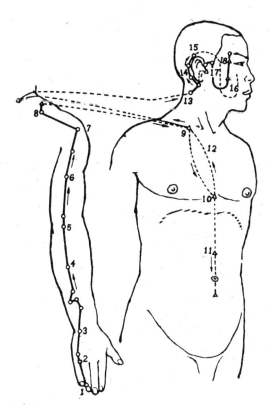

Fig. 32

emerges in front of it, descends a short way, and then reverts to the *canthus lateralis* (18).[96]

SYMPTOMS

Deafness; confusion; absent-mindedness; narrowed, swollen, painful fauces. Symptoms associated with disturbance of the active physiological energy (*ch'i*): spontaneous perspiration, pains in the *canthus lateralis*, swellings of the cheek [parotitis ...]; pains in the regions touched by the conduit, especially in front of the ear, in the shoulder, in the upper arm and forearm, in the elbow; stiffness of the ring finger.

[96]*Ling-shu* 10/1017.

Foramina propria cardinalis tricalorii:
 1 *Impedimentale clusae* (1)
   kuan-ch'ung 關衝
   p—cT1
 2 *Porta suci* (1)
   yeh-men 液門; 腋門, 掖門
   e—cT2
 3 *Insula media* (2)
   chung-chu[97] 中渚
   i—cT3
 4 *Stagnum yang* (1)
   yang-ch'ih 陽池; *pieh-yang* 別陽
   O—cT4
 5 *Clusa externa* (1)
   wai-kuan 外關
   N—cT5
 6 *Tigris volans* (5)
   chih-kou 支溝; *fei-hu* 飛虎*
   t—cT6
 7 *Genus conventum* (1)
   hui-tsung 會宗
   R—cT7
 8 *Porta communicans* (5)
   san-yang-luo 三陽絡; *t'ung-chien* 通間, *t'ung-kuan* 通關, *t'ung-men* 通門
   (*Nexorium trium yang*)
   cT8
 9 *Quattuor incilium* (1)
   szu-tu 四瀆
   cT9
10 *Puteus caelestis* (1)
   t'ien-ching 天井
   c—cT10
11 *Fons limpidus ac frigidus* (5)

[97]*Chu* 渚 = an islet in a river.

ch'ing-leng-yüan 清冷淵; *ch'ing-leng-ch'üan* 清冷泉,* *ch'ing-ling* 青靈
cT11

12 *Quod dispellit* (2, 5)
hsiao-shuo[98] 消鑠; *hsiao-li* 消瀝, *hsiao-shuo* 消爍, *hsiao-luo* 消濼
cT12

13 *Conventus lacerti* (1)
nao-hui 臑會; *nao-chiao* 臑交, *nao-liao* 臑髎
cT13 [cIC15]

14 *Cella alae* (1)
chien-chiao 肩窌; *chien-liao* 肩髎
cT14 [cIC16]

15 *Cella caelestis* (1)
t'ien-chiao 天窌; *t'ien-liao* 天髎
cT15 [cT17]

16 *Apertura caeli* (1)
t'ien-yu 天牖
cT16 [cT18]

17 *Pluteus venti* (1)
i-feng 翳風
cT17 [cT20]

18 *Foramen spasticum* (3, 2)
chi-mo[99] 瘈脈; *tzu-mo* 資脈, *t'i-mo* 體脈
cT18 [cT21]

19 *Auriculare posterius*[100] (4, 3)
lu-hsi 顱息; *lu-hsin* 顱顖
cT19 [cF12]

20 *Temporale superius* (4)
chüeh-sun 角孫
cT20 [cT22]

21 *Porta auris* (1)
erh-men 耳門
cT21 [cT24]

---

[98]*Shuo* 鑠, "to dispel."
[99]The technical term *chi* 瘈 designates diverse forms of convulsions, more particularly the *paralysis infantilis spastica*.
[100]That is, the foramen situated in the *m. auricularis posterior*.

22 *Cella harmoniae* (1)
   ho-chiao 和窌; *ho-liao* 和髎
   cT22 [cT23]
23 *Fides et fistulae* (2)
   szu-chu-k'ung[101] 絲竹空; *chü-liao* 巨髎, *mu-liao* 目髎, *yüeh-liao* 月髎
   cT23 [cF1]

Foramina copulo-conventoria cardinalis tricalorii:
Continens ventum (*ping-feng*) [cIT12]
Cella zygomatica (*ch'üan-chiao*) [cIT18]
Conclave auditus (*t'ing-kung*) [cIT19]
Conquisitorium stomachi (*chung-kuan*) [Rs12]
Cella pupillae (*t'ung-tzu-chiao*) [cF1]
Clusa superior (*shang-kuan*) [cF3]
In angulo sphenoidalis (*han-yen*) [cF4]
Foramen medullae (*hsüan-lu*) [cF5]
Lobulus suspensus (*hsüan-li*) [cF6]
Puteus alae (*chien-ching*) [cF21]
Omnium defatigationum (*ta-chui*) [Rg14]

THE *CARDINALIS FELLEA YANG MINORIS PEDIS* (足少陽膽經)

COURSE

This sinartery (Fig. 33) originates in the *canthus lateralis* (1), runs straight upward to the hairline along which it extends (2), first obliquely backward and then in a more downward direction (3) to a point above the ear, whence it skirts the ear from behind and descends in front of the *cardinalis tricalorii* through the nuchal and lateral cervical regions (4) into the *fossa supraclavicularis* (5).[102]

This is the classical description in the *Ling-shu* which, in the main, still guided Liao Jun-hung 廖潤鴻 in his *Chen-chiu chi-ch'eng* 針灸集成 (Compendium of acu-moxi-therapy, 1874). In modern descriptions and figures, however, several variant courses for the cardinal conduit are adopted without affect-

---

[101]The Chinese words *szu* 絲 ("strings") and 竹 *chu* ("bamboo tubes") designate the string and wind instruments, in Latin *fides* ("strings") *et fistulae* ("pipes").
[102]*Chen-chiu-hsüeh chiang-i*, p. 69; *Nei-ching chiang-i*, p. 70.

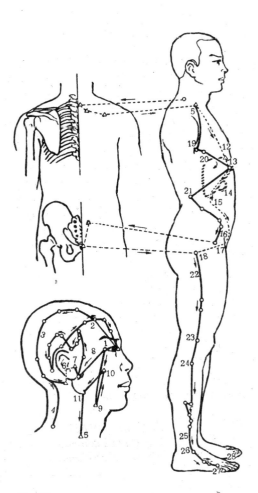

Fig. 33

ing the functions and attributions of the basic foramina such as the *stagnum venti* (cF20) or the *impedimentale caeleste* (cF9).

A ramification leaves the conduit behind the ear, penetrates into the ear (6), emerges in front of it (7), and extends close to the *canthus lateralis* (8). A secondary ramification extends from the *canthus lateralis* (1) in the direction of the *foramen magnum accipiens* (cS5) (9) situated on the mandible, and reverts together with the *cardinalis tricalorii* to a point below the eye (10), only to return again across the mandible (11) and lateral cervical region into the *fossa supraclavicularis* (5). There it penetrates into the thorax, traverses the diaphragm (12), attaches to the *orbis hepaticus* (13), unites with the *orbis felleus* (14), and then descends along the inner side of the ribs (15) and the abdominal peritoneum to the *foramen impedimentale ch'i* (cS30) (16), in which it emerges, then briefly continues along the border of pubic hair in a median direction (17), and deflects again to end in the *foramen cardo femoralis* (cF30) on the joint of the hip (18). The direct continuation of the cardinal conduit descends from the *fossa supraclavicularis* (5) to the axilla (19) and from there runs along the outside of the thorax (20) and abdomen (21) down to the *foramen cardo femoralis* (18). It continues downward along the external side of the upper leg (22), knee (23), and lower leg to the *malleolus lateralis* (24, 25, 26), and across the dorsum of the foot straight to the tip of the fourth toe (27). A ramification leaves the *cardinalis* on the dorsum of the foot, penetrates into the cleft between the muscles of the big toe and the second toe, and from there crosses the first and second metatarsals to the apex of the big toe, which it skirts to revert across the nail-bed to the hair on the second joint of the big toe (28).[103]

SYMPTOMS

Bitter taste in the mouth, frequent desire to sigh or to take deep breaths; pains in the muscles of the thorax accompanied by difficulties in bending and turning the body; in critical cases, sallow complexion, emaciation, fallow skin, heat in the external regions of the leg. *Flexus* and pains in the lower extremity. All

[103]*Ling-shu* 10/1019f.

symptoms associated with a dysfunction of the "bones" (*ku*), such as pains in the temple and in the pharynx, particularly in the hypopharynx and the outer canthus; swellings and pain in the *fossa supraclavicularis*, swelling in the lymphatic nodes of the axilla, spontaneous sweats, shaking chills, and malaria. Pains in the chest and flanks, in the upper and lower leg, in the knee and ankle, or generalized pains of all joints; disability of the fourth toe.

Foramina propria cardinalis felleae:
1 *Cella pupillae* (1)
   t'ung-tzu-chiao 瞳子窌; *t'ung-tzu-liao* 瞳子髎, *t'ai-yang* 太陽, *ch'ien-kuan* 前關, *hou-ch'ü* 後曲
   cF1 [cT27]
2 *Conventus auditus* (1)
   t'ing-hui 聽會; *t'ing-ho* 聽呵, *hou-kuan* 後關, *chi-kuan* 機關
   cF2 [cT25]
3 *Clusa superior* (1)
   shang-kuan 上關; *k'o-chu-jen* 客主人, *t'ai-yang* 太陽, *k'o-chu* 客主, *jung-chu* 容主
   cF3 [cT26]
4 *In angulo sphenoidalis* (4)
   han-yen[104] 頷厭
   cF4 [cF3]
5 *Foramen medullae* (5, 2)
   hsüan-lu 懸顱; *sui-chung* 髓中, *sui-k'ung* 髓孔,* *mi-nieh* 米(嚙)齧
   cF5 [cF4]
6 *Lobulus suspensus* (3, 2)
   hsüan-li[105] 懸釐
   cF6 [cF5]

[104]This foramen is situated at the tip of the sphenoid bone advancing between the parietal and temporal bones. Its somewhat obscure Chinese name *han-yen* 頷厭, "full chin-line," possibly points to a position of the head during treatment which causes a bulge to appear below the chin.
[105]*Li* 釐 originally designates the meat used at sacrifices to the ancestors, from which are derived the meanings of "an infinitesimal quantity" and "the thousandth part of an ounce or a foot."

7 *Curvatura coruli* (1, 2)
  ch'ü-pin[106] 曲鬢; *ch'ü-fa* 曲髮
  cF7 [cF6]

8 *Apex auriculi* (5)
  shuai-chüeh 率角; *shuai-ku* 蜂谷, 率骨, *erh-chien* 耳尖
  cF8 [cF7]

9 *Impedimentale caeleste* (1)
  t'ien-ch'ung 天衝; *t'ien-ch'ü* 天衢*
  cF9 [cF8]

10 *Candor superficialis* (1)
   fu-pai 浮白
   cF10 [cF9]

11 *Yin penetrans capitis* (1, 2)
   ch'iao-yin[107] 竅陰; *chen-ku* 枕骨
   (*Protuberantia occipitalis*)
   cF11 [cF10]

12 *Processus mastoideus* (4)
   wan-ku 完骨
   cF12 [cF11]

13 *Shen stirpis* (1)
   pen-shen 本神
   cF13

14 *Candor yang* (1)
   yang-pai 陽白
   cF14

15 *Lacrimarum instantium capitis* (1, 2)
   lin-ch'i 臨泣 [sc. *foramen*]
   cF15

16 *Fenestra oculi* (1)
   mu-ch'uang 目窗; *chih-jung* 至榮
   cF16 [cF17]

17 *Castra praetoriana* (1, 3)
   cheng-ying 正營
   cF17 [cF18]

---

[106]*Pin* 鬢, "the hair at the temples"; *corulus* = hazel (bush) →a tuft.
[107]*Ch'iao* 竅 has the verbal meaning "to project," "to penetrate" (= *t'ung* 通).

18 *Recipiens vis responsiva* (1,3)
   ch'eng-ling[108] 承靈
   cF18 [cF19]
19 *Hiatus cerebri* (2)
   nao-k'ung 腦空; *nieh-ju* 顳顬
   cF19 [cF20]
20 *Stagnum venti* (1)
   feng-ch'ih 風池
   cF20 [cF21]
21 *Puteus alae* (1)
   chien-ching 肩井; *po-ching* 膊井
   cF21
22 *Porta axillae* (5)
   yüan-yeh 淵腋; *ch'üan-yeh* 泉腋, *yeh-men* 腋門,* 液門, *yüan-yeh* 淵液
   cF22
23 *Atrium axillae* (4, 3)
   che-chin 輒筋
   cF23
24 *Sol et luna* (1)
   jih-yüeh 日月; *shen-kuang* 神光, *tan-mu* 膽募*
   (*Conquisitorium felleum*)
   C—cF24
25 *Porta pyramidis* (1)
   ching-men 京門; *ch'i-fu* 氣府, *ch'i-shu* 氣俞, *shen-mu* 腎募*
   (*Conquisitorium renale*)
   C^{cR}—cF25
26 *Foramen sinarteriae zonalis* (2, 1)
   tai-mo 帶脈
   cF26
27 *Cardo quintus* (1)
   wu-shu 五樞
   cF27
28 *Via retinentis* (1)
   wei-tao 維道; *wai-shu* 外樞* [sc. *foramen*]

[108]See note 92 and p. 193 above.

(*Cardo externus*)
cF28
29 *Cella habitationis* (1)
chü-chiao 居窌; *chü-liao* 居髎
cF29
30 *Cardo femoralis* (5)
huan-t'iao 環跳; *huan-ku* 環骨, *huan-t'iao* 鐶銚, *k'uan-ku* 髖骨,
pi-shu 髀樞,* *pin-ku* 髕骨, *pi-yen* 髀厭, *shu-ho-chung* 樞合中,
shu-chung 樞中
(*Articulatio coxae*)
cF30
31 *Forum ventorum* (1)
feng-shih 風市
cF31
32 *Incile medium* (1)
chung-tu 中瀆, 中犢
cF32
33 *Clusa yang fellea* (1, 2)[109]
yang-kuan 陽關; *kuan-yang* 關陽, *kuan-ling* 關陵, *han-fu* 寒府
cF33
34 *Fons tumuli yang* (1)
yang-ling-ch'üan 陽陵泉; *yang-ling* 陽陵, *yang chih ling-ch'üan*
陽之陵泉
c—cF34
35 *Copulatio yang* (1)
yang-chiao 陽交; *pieh-yang* 別陽, *tsu-chiao* 足窌, *tsu-liao* 足髎
cF35
36 *Monticulus externus* (1)
wai-ch'iu 外丘
R—cF36
37 *Lumen ac splendor* (1)
kuang-ming 光明
N—cF37

---

[109]In this normative Latin equivalent we have added the epithet *fellea*
to distinguish the foramen from a point of the same name situated on the
sinarteria regens: clusa yang regentis (Rg3 [Rg6]).

38 *Divisio carnis* (5)
  yang-fu 陽輔; *fen-jou* 分肉*
  t—cF38
39 *Campana suspensa* (1)
  hsüan-chung 懸鍾; *chüeh-ku* 絕骨
  cF39
40 *Agger monticuli* (1)
  ch'iu-hsü 丘墟
  O—cF40
41 *Lacrimarum instantium pedis* (1, 2)
  lin-ch'i 臨泣 [sc. *foramen*; cf. cF15]
  i—cF41
42 *Conventus quintus terrae* (1)
  ti wu-hui 地五會; *ti-wu* 地五
  cF42
43 *Rivulus coercitus* (1, 2)
  chia-hsi 俠谿; *chia-hsi* 夾谿
  e—cF43
44 *Yin penetrans pedis* (1, 2)
  ch'iao-yin 竅陰 [cf. cF11]
  p—cF44
Foramina copulo-conventoria cardinalis felleae:
Retinens capitis (*t'ou-wei*) [cS8]
Clusa inferior (*hsia-kuan*) [cS7]
Cella caelestis (*t'ien-chiao*) [cT15]
Pluteus venti (*i-feng*) [cT17]
Temporale superius (*kung-sun*) [cT20]
Cella harmoniae (*ho-chiao*) [cT22]
Conclave auditus (*t'ing-kung*) [cIT19]
Continens ventum (*ping-feng*) [cIT12]
Omnium defatigationum (*ta-chui*) [RG14]
Conventus omnium (*pai-hui*) [Rg20]
Incrementum et vigor (*chang-ch'iang*) [Rg1]
Conquisitorium lienale (*chang-men*) [cH13]
Cella superior (*shang-chiao*) [cV31]
Cella media (*chung-chiao*) [cV33]

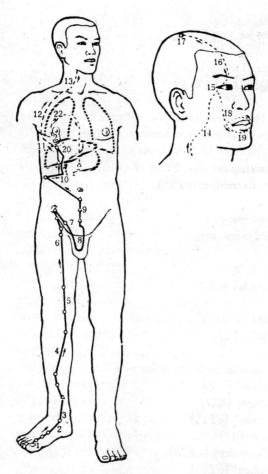

Fig. 34

Cella inferior (hsia-chiao) [cV34]
Stagnum caeleste (t'ien-ch'ih) [cPC1]

THE *CARDINALIS HEPATICA YIN FLECTENTIS PEDIS* (足厥陰肝經)

COURSE

This conduit (Fig. 34) originates on the dorsum of the big toe in the hair of its second joint (1), extends across the dorsum of the foot (2), and passes one inch in front of the *malleolus medialis* to the intercrural region (3). There it crosses the *cardinalis lienalis* eight inches above the *malleolus* (4) and continues behind the *cardinalis lienalis* up to the lower, medial internal border of the patellar region (5). From there it runs across the internal femoral region (6) up to the pubic-hair border in the inguinal region (7), and then reverts toward the genitals, which it skirts (8). It ascends again and penetrates into the hypogastrium (9) and then runs along the stomach (10), unites with the *orbis hepaticus*, and attaches to the *orbis felleus*. After traversing the diaphragm (11) it first radiates along the ribs (12), then continues on the backside of the trachea and larynx (13) to the pharynx and the fauces (14), connects to the conduits of the ocular system (15), and, after crossing the frontal (16), ends in the parietal bone (17). A ramification leaves the *cardinalis* in the ocular system (15), extends to the mandible (18), and surrounds the mouth opening on the inside (19). Another ramification emanates from the *orbis hepaticus* (20), traverses the diaphragm (21), and ends in the *orbis pulmonalis* (22).[110]

SYMPTOMS

Pains in the waist which render bending backward or forward difficult; hernias, especially scrotal hernia and complications; distended abdomen (gynecological symptoms); parched throat, sallow complexion. Plethora of the chest and the epigastrium, vomiting, eructations, retching, diarrhea, total digestive prostration, urinary incontinence or inability to urinate, obstipation.

Foramina propria cardinalis hepaticae:

1 *Lanx magna* (1)
   ta-tui[111] 大敦; *ta-shun* 大順, *shui-ch'üan* 水泉
   p—cH1

2 *Interstitium ambulatorium* (2)
   hsing-chien 行間
   e—cH2

3 *Impedimentale maius* (1)
   t'ai-ch'ung 太衝
   Oi—cH3

4 *Altare medium* (1)
   chung-feng 中封; *hsüan-ch'üan* 懸泉
   t—cH4

5 *Canalis teredinis* (1)
   li-kou[112] 蠡溝; *chiao-i* 交儀
   N—cH5

6 *Urbs media* (1)
   chung-tu 中都; *chung-hsi* 中郄,* *t'ai-yin* 太陰
   (*Rimicum medium*)
   R—cH6

7 *Clusa genus* (1)
   hsi-kuan 膝關
   cH7

8 *Fons curvus* (1)
   ch'ü-ch'üan 曲泉
   c—cH8

9 *Foramen uteri* (3, 2)
   yin-pao 陰包
   cH9

10 *Vicus quintus pedis* (1, 2)
   wu-li 五里
   cH10

11 *Angustiae yin* (1)
   yin-lien 陰廉

[111]The character 敦 when pronounced *tui* designates a large bowl or vessel for grain; *lanx* = metal bowl used at sacrifices.
[112]*Li* 蠡, "wood-worm" (Latin *teredo*).

cH11

12 *Pulsus excitatus* (1)
 chi-mo 急脈
 cH12

13 *Conquisitorium lienale* (5)
 chang-men 章門; *ch'ang-p'ing* 長平, *chou-chien* 肘尖, *p'i-mu* 脾募,* *lei-liao* 肋髎, *chi-lei* 季肋, *hsieh-chiao* 脇髎
 C^{cL}—cH13

14 *Conquisitorium hepaticum* (5)
 ch'i-men 期門; *kan-mu* 肝募*
 C—cH14

Foramina copulo-conventoria cardinalis hepaticae:
Copulatio trium yin (*san-yin-chiao*) [cL6]
Porta impedimentalis (*ch'ung-men*) [cL12]
Domus aulicus (*fu-she*) [cL13]
Os curvum (*ch'ü-ku*) [Rs2]
Conquisitorium vesicale (*chung-chi*) [Rs3]
Prima clusarum (*kuan-yüan*) [Rs4]
Conventus omnium (*pai-hui*) [Rg20]

The Eight Odd Conduits (Cardinales impares, chi-ching pa-mo 奇經八脈)

The odd conduits (*chi-ching pa-mo*) are in various ways intertwined with the cardinal conduits and thus are indirectly connected with various orbs; no odd conduit, however, directly belongs (*shu* 屬) to a particular orb. With the exception of the first two odd conduits, the *sinarteriae regens et respondens*, none has foramina of its own (*foramina propria*).

THE *SINARTERIA REGENS* (*TU-MO* 督脈)

COURSE

This sinartery (Fig. 35) originates at the perineum (1) and follows the spine (2) straight to the indentation between the atlas and the occipital bone (= *foramen aula venti*, Rg16) (3), where it penetrates into the brain, emerges again on top of the skull

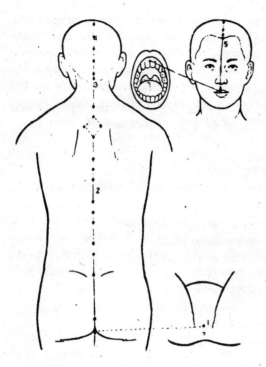

Fig. 35

and descends across the frontal bone (5) and the nose to the philtrum. There it meets the *sinarteria respondens* and the *cardinalis stomachi splendoris yang pedis*.[113]

SYMPTOMS

Stiffness or spastic contortion of the back. Daze, epileptiform symptoms [meningitis or encephalitis]; urinary incontinence; female sterility.

FUNCTIONS

The *sinarteria regens* extends along the back (= yang) and is connected with all the yang cardinal conduits. For this reason it may act as the regulatory and stimulating agent (a pacemaker, so to speak) for all activated configurational energy

[113]*Su-wen* 60/518f.

(*yang-ch'i*) of the body. For the *sinarteria regens* is directly connected to the sexual organs, to the yang conduits and to the
head, which latter is called "the junction of all yang" (*conventus
omnium yang*), and its reticular conduit indirectly touches the
orbis renalis. In this way it has a decisive influence on the
coordination and distribution of the inborn vital structive
potential (*ch'i primum*).[114]

Foramina propria sinarteriae regentis:

1 *Incrementum et vigor* (1, 2)

   chang-ch'iang 長強;ʹ *ch'iung-ku* 窮骨, *chüeh-ku* 撅骨, *wei
ch'iung-ku* 尾窮骨, *ti-ku* 骶骨, *wei-lü* 尾閭, *lung-hu-hsüeh*
龍虎穴, *ts'ao-hsi-lu* 曹溪路, *san-fen-lü* 三分閭, *ho-ch'e-lu* 河車
路, *ch'ao-t'ien-tien* 朝天巔, *shang-t'ien-t'i* 上天梯, *ch'i yin-hsi*
氣陰郄, *wei-ch'iung-ku* 尾窮骨, *wei ts'ui-ku* 尾翠骨, *ch'i-hsi*
氣郄, *chi-ku hsia-k'ung* 脊骨下空, *kuei-wei chang-ch'iang* 龜尾
長強, *ti shang* 骶上, *ku-ti* 骨骶

   Rg1 [Rg4]

2 *Inductorium lumbale* (1)

   yao-shu 腰俞; *pei-chieh* 背解, *sui-k'ung* 髓空, *yao-hu* 腰戶,
yao-chu 腰柱, *pei-hsien* 背鮮, *sui-shu* 髓俞, *sui-fu* 髓府, *sui-
k'ung* 髓孔

   Rg2 [Rg5]

3 *Clusa yang regentis* (1, 2)

   yang-kuan 陽關 [cf. *Clusa yang fellea,* cF33]

   Rg3 [Rg6]

4 *Porta fortunae* (1)

   ming-men 命門; *shu-lei* 屬累,

   Rg4 [Rg7]

5 *Cardo suspensus* (1)

   hsüan-shu 懸樞.

   Rg5 [Rg8]

6 *Medium spinae* (1)

   chi-chung 脊中; *shen-tsung* 神宗, *chi-shu* 脊俞, *chi-chu* 脊柱

   Rg6 [Rg9]

[114]See p. 173 above. *Chen-chiu-hsüeh chiang-i,* p. 76.

7 *Cardo medius* (1)
chung-shu 中樞
Rg7 [Rg10]

8 *Nervi constricti* (1)
chin-su 筋縮; *chin-shu* 筋束
Rg8 [Rg11]

9 *Yang supremus* (1)
chih-yang 至陽
Rg9 [Rg12]

10 *Turris responsiva* (3)
ling-t'ai[115] 靈臺
Rg10 [Rg13]

11 *Via shen* (1)
shen-tao 神道; *tsang-shu* 臟兪*
(*Inductorium orbium*)
Rg11 [Rg14]

12 *Columna personae* (1)
shen-chu[116] 身柱; *ch'en-ch'i* 塵氣, *chih li-ch'i* 知利氣, *chih li-chieh* 知利介, *chih-li-mao* 智利毛
Rg12 [Rg15]

13 *Via figulina* (1)
t'ao-tao[117] 陶道
Rg13 [Rg 16]

14 *Omnium defatigationum* (5, 2)
ta-chui 大椎; *pai-lao* 百勞*
Rg14 [Rg17]

15 *Porta infantiae* (1)
ya-men[118] 啞門; *she-heng* 舌橫, *she-yen* 舌厭, *yen-she* 厭舌, *she-ken* 舌根, *she-chung* 舌腫, *yin-men* 瘖門, *ya-men* 瘂門
Rg15 [Rg18]

16 *Aula venti* (1)

---

[115]The term *t'ai* 臺 designates a belvedere, an exalted vantage point; for the term *ling* see note 92 and p. 193 above. The composite term *ling-t'ai* 靈臺, an ancient term for astronomical observatories, is a metaphor for the heart.

[116]*Shen* 身 = body, status, individuality; *persona* = status, rank, individuality.

[117]*Figulus* = potter.

[118]*Yin-ya* 瘖瘂 = *infans* = mute, speechless.

feng-fu 風府; *she-pen* 舌本, *kuei-chen* 鬼枕, *ts'ao-hsi* 曹谿, *kuei-hsüeh* 鬼穴, *hsing-hsing* 惺惺
Rg16 [Rg19]

17 *Ostium cerebri* (1)
nao-hu 腦戶; *tsa-feng* 匝風, *hui-eh* 會額, *ho-lu* 合顱
Rg17 [Rg20]

18 *Interstitium vigoris* (1)
ch'iang-chien 强間; *ta-yü* 大羽
Rg18 [Rg21]

19 *Parietale posterius* (1, 4)
hou-ting 後頂; *chiao-ch'ung* 交衝
Rg19 [Rg22]

20 *Conventus omnium* (2)
pai-hui 百會; *san-yang wu-hui* 三陽五會, *tien-shang* 巔上, *t'ien-man* 天滿, *wei-hui* 維會, *ni-wan-kung* 泥丸宮, *ling-shang* 嶺上, *san-yang* 三陽, *wu-hui* 五會, *ling-shang t'ien-man* 嶺上天滿
Rg20 [Rg23]

21 *Parietale anterius* (1, 4)
ch'ien-ting 前頂
Rg21 [Rg24]

22 *Fonticulus maior* (4, 2)
hsin-hui[119] 囟會; *hsin-men* 囟門, *ting-men* 頂門, *kuei-men* 鬼門, *hsin-shang* 囟上
Rg22 [Rg25]

23 *Stella superior* (1)
shang-hsing 上星; *shen-t'ang* 神堂, *kuei-t'ang* 鬼堂, *ming-t'ang* 明堂, *kuei-kung* 鬼宮
Rg23 [Rg26]

24 *Vestibulum shen* (1)
shen-t'ing 神庭; *fa-chi* 髮際
Rg24 [Rg27]

25 *Rex faciei* (5)
su-chiao 素窌; *su-liao* 素髎, *mien-wang* 面王,* *mien-cheng* 面正, *pi-chun* 鼻準, *chun-t'ou* 準頭
Rg25 [Rg28]

---

[119]*Hsin* 囟 = *fonticulus maior sive frontalis.*

26 *Canalis aquae* (1)
   shui-kou 水溝; *jen-chung* 人中, *kuei-kung* 鬼宮, *kuei-k'o-t'ing*
   鬼客廳, *kuei-shih* 鬼市, *pi-jen-chung* 鼻人中
   (*Philtrum, Medium mominis*)
   Rg26 [Rg29]
27 *Promuntorium laetitiae* (1, 2)
   tui-tuan 兌端; *ch'un shang-tuan* 唇上端, *tui-t'ung-jui* 兌通銳,
   chuang-ku 壯骨, *tui-ku* 兌骨
   Rg27 [cIC21]
28 *Copulatio gingivalis* (1)
   yin-chiao 齦交; *yin-feng chin-chung* 齦縫筋中
   Rg28 [Rs24]

THE *SINARTERIA RESPONDENS* (*JEN-MO* 任脈)

COURSE

This sinartery (Fig. 36) originates on the perineum (1), from

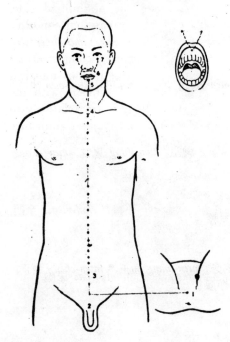

Fig. 36

where it traverses the genitals, the pubic hair, and the hypogastrium (2), and emerges below the navel in the *foramen prima clusarum* (Rs3) (3), whence it runs in a straight line to the larynx (4), and continues over the throat and chin (5, 6) to the eyes (7).[120]

Elsewhere In the *Nei-ching*,[121] however, it is stated that (together with the *sinarteria impedimentalis*) the *sinarteria respondens* originates in the uterus. This is only verbally contradictory to the *Su-wen* theory, for we should keep in mind that the conduits postulated within the body correspond to empirical data tailored to fit a speculative system by means of conventional terms and metaphors, and that branches of a conduit specified by one author may be considered by some other author an integral part of the conduit rather than a ramification.

SYMPTOMS

(In the male:) All kinds of pains and swellings of the testes and seminal chords, premature ejaculation and impotence. (In the female:) All kinds of disturbances of the menses with concomitant pains in the abdomen, heat flushes, sterility, and epilepsy.

FUNCTIONS

The *sinarteria respondens* extends along the abdominal side, which is yin, and is connected with all yin cardinal conduits, with the *sinarteria retinens yin* and with the *sinarteria impedimentalis*. For these reasons it may function as an equalizing reservoir (*mare, hai*) and regulating agent for all structive physiological energy (*yin-ch'i*). Because of its functional linkage with the *paraorbis uteri* and also because the female is yin relatively to the male, the *sinarteria respondens* is of particular significance for gynecological functions and symptoms.[122]

Foramina propria sinarteriae respondentis:

1 *Yin conventi* (1)
  hui-yin 陰會; *p'ing-i* 平翳, *hsia-chi* 下機, *chin-men,* 金門, *ping-i* 屏翳, *hai-ti* 海底, *hsia-yin-pieh* 下陰別
  Rs1 [Rg2]

2 *Os curvum* (1)
  ch'ü-ku 曲骨; 屈骨, *ch'ü-ku-tuan* 屈骨端, *niao-pao* 尿胞
  Rs2 [Rs1]

---

[120]*Su-wen* 60/517.
[121]*Ling-shu* 65/129f.
[122]*Chen-chiu-hsüeh chiang-i*, p. 77.

3 *Conquisitorium vesicale* (5)
chung-chi 中極; *ch'i-yüan* 氣原, *yü-ch'uan* 玉泉, *p'ang-kuang-mu*
膀胱募*
(*Culmen medium*)
C^{cV}—Rs3 [Rs2]

4 *Prima clusarum* (1)
kuan-yüan 關元; *hsia-chi* 下紀, *tz'u-men* 次門, *tan-t'ien* 丹田,
ta-chung-chi 大中極, *hsiao-ch'ang-mu* 小腸募,* *kuan-yüan* 關原,
ta-chung 大中, *san-chieh-chiao* 三結交, *ta-hai* 大海, *niao-shui*
溺水, *ta-k'un* 大涃, *k'un-lun* 崑崙, *ch'ih-shu* 持樞, *wu-ch'eng*
五城, *ch'an-men* 產門, *tzu-ch'u* 子處, *hsüeh-hai* 血海, *hsüeh-shih*
血室, *pao-men* 胞門, *tzu-kung* 子宮, *tzu-ch'ang* 子腸, *ming-men*
命門, *tzu-hu* 子戶
(*Conquisitorium intestini tenuis*)
C^{cIT}—Rs4[Rs3]

5 *Porta lapidea* (1)
shih-men 石門; *li-chi* 利機, *ching-lu* 情露, *tan-t'ien* 丹田, *ming-
men* 命門, *chüeh-yün* 絕孕, *shu-men* 俞門, *san-chiao-mu* 三焦募*
(*Conquisitorium tricalorii*)
C^{cT}—Rs5 [Rs4]

6 *Mare ch'i* (1)
ch'i-hai 氣海; *tan-t'ien* 丹田, *po-yang* 脖胦, *hsia-huang* 上肓,
chi-yang 季胦, *huang-chih-yüan* 肓之原, *hsia ch'i-hai* 下氣海
Rs6 [Rs5]

7 *Copulatio yin* (1)
yin-chiao 陰交; *shao-kuan* 少關, *heng-hu* 橫戶, *tan-t'ien* 丹田,
hsiao-kuan 小關
Rs7 [Rs6]

8 *Medium umbilici* (4, 5)
shen-ch'üeh 神闕; *ch'i-she* 氣舍, *ch'i-chung* 臍中,* *ch'i-ho* 氣合,
ming-ti 命蒂, *wei-hui* 維會
Rs8[Rs7]

9 *Aquae divisae* (1, 5)
shui-fen 水分; *fen-shui* 分水, *chung-shou* 中守
Rs9 [Rs8]

10 *Foramen pyloricum* (3, 4)
hsia-kuan 下脘; *yu-men* 幽門 [*hsia-kuan* 下管 = *pars pylorica*]
Rs10 [Rs9]

11 *Vicus constitutus* (1)

chien-li 建里
Rs11 [Rs10]
12 *Conquisitorium stomachi* (5)
chung-kuan 中脘; *t'ai-ts'ang* 太倉, *wei-mu* 胃募* [*chung-kuan* 中管 = *pars stomachi*]
C^{cs}—Rs12 [Rs11]
13 *Foramen cardiacum* (3, 4)
shang-kuan 上脘; *wei-kuan* 胃脘, 胃管, *shang-chi* 上紀, [*shang-kuan* 上管 = *pars cardiaca*]
Rs13 [Rs12]
14 *Conquisitorium cardiale* (5)
chü-ch'üeh 巨闕; *hsin-mu* 心募*
C^{cC}—Rs14 [Rs13]
15 *Cauda columbina* (1)
chiu-wei 鳩尾; *ho-ho* 𩨗𩨗, *wei-i* 尾翳, *ho-yü* 𩨗骬, *i-ch'ien* 臆前, *shen-fu* 神府, *kan-yü* 骭骬
Rs15 [Rs14]
16 *Vestibulum medium* (1)
chung-t'ing 中庭
Rs16 [Rs15]
17 *Atrium pectoris* (5)
tan-chung 膻中; *shang-ch'i-hai* 上氣海, *hsiung-t'ang* 胸堂,* *yüan-erh* 元兒, *yüan-chien* 元見
(*Conquisitorium pericardiale*)
C^{cPC} Rs17 [Rs16]
18 *Atrium iaspidis* (1)
yü-t'ang 玉堂; *yü-ying* 玉英
Rs18 [Rs17]
19 *Conclave purpureum* (1)
tzu-kung 紫宮
Rs19 [Rs18]
20 *Tegmen floreum* (1)
hua-kai 華蓋
Rs20 [Rs19]
21 *Dioptra mobilis* (3)
hsüan-chi[123] 璇機; 旋機

---

[123]*Hsüan-chi* 璇璣 = an astronomical sighting-tube; see Needham, *Science and Civilisation in China*, Vol. III, p. 334.

Rs21 [Rs20]
22 *Processus caelestis* (1)
   t'ien-t'u 天突; *t'ien-ch'ü* 天瞿, *yü-hu* 玉戶
   Rs22 [Rs21]
23 *Fons in angustiis* (1)
   lien-ch'üan 廉泉; *pen-ch'ih* 本池, *she-pen* 舌本
   Rs23 [Rs22]
24 *Recipiens liquoris* (1, 2)
   ch'eng-chiang 承漿; *t'ien-ch'ih* 天池, *hsüan-chiang* 懸漿, *ch'ui-chiang* 垂漿, *kuei-shih* 鬼市, *chung-chiang* 重漿
   Rs24 [cS6]

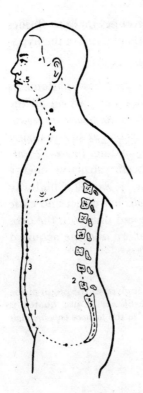

Fig. 37

THE *SINARTERIA IMPEDIMENTALIS* (*CH'UNG-MO* 衝脈)

COURSE

According to the *Su-wen,* this sinartery (Fig. 37) originates in the inguinal region at the *foramen impedimentale ch'i* (cS30) (1), passes the navel (3) in company of the *cardinalis renalis yin minoris pedis,* and radiates within the chest.[124] According to complementary statements in the *Ling-shu,* this sinartery or one of its ramifications extends upward within the back (2), constituting a sinarterial reservoir (*mare sinarteriarum, ching-luo chih hai* 經絡之海), whereas its superficial part ascends in front, combines in the larynx (4) with the ramification ascending within the chest, and ends in a network surrounding the mouth.[125]

SYMPTOMS

Generalized contravection (*ch'i-ni*) resulting in heat flushes toward the head with cold limbs, and violent pains in the hypogastrium.[126]

FUNCTIONS

The *sinarteria impedimentalis* in its upper part has anastomoses on all yang cardinal conduits and in its lower part on all the yin conduits.[127] In addition it is attached to the *sinarteriae regens, respondens, et zonalis.* In this way it may function as an equalizing reservoir not only for all the cardinal conduits (*mare 12 cardinalium*[128]) but for all individually specific structive energy (*hsüeh*). This suffices to justify its name, *ch'ung* 衝, "highway conduit."[129] In addition, the *impedimentalis* has direct and close links with the *cardinales renalis et stomachi* and thus with the orbs that constitute the foundation of the inborn and the acquired constitutions (*ch'i nativum et ch'i ascitum*).[130]

---

[124]*Su-wen* 60/517.
[125]*Ling-shu* 65/1292f. In this passage the uterus is given as the origin of the *sinarteria impedimentalis.* The conflict with the *Su-wen* as just quoted is probably due to the propinquity of the ovaries to the *foramen impedimentale ch'i.*
[126]*Su-wen* 60/518.
[127]*Ling-shu* 38/1173 and 65/1292f; *Su-wen* 44/405.
[128]*Ling-shu* 33/1156f.
[129]See note 64 on page 231 above.
[130]See pp. 164 and 172 above; *Chen-chiu-hsüeh chiang-i,* p. 77.

Foramina copulo-conventoria sinarteriae impedimentalis:
Yin conventi (hui-yin) [Rs1]
Impedimentale ch'i (ch'i-ch'ung) [cS30]
Os transversum (heng-ku) [cR11]
Clusa yin (ta-ho) [cR12]
Foramen ch'i (ch'i-hsüeh) [cR13]
Plenum quartum (szu-man) [cR14]
Infusio media (chung-chu) [cR15]
Inductorium viscerum (huang-shu) [cR16]
Curvatura alta (shang-ch'ü) [cR17]
Clusa lapidea (shih-kuan) [cR18]
Urbs yin (yin-tu) [cR19]
Vallis communicans renalis (t'ung-ku) [cR20]
Porta pylorica (yu-men) [cR21]

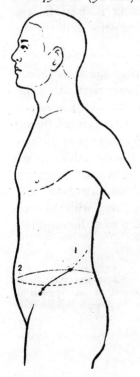

Fig. 38

THE *SINARTERIA ZONALIS* (*TAI-MO* 帶脈)

COURSE

This sinartery (Fig. 38) originates in the floating ribs (1) and surrounds the body like a belt (*tai* 帶, *zona*) (2).[131]

SYMPTOMS

Plethora abdominalis, quivering feeling as if one were sitting in water, irregular menses, paretic atrophies of the extremities, pains in the hypogastrium and in the loins.

FUNCTIONS

The *sinarteria zonalis,* as its name implies, cinctures the body above the waist like a belt. It touches all the cardinal and reticular conduits extending vertically along the back, the front, and the flanks. Whereas the anastomoses of all odd conduits considered up to now, as well as those of the cardinal conduits, are situated either at the lower end of the trunk or on the head, the *sinarteria zonalis* insures the equalization of energies in the middle of the trunk.[132]

Foramina copulo-conventoria sinarteriae zonalis:
Conquisitorium lienale (*chang-men*) [cH13]
Foramen sinarteriae zonalis (*tai-mo*) [cF26]
Cardo quintus (*wu-shu*) [cF27]
Via retinentis (*wei-tao*) [cF28]

THE *SINARTERIA ASCENDENS YIN* (*YIN CH'IAO-MO* 陰蹻脈)

COURSE

This sinartery (Fig. 39) is a ramification of the *cardinalis renalis yin minoris pedis.* It originates back of the *protuberantia navicularis* (*foramen fons draconis,* cR2) (1) and ascends in front of the *malleolus lateralis* (2) and medially across the anterior crural region (3), and along the inward side of the knee and upper leg to the genitals (4), where it penetrates into the trunk to emerge again in the *fossa supraclavicularis* (5). From there it continues across the throat (6) and chin (7) to the *foramen accipiens homi-*

---

[131]*Nan* 21 = *Nan-ching* 3/87.
[132]*Chen-chiu-hsüeh chiang-i,* p. 78.

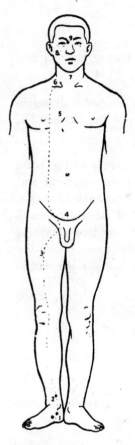

Fig. 39

num (cS9) (8) and ascends across the medial part of the zygo-matic to the inner canthus (9).[133]

SYMPTOMS

Fatigue, powerlessness of the active (yang) functions and organs, spastic tension of the structure (yin) functions and organs. Epilepsy, spasms, and pareses. Because of specific affinity to the *orbis renalis*, impotence and diseases of the genital organs.

[133]*Nan* 28 = *Nan-ching* 3/87.

Fig. 40

FUNCTIONS
Accessory conduit for the distribution of the unattached configurational energy (*ching-ch'i*) stored in the *orbis renalis*.[134]

Foramina copulo-conventoria sinarteriae ascendentis yin:
Mare illustratum (*chao-hai*) [cR6]
Cursores copulati (*chiao-hsin*) [cR8]
Canthus nasalis (*ching-ming*) [cV1]

[134]*Chen-chiu-hsüeh chiang-i*, p. 78.

THE *SINARTERIA ASCENDENS YANG (YANG CH'IAO-MO* 陽蹻脈)

COURSE

This sinartery (Fig. 40) originates in the heel (1) and ascends along the external side of the leg (2) and the lateral side of the trunk to the *foramen stagnum venti* (cF20) situated laterally in the occipital region (3).[135]

SYMPTOMS

The symptoms of this sinartery are complementary to those of the *ascendens yin*: Fatigue and powerlessness of the yin organs and functions and spastic tensions of the yang. General myalgias, more particularly in the back and in the loins; stiffness; painful eyes.

FUNCTIONS

The *sinarteria ascendens yang* is an accessory conduit for distribution and coordination of structive energy about to be activated.[136]

Foramina copulo-conventoria sinarteriae ascendentis yang:
Origo ascendentis yang (shen-mo) [cV62]
Servi salutatio (p'u-ts'an) [cV61]
Yang tarsi (fu-yang) [cV59]
Cella habitationis (chü-chiao) [cF29]
Inductorium lacerti (nao-shu) [cIT10]
Os amplum (chü-ku) [cIC16]
Promunturium humeri (chien-yü) [cIC15]
Granarium terrestre (ti-ts'ang) [cS4]
Cella ampla (chü-chiao) [cS3]
Recipiens lacrimarum (ch'eng-ch'i) [cS1]
Canthus nasalis (ching-ming) [cV1]
Stagnum venti (feng-ch'ih) [cF20]

THE *SINARTERIA RETINENS YIN (YIN WEI-MO* 陰維脈)

COURSE

This sinartery (Fig. 41) originates in the *foramen copulatio yin* (1) (Rs7), ascends along the internal side of the leg up to the groin,

---

[135]*Nan* 28 = *Nan-ching* 3/87.
[136]*Chen-chiu-hsüeh chiang-i*, pp. 78f.

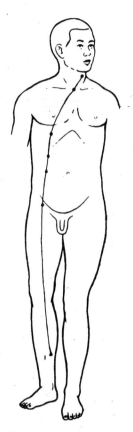

Fig. 41

penetrates into the hypogastrium, continues along the inner side of the abdomen and thorax penetrating the diaphragm, and terminates laterally on the larynx.[137]

SYMPTOMS

Chronic pains of the throat and pains in the epigastrium, the loins, and the genitals.

FUNCTIONS

The *retinens yin* communicates with the yin cardinal conduits and joins the *sinarteria respondens*. In this way it constitutes a

---

[137]*Nan-ching* 3/87; *Chi-ching pa-mo k'ao* 奇經八脈考, pp. 68f.

kind of net (*wang* 網) trussing up all the yin conduits. It controls the constructive energy (*ying*) congruent with the individually specific structive energy (*hsüeh*).[138]

Foramina copulo-conventoria sinarteriae retinentis yin:
Ripa spissa (*chu-pin*) [cR9]
Porta impedimentalis (*ch'ung-men*) [cL12]
Domus aulicus (*fu-she*) [cL13]
Transversum magnum (*ta-heng*) [cL15]
Aegritudo abdominis (*fu-ai*) [cL16]
Conquisitorium hepaticum (*ch'i-men*) [cH14]
Processus caelestis (*t'ien-t'u*) [Rs22]
Fons in angustiis (*lien-ch'üan)* [Rs23]

THE *SINARTERIA RETINENS YANG* (*YANG WEI-MO* 陽維脈)

COURSE

This sinartery (Fig. 42) originates at the outer side of the foot in the *foramen porta metalli* (1) (cV63). It ascends along the external side of the lower leg, knee, and upper leg to the lateral side of the epigastrium. It crosses the ribs to reach the shoulder, at which point it reverts briefly downward, then crosses the nuchal region to reach a spot behind the ear, and runs across the lateral part of the parietal bone and across the temporal bone to the lateral part of the frontal bone.[139]

SYMPTOMS

Frequently alternating flushes and shivers.

FUNCTIONS

The *sinarteria retinens yang* generally communicates with the yang cardinal conduits, and is particularly closely connected with the *cardinalis vesicalis yang maioris pedis* and the *cardinalis fellea yang minoris pedis*. As a connecting link between all the yang conduits, the *retinens yang* influences the expenditure of active energy and controls the defensive energy (*wei*).[140]

---

[138]*Chen-chiu-hsüeh chiang-i*, pp. 79f.
[139]*Nan-ching* 3/87; *Chi-ching pa-mo k'ao*, pp. 69f.
[140]*Chen-chiu-hsüeh chiang-i*, p. 79.

Fig. 42

Foramina copulo-conventoria sinarteriae retinentis yang:
Porta metalli (chin-men) [cV63]
Copulatio yang (yang-chiao) [cF35]
Conventus lacerti (ju-hui) [cT13]
Cella caelestis (t'ien-chiao) [cT15]
Latus lacerti (pi-ju) [cIC14]
Puteus alae (chien-ching) [cF21]
Inductorium lacerti (ju-shu) [cIT10]
Stagnum venti (feng-ch'ih) [cF20]
Porta infantiae (ya-men) [Rg15]

Aula venti (*feng-fu*) [Rg16]
Hiatus cerebri (*nao-k'ung*) [cF19]
Recipiens vis responsiva (*ch'eng-ling*) [cF18]
Castra praetoriana (*cheng-ying*) [cF17]
Fenestra oculi (*mu-ch'uang*) [cF16]
Lacrimărum instantium capitis (*lin-ch'i*) [cF15]
Candor yang (*yang-pai*) [cF14]
Shen stirpis (*pen-shen*) [cF13]
Retinens capitis (*t'ou-wei*) [cS8]

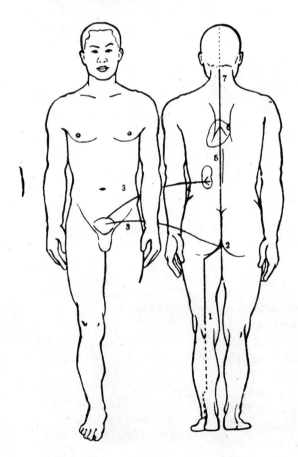

Fig. 43

The Cardinal Branch Conduits (Sinarteriae paracardinales, ching-pieh 經別)

As their name suggests, the cardinal branch conduits are integral parts of the cardinal conduits. Hence they have no foramina of their own, nor are they associated with symptoms distinct from those of the respective cardinal conduits. We thus need sketch their course only briefly.[141]

THE *PARACARDINALIS VESICALIS YANG MAIORIS PEDIS* (足太陽膀胱經別)

This conduit originates in the hollow of the knee (at the *foramen medium lacunae,* cV40). A branch penetrates the anus five inches below the coccyx, unites with the *orbis vesicalis,* and radiates into the *orbis renalis.* From there it extends through the muscles of the back, paralleling both sides of the spine. Branches penetrate the *orbis cardialis,* while the main part continues in the muscles of the back to the neck and reenters the cardinal conduit at the *foramen canthus nasalis* (cV1) (Fig. 43).

THE *PARACARDINALIS RENALIS YIN MINORIS PEDIS* (足少陰腎經別)

This conduit originates in the hollow of the knee and ascends in company with the *paracardinalis yang maioris,* also penetrating the *orbis renalis.* It then connects with the *sinarteria zonalis* at the height of the fourteenth vertebra (second lumbar vertebra). It leaves the *sinarteria zonalis* on the abdominal side of the body, ascends to the hypoglottis, reemerges at the surface of the throat, and unites with its outer sinartery (*cardinalis speciei,* i.e., the *cardinalis vesicalis yang minoris pedis*) at the *foramen canthus nasalis* (cV1). This is called the first of the Six Conjunctions (*coniunctiones, ho* 合) (Fig. 44).

THE *PARACARDINALIS FELLEA YANG MINORIS PEDIS* (足少陽膽經別)

This conduit originates in the joint of the hip (*foramen cardo femoralis,* cF30), which it skirts, extending to the pubic hair, where it unites with the *paracardinalis yin flectentis.* It then ascends to the floating ribs, extends within the chest, unites with

---

[141]See *Ling-shu* 11/1043; *Chen-chiu-hsüeh chiang-i,* pp. 80ff.

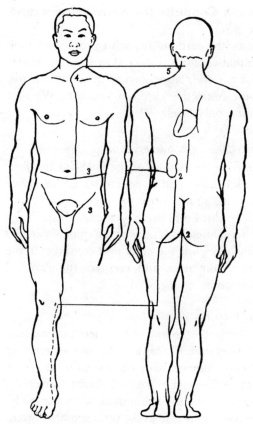

Fig. 44

the *orbis felleus,* radiates upwards, spreads in the *orbis hepaticus,* traverses the *orbis cardialis,* ascends to the side of the larynx, runs laterally across the cheek and mandible, radiates into the face, and reunites with its *cardinalis* at the *canthus lateralis* (*foramen cella pupillae,* cF1) (Fig. 45).

THE *PARACARDINALIS HEPATICA YIN FLECTENTIS PEDIS* (足厥陰肝經別)

The *paracardinalis* originates on the dorsum of the foot close to the joint (*foramen altare medium,* cH4). First it ascends to the

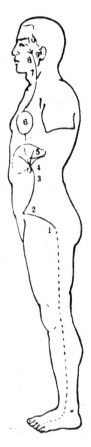

Fig. 45

border of the pubic hair, whence it continues in company of the *paracardinalis fellea yang minoris pedis* up to the *canthus lateralis* (*foramen cella pupillae,* cF1). This is the second of the Six Conjunctions (Fig. 46).

THE *PARACARDINALIS STOMACHI SPLENDORIS YANG PEDIS* (足陽明胃經別)
This conduit originates at the *foramen lepus subreptus* (cS32) situated in the anterior femoral region, ascends to penetrate into the mesogastrium, unites with the *orbis stomachi,* radiates

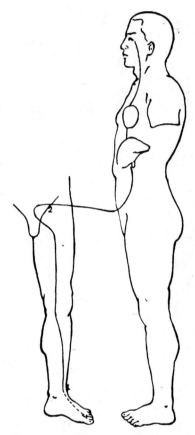

Fig. 46

into the *orbis lienalis,* and joins the *orbis cardialis.* It then ascends again along the esophagus into the mouth, emerges at the surface of the face, extends to the base of the nose and to the eye sockets, where it reunites with its cardinal conduit (Fig. 47).

THE *PARACARDINALIS LIENALIS YIN MAIORIS PEDIS* (足太陰脾經別)
This conduit originates in the anterior femoral region, ascends in company with the *paracardinalis stomachi,* attaches to the

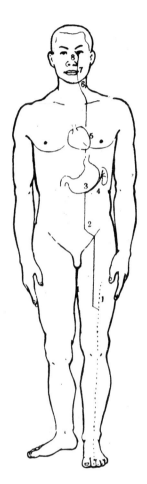

Fig. 47

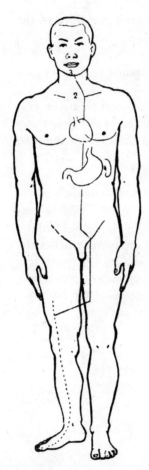

Fig. 48

larynx, and radiates into the tongue. This is the third of the Six Conjunctions (Fig. 48).

THE *PARACARDINALIS INTESTINI TENUIS YANG MAIORIS MANUS* (手太陽小腸經別)
This conduit originates and extends downward from the posterior side of the shoulder (*foramen rectum alae,* cIT9), penetrates the axilla, enters the *orbis cardialis,* and unites with the *orbis intestini tenuis* (Fig. 49).

THE *PARACARDINALIS CARDIALIS YIN MINORIS MANUS* (手少陰心經別)
This conduit originates deep within the axilla (*foramen porta axillae,* cF22), penetrates into the thorax, and there unites with the *orbis cardialis.* Then it deflects upward, reaches the larynx, emerges in the face, and unites with its outer sinartery (*cardinalis speciei*) in the *canthus medialis* (*foramen canthus nasalis,* cV1). This is the fourth of the Six Conjunctions (Fig. 50).

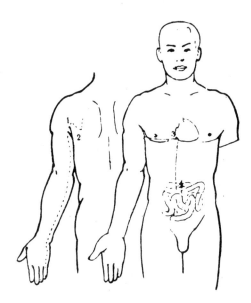

Fig. 49

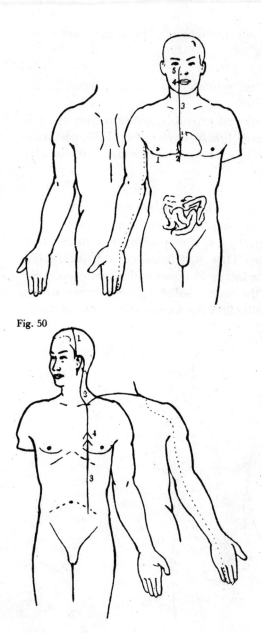

Fig. 50

Fig. 51

THE *PARACARDINALIS TRICALORII YANG MINORIS MANUS* (手少陽三焦經別)

This conduit extends from the top of the skull, the highest point of the body, down into the *fossa supraclavicularis,* and continues downward through the *orbis tricalorii,* finally radiating out within the thorax (Fig. 51).

THE *PARACARDINALIS PERICARDIALIS YIN FLECTENTIS MANUS* (手厥陰心包經別)

This conduit originates three inches below the axilla (in the *foramen stagnum caeleste,* cPC1), penetrates into the thorax, unites with the *orbis tricalorii,* ascends along the trachea, and curves to a spot behind the ear, where it unites with its outer sinartery near the *foramen processus mastoideus* (cF12). This is the fifth of the Six Conjunctions (Fig. 52).

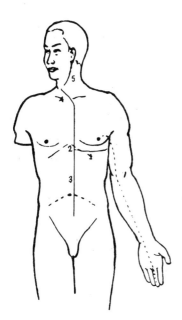

Fig. 52

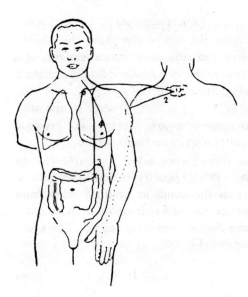

Fig. 53

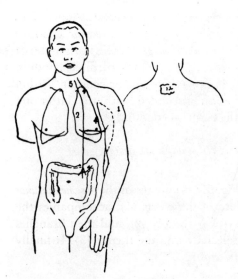

Fig. 54

THE *PARACARDINALIS INTESTINI CRASSI SPLENDORIS YANG MANUS*
（手陽明大腸經別）

This branch conduit leaves its cardinal conduit in the shoulder (*foramen promunturium humeri*, cIC15), enters the spine slightly higher (at the *foramen omnium defatigationum*, Rg14), and descends to the *orbis intestini crassi*. It then reverts to the *orbis pulmonalis*, ascends along the trachea, emerges in the *fossa supraclavicularis*, and reunites with its *cardinalis* (Fig. 53).

THE *PARACARDINALIS PULMONALIS YIN MAIORIS MANUS* （手太陰肺經別）

This conduit originates in the axilla in front of the *foramen porta axillae* (cF22), penetrates into the *orbis pulmonalis*, and radiates into the *orbis intestini crassi*. It then ascends again and emerges in the *fossa supraclavicularis* and runs to the larynx, where it unites with its outer sinartery (*cardinalis speciei*), the *cardinalis intestini crassi*. This is the last of the Six Conjunctions (Fig. 54).

The Reticular Conduits (Sinarteriae reticulares, luo-mo 絡脈)

The reticular conduits (*luo-mo* 絡脈) are the distal ramifications of the conduit system. Each of the fifteen reticular conduits (with the exception of the *reticularis magna lienalis*) originates at the *foramen nexorium* (*luo-hsüeh* 絡穴)[142] of a cardinal conduit, which latter also lends its name to the reticular conduit. Within narrow limits, the symptoms associated with the latter are independent of those of the cardinal conduit.[143]

THE *RETICULARIS PULMONALIS YIN MAIORIS MANUS*（手太陰肺絡）

COURSE   •

This reticular conduit (Fig. 55) originates in the *foramen lacunae* (cP7) between the tendons of the wrists (1), accompanies the *cardinalis pulmonalis* a short way distally (2), and then branches out into the palm and especially into the thenar (3). It finally joins the *cardinalis intestini crassi*.

[142]See p. 199 above and p. 338 below.
[143]*Ling-shu* 10/1036ff and the *Chen-chiu-hsüeh chiang-i*, pp. 83ff.

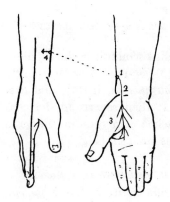

Fig. 55

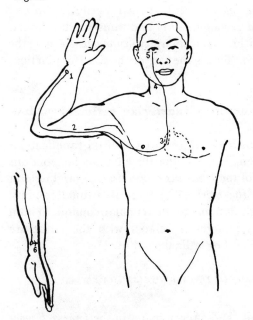

Fig. 56

SYMPTOMS
In case of repletion, heat in the *eminentia carpi radialis* and in the palm; in case of exhaustion, frequent sneezes or urinary incontinence.

THE *RETICULARIS CARDIALIS YIN MINORIS MANUS* (手少陰心絡)

COURSE
This conduit (Fig. 56) originates in the *foramen vicus communicans* (cC5) one inch proximally of the wrist (1), penetrates into the *orbis cardialis* (2, 3) in company of its *cardinalis,* from where it establishes communications to the hypoglottis (4), and then enters the reticular system of the eye (5). It joins the *cardinalis intestini tenuis.*
SYMPTOMS
In case of repletion, tension and pressure on the chest; in case of exhaustion, aphasia.

THE *RETICULARIS PERICARDIALIS YIN FLECTENTIS MANUS* (手厥陰心包絡)

COURSE
This conduit originates at the *foramen clusa interna* (cPC6) two inches above the wrist (1), emerges between the tendons of the *mm. palmaris longus et flexor carpi radialis* (2), and accompanies the *cardinalis pericardialis* (3) into its orb.
SYMPTOMS
In case of repletion, pains in the heart; in case of exhaustion, stiffness of the neck.

THE *RETICULARIS INTESTINI TENUIS YANG MAIORIS MANUS* (手太陽小腸絡)

COURSE
This conduit (Fig. 58) originates at the *foramen adminiculans orthopathiam* (cIT7) five inches above the wrist (2), and joins the *cardinalis cardialis yin minoris manus* in the ulnar antebrachial region (3). A ramification runs upward to the elbow (3) and finally surrounds the *promunturium humeri* (cIC15) (4) in the form of a plexus.

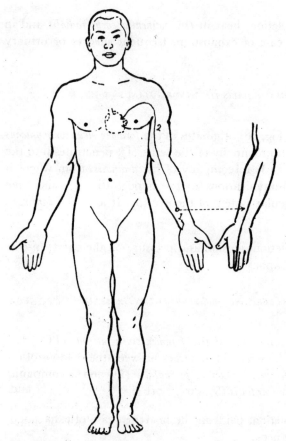

Fig. 57

SYMPTOMS

In case of repletion, limpness of the joints (which probably means the muscles of the motive apparatus), and incapacity' to bend the elbow; in case of exhaustion, granulations, scabs, and scaling.

THE *RETICULARIS INTESTINI CRASSI SPLENDORIS YANG MANUS* (手陽明大腸絡)

COURSE

This conduit (Fig. 59) originates at the *foramen pervium obliquum*

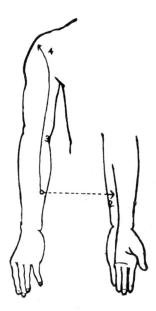

Fig. 58

(cIC6) (1) three inches above the wrist and joins the *cardinalis pulmonalis* (2). A ramification extends upward on the arm (3), passes through the *foramen promunturium humeri* (cIC15) (4) and through the cheek (5) to the teeth (6); a secondary rämification penetrates into the ear (7) and unites with the plexus of sinarteries of the ear.[144]

SYMPTOMS

In case of repletion, carious teeth and deafness; in case of exhaustion, feeling of cold in the teeth and tension in the medias-tinum.

THE *RETICULARIS TRICALORII YANG MINORIS MANUS* (手少陽三焦絡)

COURSE

This conduit (Fig. 60) originates at the *foramen clusa externa* (cT5) (1) two inches above the wrist, extends upward on the

[144]See the commentary in the *Chen-chiu-hsüeh chiang-i*, p. 85, concerning the term *tsung-mo* 宗脈.

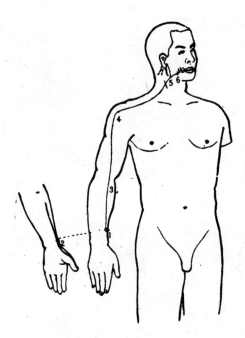

Fig. 59

arm (2), and penetrates into the thorax (3), where it unites with the *orbes cardialis et pericardialis.*

SYMPTOMS

In case of repletion, spastic pareses of the elbow; in case of exhaustion, paretic limpness of the elbow.

THE *RETICULARIS VESICALIS YANG MAIORIS PEDIS* (足太陽膀胱絡)

COURSE

This sinartery (Fig. 61) originates at the *foramen yang flectens* (cV58) seven inches above the *malleolus lateralis,* and immediately joins the *cardinalis renalis.*

SYMPTOMS

In case of repletion, clogged nose and edematous coryza, pains in the head and back; in case of exhaustion, cold in the head and nosebleed.

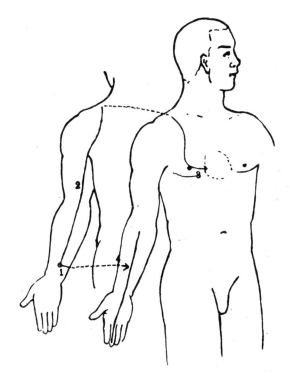

Fig. 60

Fig. 61

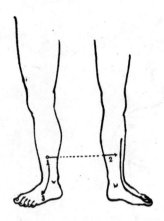

Fig. 62

THE *RETICULARIS FELLEA YANG MINORIS PEDIS* （足少陽膽絡）

COURSE

This conduit (Fig. 62) originates at the *foramen lumen ac splendor* (cF37) (1) five inches above the *malleolus lateralis*. One branch joins the *cardinalis hepatica* (2), while another descends to the dorsum of the foot (3), where it spreads to form a plexus.

SYMPTOMS

In case of repletion: *contravectio flectens* (*chüeh-ni* 厥逆) [nervous circulation and collapse of the circulation]; in case of exhaustion: powerlessness or pareses of the feet and inability to rise when seated.

THE *RETICULARIS STOMACHI SPLENDORIS YANG PEDIS* （足陽明胃絡）

COURSE

This conduit (Fig. 63) originates at the *foramen abundantia* (cS40) (1), seven to eight inches above the *malleolus lateralis*, and joins the *cardinalis lienalis* (2). A ramification extends along the outward side of the leg upward and continues across the abdominal side of the trunk to the head. There one branch (4) forms a plexus on top of the skull and another forms a plexus around the larynx (5).

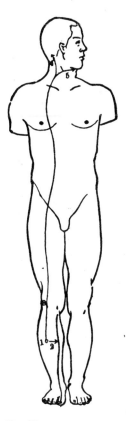

Fig. 63

SYMPTOMS

All symptoms are due to a contravection of energy in the conduit manifesting itself by such symptoms as laryngeal paralysis with aphasia. In case of repletion, epileptiform symptoms; in case of exhaustion, powerlessness, paresis, or paralysis of the foot and lower leg.

THE *RETICULARIS LIENALIS YIN MAIORIS PEDIS* (足太陰脾絡)

COURSE

This conduit (Fig. 64) originates at the *foramen caput metatarsalis hallucis* (cL4) (1) one inch behind the base of the big toe

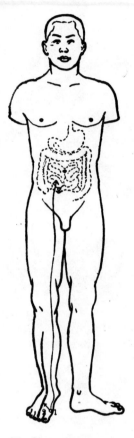

Fig. 64

and immediately joins the *cardinalis stomachi* (2). A ramification ascends on the inner side of the leg and spreads with numerous branches in the *orbes intestinorum et stomachi* (2).

SYMPTOMS.

In case of contravection, cholera; in case of repletion, violent colic pains in the intestines; in case of exhaustion, chronic pains in the intestines and tympanites.

THE *RETICULARIS RENALIS YIN MINORIS PEDIS* (足少陰腎絡)

COURSE

This sinartery (Fig. 65) originates at the *foramen campana*

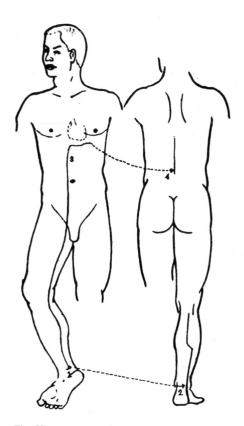

Fig. 65

magna (cR4) (1) situated behind the *malleolus medialis,* skirts the Achilles tendon (2), and joins the *cardinalis vesicalis* (3). A ramification accompanies the latter upward and shortly below the *orbis pericardialis* radiates into the lumbar region and the spine (4).

SYMPTOMS

In case of contraction, depressive moods; in case of repletion, inability to u   , in case of exhaustion, pains in the loins.

THE *RETICULARIS HEPATICA YIN FLECTENTIS PEDIS* (足厥陰肝絡)

COURSE

This sinartery (Fig. 66) originates at the *foramen canalis teredinis*

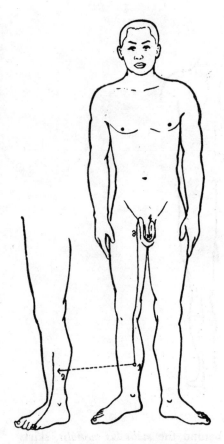

Fig. 66

(cH5) (1) five inches above the *malleolus medialis*, and immediately joins the *cardinalis fellea* (2). A ramification extends upward from the calf to the scrotum (3) and unites with the penis.
SYMPTOMS
In case of contravection, swellings of the scrotum; in case of repletion, scrotal hernia, painful erection; in case of exhaustion, itching of the genitals.

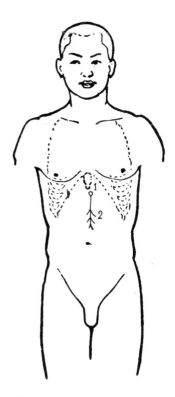

Fig. 67

THE *RETICULARIS SINARTERIAE RESPONDENTIS* (任脈絡)

COURSE

This conduit (Fig. 67) originates at the *foramen cauda columbina* (RS15)(1) and descends to radiate within the mesogastrium (2).

SYMPTOMS

In case of repletion, pains in the abdominal wall; in case of exhaustion, itching and formication of the abdomen.

THE *RETICULARIS SINARTERIAE REGENTIS*(督脈絡)

COURSE

This conduit (Fig. 68) originates at the *foramen incrementum*

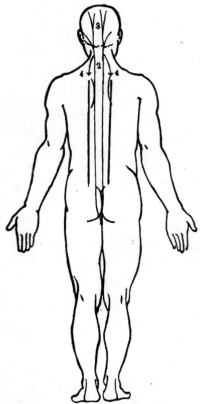

Fig. 68

et vigor (Rg1) (1), ascends within the flesh at both sides of the spine to the neck (2), radiates on the head (3), again descends to the shoulder blades (4), and penetrates into the *cardinalis vesicalis* and the deep muscle layers of the back.

SYMPTOMS

In case of repletion, spastic tension or stiffness of the back; in case of exhaustion, daze and heaviness or shaking motions of the head.

THE *RETICULARIS MAGNA LIENALIS* (脾之大絡)

COURSE

This reticular conduit (Fig. 69) originates in the *foramen*

Fig. 69

nexorium lienalis (cL21) (1) about three inches below the *foramen porta axillae* (cF22) and radiates on the thorax and on the ribs (2).

SYMPTOMS

In case of repletion, diffuse pains throughout the body; in case of exhaustion, powerlessness and weakness of all joints.

The Twelve Muscle Conduits (Sinarteriae nervocardinales, ching-chin 經筋)

The muscle conduits, as their name indicates, extend within the muscle of the motive apparatus and never directly touch any orb. Within the sinarteriological system they figure as peripheral conduits. They are associated with symptoms that, within limits, are independent of those of the cardinal conduits.[145]

THE *NERVOCARDINALIS VESICALIS YANG MAIORIS PEDIS* (足太陽膀胱經筋)

COURSE

This muscle conduit (Fig. 70) originates on the small toe (1). It is tied to the *malleolus lateralis* (2), whence it ascends obliquely to make another tie at the outside posterior side of the knee (3). From the tie on the *malleolus lateralis* (4) a ramification runs to a tie on the heel (4) and thence to another tie in the hollow of the knee (5). A second ramification extending across the calf (6) establishes a link between the last mentioned tie and that on the malleolus and then extends from the hollow of the knee across the posterior femoral region (7) to a tie on the *gluteus maximus* (8). It continues within the muscles of the back (9) to a tie on the *gluteus maximus* (8). It continues within the muscles of the back (9) to a tie on the occiput (12), crosses the parietal bone (13), and ends in a tie at the root of the nose (15). A further ramification extends from the neck to the hypoglottis (11), and another leaves the root of the nose, forms the so-called upper plexus of the eye (*mu chih shang-wang* 目之上網) (16), and descends to a tie on the *os zygomaticum* (17). Still another secondary branch leaves the muscle conduit at shoulder height (18), passes below the shoulder and through the *fossa supraclavicularis* (19), and from there continues to the *processus mastoideus* (22). A tertiary ramification leaves the branch last mentioned and extends upward to a tie on the shoulder. Finally a ramification extends obliquely from the *fossa supraclavicularis* (19) across the mandible and cheek to a tie on the *os zygomaticum* (17).

SYMPTOMS

Swellings and pains radiating from the small toe; spasms in the hollow of the knee; tensions and spasms of the muscles of the back and neck; inability to lift the arm; boring pain between the axilla and the *fossa supraclavicularis* that prevents the patient from moving the arm. These symptoms are called collectively "spasms and pareses of the second spring month" (*chung-ch'un-pi* 仲春痺).

[145]*Ling-shu* 13/1054ff; *Chen-chiu-hsüeh chiang-i*, pp. 89ff.

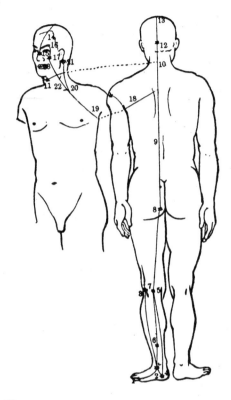

Fig. 70

THE *NERVOCARDINALIS FELLEA YANG MINORIS PEDIS* (足少陽膽經筋)

COURSE

This muscle conduit (Fig. 71) originates on the fourth toe (1) and runs to a tie on the *malleolus lateralis* (2), continuing across the external crural region to a tie on the knee (3). A branch leaves the conduit at the head of the fibula (4) and bifurcates on the upper leg into a short branch ending in a tie on the anterior femoral region (5), and a longer continuation from which another ramification branches out to a tie on the *gluteus maximus* at approximately the height of the *articulatio coxae* (6). The continuation itself again bifurcates on the ribs (7), one branch extending to the nipple (8) and from there to a tie in the *fossa supraclavicularis* (9), and the second reaching the same spot via the axilla (10). From the *fossa supraclavicularis* (11) the continuation circles the ear in front of the *cardinalis vesicalis* (12), and then ascends to the parietal bone (13, 14), where it meets its counterpart from the other side of the body. It then descends on the other side across the temporal bone down to the cheek (15) and deflects upward to a tie on the *os zygomaticum,* with a short ramification ending in a tie to the outer canthus.

SYMPTOMS

Clonic and tonic spasms, tenseness, or stiffness in the muscle regions touched by the conduits, especially in the fourth toe, the knee, the upper leg, the glutei, the bow of the ribs, the

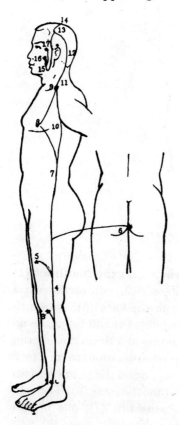

Fig. 71

pectoral muscles, and the neck. The chiasma of the muscle conduit on the parietal bone is responsible for a crosswise combination of symptoms of the parallel conduits, e.g:, paresis of the left eyelid and pains in the right muscle conduit. The symptoms enumerated are collectively called "spasms and pareses of the first spring month" (*meng-ch'un-pi* 孟春痹).

THE *NERVOCARDINALIS STOMACHI SPLENDORIS YANG PEDIS* (足陽明胃經筋)

COURSE

This muscle conduit (Fig. 72) originates on the second, third, and fourth toes (1) in three equivalent branches meeting in a tie on the dorsum of the foot (2), from where it continues obliquely to a tie behind the top of the fibula (3), ascending first to a tie on the *articulatio coxae* (4) and then to the floating ribs (5), where it deflects backward toward the spine (6). The main branch of the conduit runs from the tie on the *dorsum pedis* (2) along the tibia to a tie in the patellar region (7). A short branch connects to a tie on the top of the fibula (8), establishing a link with the *nervocardinalis fellea*. From the tie in the patellar region the conduit ascends through the anterior femoral region (9) to a tie at the highest point of the lower bonder of the ischium (10) and then to a tie in the genitals (11), from where it radiates into the abdominal and thoracic walls (12). It is tied again in the *fossa supraclavicularis* (13), continues across the throat and cheek, approaches the mouth from below by a side branch (14), reaches the *os zygomaticum*, extends to a tie at the lower border of the nose (16), and reascends to the inner canthus (17), where it unites with the *nervocardinalis vesicalis* (17), after which it forms the lower plexus of the eye (*mu chih hsia-wang* 目之下網). This is complementary to the upper plexus formed by the *nervocardinalis vesicalis*. A branch leaves the conduit on the cheek and ends in a tie directly in front of the ear.

SYMPTOMS

Spasms, spastic pains, twitchings, paresses, and paralyses in the regions touched by the muscle conduit, especially radiating from the third toe in the direction of the tibia, on the dorsum

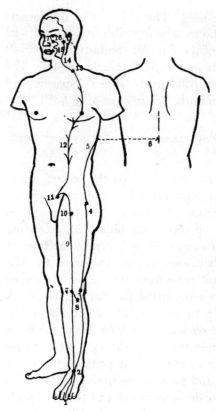

Fig. 72

of the foot, in the anterior femoral region, on the *gluteus maximus*, and from the abdominal wall through the *fossa supraclavicularis* up to the cheek. If the muscles of the cheek are implicated, distorted mouth and an inability to open or to close the eye; oozing tumors on the genitals. These symptoms are collectively designated "spasms and pareses of the third spring month" (*chi-ch'un-pi* 季春痹).

THE *NERVOCARDINALIS LIENALIS YIN MAIORIS PEDIS*(足太陰脾經筋)
COURSE
This muscle conduit (Fig. 73) originates at the tip of the large

toe (1), extends backward to a tie on the *malleolus medialis* (2), and from there into a plexus around the *condylus medialis tibiae* (3). It continues through the internal femoral region to a tie at the height of the lower border of the ischium (4), and from there to a tie in the genitals (5), from which it ascends to a tie in the navel (6). There it traverses the abdomen sagittally and reaches the spine at the height of the last lumbar vertebra. The conduit then ascends along the inner side of the

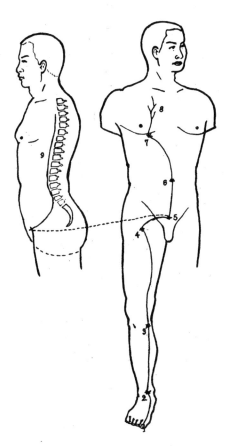

Fig. 73

spine (9) and also radiates into the walls of the abdomen and the thorax, where it is tied once more.

SYMPTOMS

Pains and spasms radiating from the big toe toward the *malleolus medialis*; pains at the *condylus medialis tibiae*; pains radiating forward and upward from the internal femoral region; tearing pains in the genitals, radiating upward toward the navel; simultaneous pains in the thorax and spine. These symptoms make up the "spasms and pareses of the first autumn month" (*meng-ch'iu-pi* 孟秋痹).

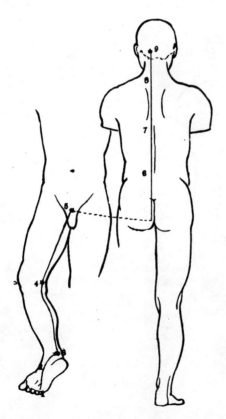

Fig. 74

THE *NERVOCARDINALIS RENALIS YIN MINORIS PEDIS* (足少陰腎經筋)

COURSE

This muscle conduit (Fig. 74) originates on the plantar side of the tip of the small toe (1), traverses the arch (2), and in company with the *nervocardinalis lienalis* enters a tie situated back and below the *malleolus medialis* on the heel (3). From there it ascends with the *nervocardinalis vesicalis* to a tie within the hollow of the knee (4), from where it returns to join the *nervocardinalis lienalis*. After traversing the internal femoral region it arrives at a tie in the genitals (5) and ascends through the muscles along the inner side of the spine (6, 7) up to the occiput (8), where it unites in a tie with the *nervocardinalis vesicalis* (9).

SYMPTOMS

Spasms and twitching in all regions (especially the lower extremities) touched by the muscle conduit. Spastic paralyses, contortions, atrophy. A general symptom associated with this conduit is that the extremity or the whole body cannot be bent toward the side opposite the one affected. There is an infaust prognosis if the recurrence of spasms in the regions touched by this conduit is too violent or too frequent. The enumerated symptoms are collectively designated "spasms and pareses of the second autumn month" (*chung-ch'iu-pi* 仲秋痹).

THE *NERVOCARDINALIS HEPATICA YIN FLECTENTIS PEDIS* (足厥陰肝經筋)

COURSE

This muscle conduit (Fig. 75) originates on the big toe (1) medially near its tip, runs to the tie in front of the *malleolus medialis* (2), and then ascends through the internal crural region to the tie on the *condylus medialis tibiae* (3), whence it continues across the interior femoral region to the tie in the genitals (4). There it attaches to all the other yin muscle conduits (*nervocardinales yin*) as well as to the *nervocardinales splendoris yang*.

SYMPTOMS

Pains radiating from the big toe toward the *malleolus medialis,*

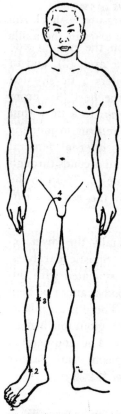

Fig. 75

pains at the *condylus medialis tibiae;* pains and spasms in the
internal femoral region; impotence. These symptoms are the
"spasms and pareses of the third autumn month" (*chi-ch'iu-pi*
季秋痹).

THE *NERVOCARDINALIS INTESTINI TENUIS YANG MAIORIS MANUS*
(手太陽小腸經筋)

COURSE

This muscle conduit (Fig. 76) originates dorsally on the tip of
the small finger (1), is tied at the wrist (2), ascends through the
ulnar antebrachial region to a tie behind the *epicondylus medialis*

humeri (3) (at the place where, on slight pressure, a shock runs down the little finger), and continues into a tie in the axilla. A branch out of the axilla from behind (4) extends across the shoulder blade up to the neck (5), where it ascends in front of the *nervocardinalis vesicalis* (6) to the tie on the mastoid process (7). One branch enters the ear (8) and another skirts the ear from behind, descending across the cheek to a tie on the mandible (9), from which it reascends to unite with the outer canthus (10). Another ramification leaves the preceding one on the neck (11), ascends across the mandibular angle (12) and in front of the ear to the junction in the outer canthus, after which it ends in a tie at the angle of the hair border (13).

SYMPTOMS

Pains in those parts of the arm that are supplied by the muscle conduit; ringing and pains in the ears, pain radiating from the ear toward the mandible; dim eyesight remedied only by closing the eyes for a long moment; tensions in the muscles of

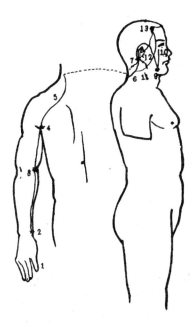

Fig. 76

the neck; carbuncles on the neck. These symptoms make up what is called "the spasms and pareses of the second summer month" (*chung-hsia-pi* 仲夏痹).

THE *NERVOCARDINALIS TRICALORII YANG MINORIS MANUS* (手少陽三焦經筋)

COURSE

This muscle conduit (Fig. 77) originates at the tip of the ring finger (1) and is tied in the middle of the wrist (2). It continues through the dorsal antebrachial region to a tie at the elbow joint (3) and ascends through the posterior brachial region (4) and across the shoulder to the neck (5). There it unites with the *nervocardinalis intestini crassi yang maioris manus*. A branch extends around the mandibular angle to the root of the tongue; another crosses the mandibular ramus (6), passes in front of the ear (7), unites with the outer canthus, and, after traversing the temple, ends at a tie in the angle of the hair border (8).

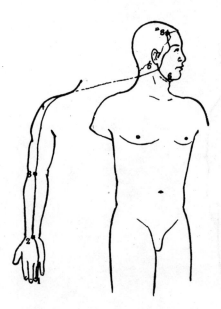

Fig. 77

SYMPTOMS

Tensions and spasms in the regions served by this muscle conduit; spastic rolling up of the tongue. These symptoms are collectively known as the "spasms and pareses of the third summer month" (*chi-hsia-pi* 季夏痹).

THE *NERVOCARDINALIS INTESTINI CRASSI SPLENDORIS YANG MANUS* (手太陽大腸經筋)

COURSE

This muscle conduit (Fig. 78) originates at the tip of the index finger (1), extends dorsally to a tie at the radial border of the wrist (2), and continues through a tie situated at the border of the anterior and middle cubital regions (3) and through the anterior brachial and deltoid regions to a tie in the shoulder

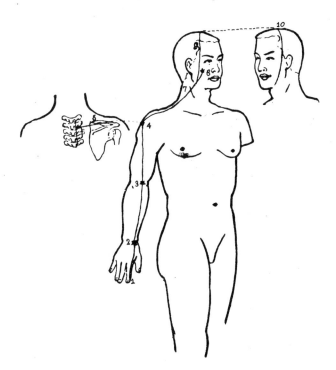

Fig. 78

joint (4). From there a ramification crosses the shoulder blade
(5) and attaches to the spine (6); the main conduit continues
across the neck to the throat (7), where it divides. A short
branch ends in a tie on the *os zygomaticum* (8); a longer
branch passes to the angle of the border of hair in front of the
nervocardinalis intestini tenuis yang maioris manus (10), radiates on
the parietal bone, and finally redescends on the opposite side,
crossing the cheek and ending on the mandible.

SYMPTOMS

Twitching, spasms, and stiffness in the regions touched by this
muscle conduit. Inability to lift the arm or turn the head. These
symptoms are collectively called the "spasms and pareses of the
first summer month" (*meng-hsia-pi* 孟夏痹).

THE *NERVOCARDINALIS PULMONALIS YIN MAIORIS MANUS* (手太陰肺經筋)

COURSE

This muscle conduit (Fig. 79) originates near the tip of the
thumb (1), runs to a tie on the proximal border of the thenar
(2), and continues along the radius and through the volar

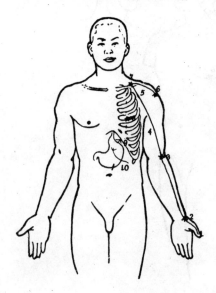

Fig. 79

antebrachial region to a tie in the hollow of the elbow (3). From there it ascends through the anterior brachial region (4) to the axilla (5) and submerges to emerge again in the *fossa supraclavicularis* (6). It extends to the tie in the shoulder joint (7), reverts into the *fossa supraclavicularis,* descends into the thorax to a tie in the chest (8), radiates on and penetrates through the diaphragm (9), with which it unites, and finally touches the floating ribs (10).

SYMPTOMS

Pains and tensions in the regions touched by the conduit. In the case of violent pains, such organic changes as pleuritis, abscess of the lungs, and hemoptysis may be expected. These symptoms are collectively called the "spasms and pareses of the second winter month" (*chung-tung-pi* 仲冬痹).

THE *NERVOCARDINALIS PERICARDIALIS YIN FLECTENTIS MANUS* (手厥陰心包經筋)

COURSE

This muscle conduit (Fig. 80) originates on the middle finger

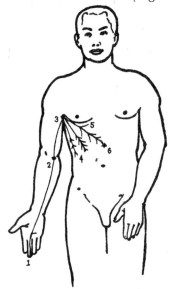

Fig. 80

(1), traverses the palm, and joins the *nervocardinalis pulmonalis* behind the wrist; both conduits then enter a tie in the hollow of the elbow (2). From there the *nervocardinalis pericardialis* ascends to a tie at the axilla (3), whence it radiates with a number of ramifications on the outside of the ribs and the inner side of the thorax (4, 5), and is tied on the diaphragm (6).

SYMPTOMS

Feelings of tension and spasms of the regions touched by this conduit. In severe cases such organic changes as pleuritis and phthisis must be espected. These symptoms are collectively known as the "spasms and pareses of the first winter month" (*meng-tung-pi* 孟冬痹).

THE *NERVOCARDINALIS CARDIALIS YIN MINORIS MANUS* (手少陰心經筋)

COURSE

This muscle conduit (Fig. 81) originates medially at the tip of the small finger (1) and extends to the ulnar tie at the wrist (2), whence it continues to a tie in the inner cubital region (3), and ascends to the axilla (4), where it crosses the *nervocardinalis pulmonalis*. It then traverses the nipple (5) to reach a tie on the

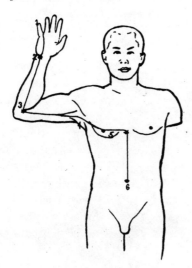

Fig. 81

sternum, and descends vertically within the wall of the thorax and abdomen to unite with the navel (6).

SYMPTOMS

Tensions and spasms in the regions served by this conduit; in severe cases, organic changes, hemoptysis, purulent sputum, and an infaust prognosis must be expected. These symptoms are collectively known as "spasms and pareses of the third winter month" (*chi-tung-pi* 季冬痹).

General Theory of the Sensitive Points: Foraminology

The descriptions of the different kinds of energetic conduits in the preceding four sections confirm a statement made at the outset:[146] that the fundamental empirically verifiable constituents of sinarteriology are not the conduits (*sinarteriae, ching-mo*) but the sensitive points (*foramina, hsüeh, shu-hsüeh*) situated on them. Only to the extent that a conduit is marked out by foramina of its own (*foramina propria*) may its course be mapped clearly and with universal significance. On the other hand, conduits without sensitive points of their own, or parts of conduits, which, because they extend deep within the body, lack sensitive points, are essentially functional models similar to those of orbisiconography.[147] Their primary purpose is to facilitate the logical or mnemonic associations of certain constant physiological and pathological relations.

The functional model represented by the system of energetic conduits consequently serves to describe actual (as opposed to potential) positive effects the substrate of which can be defined only approximately or not at all. We here meet with the apparent dilemma also encountered by modern psychiatry. Certain psychic complexes and syndromes occur with such a degree of regularity that there is no denying their positive nature. Yet there is no hope that more than the crudest outline of these psychic functions may be correlated with their substratum, the neurological organs. We call this an apparent dilemma because, until quite recently, it has never existed for

[146]See p. 198.
[147]Similar to those of orbisiconography.

Chinese medicine. For, in taking definite and rational therapeutic measures, a logically consistent model of the functional
relationships, founded upon conscientious observation of the
phenomena, is perfectly satisfactory. The point is that assertions
like " . . . the *paracardinalis fellea* unites with the *orbis felleus,*
radiates upward, spreads out in the *orbis hepaticus,* traverses the
orbis cardialis . . . " may neither be confirmed nor refuted by
anatomical arguments, because these do not apply.

THE GENERAL CLASSIFICATION OF SENSITIVE POINTS

In therapeutic disciplines such as acupuncture, moxibustion,
or massage, three kinds of sensitive points are of interest. By
distinguishing among them, we incidentally catch a glimpse of
the evolutive stages of foraminology. The first kind are the
foramina ad hoc. In Chinese these are called *ah-shih-hsüeh* 阿是穴,
because the patient exclaims "oh yes!" (*ah shih*) when one of
these foramina is pressed in exploratory palpation. These ad
hoc points, without scientific names or precise topology, are
partly identical with the "knots" that masseurs of all civilizations work to dispel. Chinese practitioners of acupuncture,
moxibustion, and massage likewise concentrate on the *foramina
ad hoc* to alleviate certain myalgias and local muscular tensions.
The anonymous *foramina ad hoc*[148] very probably correspond to
the most primitive stage in the gradual development of foraminology.

The earliest stage of systematic foraminology is reflected in
the *foramina imparia extracardinalia* (*ching-wai chi-hsüeh* 經外奇穴),
sensitive points that have a specific name, a precisely defined
location, and particular symptoms attributed to them, but that
have not been incorporated as yet into the network of a sinartery. The most recent textbooks[149] enumerate 359 *foramina
imparia.* The *foramina imparia* are treated solely on the basis of

[148]The designation *ah-shih-hsüeh* 阿是穴 was introduced comparatively late,
during the T'ang period, by Sun Szu-mo. Later still, these points come to
be called *foramina indeterminata* (*pu-ting-hsüeh* 不定穴) or *foramina naturalia*
(*t'ien-ying-hsüeh* 天應穴); in Japanese literature they are also known as
montōketsu 捫當穴 ("foramina resisting when stroked"). See the *Shu-hsüeh-
hsüeh kai-lun,* p. 5.
[149]*Shu-hsüeh-hsüeh kai-lun,* pp. 216ff.

the symptoms associated with them, but, because of their lack of integration into the system of correspondences, they have only limited diagnostic significance. However, their number and therapeutic usefulness make the *foramina imparia extracardinalia* second in importance only to the sensitive points situated on the cardinal conduits.

From their ranks come additions to the third group, the *foramina cardinalia* (*ching-hsüeh* 經穴), points situated on one of the twelve cardinal conduits or on the *sinarteriae regens et respondens*.[150] They also have names of their own, precisely defined locations, and specifically associated symptoms. In addition, the system of the conduits establishes a direct logical connection between the *foramina cardinalia* and a varying number of the orbs, which are circumscribed functional spheres. There is also an indirect yet precisely qualified relation to the organism as a whole. For these reasons the therapeutic applications of the *foramina cardinalia* are considerably more numerous than those of the first two groups of foramina; moreover, examination of the cardinal points permits inferences to be drawn about the functions of the orbs.

In addition to the classification of the *foramina cardinalia* based on the conduits (*sinarteriae*), further qualitative distinctions between the foramina grouped on a specific sinartery are made by applying the traditional qualitative conventions. This subtle and precise definition of the foramina corresponding to essential functions is described in the next section.

Functional Categories of the Foramina cardinalia

THE *INDUCTORIA DORSALIA* ([*PEI*]-*SHU* 背兪)

The Chinese term *shu* 腧前, *inductorium,* may be used on' three semantic levels with four different inflections of meaning:

---

[150]According to recent counts (*Ibid,* p. 3), the *Nei-ching* (at the beginning of the Han period) describes 160 *foramina cardinalia;* the *Chia-i-ching* of the Chin, 349; the *T'ung-jen shu-hsüeh chen-chiu t'u-ching* of the Sung, 354; the *Chen-chiu ta-ch'eng* 鍼灸大成 of the Ming, 359, and modern textbooks, 361. Since the mirror symmetry of the body requires that 309 of the 361 points be represented on both halves, today's practicioners enumerate 670 *foramina cardinalia.*

(1) *Shu* 腧 or *shu-hsüeh* 腧穴 (normative equivalents: *inductorium, foramen inductorium*) is the generic designation for every kind of sensitive point ("foramen").

(2) On a less extensive semantic level, *shu* 俞 (腧) is the pregnant designation of twelve special sensitive points assigned to the twelve orbs. Because all these foramina are situated on the back, they are more precisely designated as the *inductoria dorsalia* (*pei-shu* 脊俞). For clarity's sake we always render this meaning by the complete equivalent *inductorium dorsale* or by the abbreviation *I*, even if in the Chinese text *shu* alone is used. According to a widespread even if not general convention, in medical texts this sense of *shu* is usually written with the "ancient" character 俞 (without radical 130).

(3) *Shu* 腧 is the generic designation for the "Five Inductories" (*wu-shu* 五腧), those sensitive points of each cardinal conduit whose specialized functions correspond to the Five Evolutive Phases. Our normative equivalent is *inductorium*, without any epithet.

(4) On a third semantic level, *shu*, used with pregnant meaning, designates the third of the Five Inductories, and is rendered by the normative equivalent *foramen inductorium*, abbreviated *i*.

By definition all foramina are points of transmission of actual influences (*inductoria*). Still, a number of sensitive points seem to be "inductive transmitters" in a stricter sense than others, and consequently the name *inductoria* has special application to them. These points are all situated on the back, on a branch of the *cardinalis vesicalis yang maioris pedis,* hence their name, *inductoria dorsalia* (*pei-shu* 背俞). In the functions of an *inductorium dorsale* the active energies of a given orb or organic sphere find their purest and most powerful expression. Consequently, the *inductoria dorsalia* are of particular therapeutic significance if the expansive, active functions of an orb are to be influenced. Twelve of the *inductoria dorsalia* are designated by the name of the orb or vital sphere with which they are specifically associated, thus:

Inductorium pulmonale cV13
     yin flectentis [*pericardiale*] cV14
     cardiale cV15
     hepaticum cV18
     felleum cV19
     lienale cV20
     stomachi cV21
     tricalorii cV22
     renale cV23

intestini crassi cV25
intestini tenuis cV27
vesicale cV28

Additional *inductoria dorsalia* are the

Inductorium regentis cV16
   praecordiale cV17
   maris ch'i cV24
   prima clusarum cV26
   pro medio tergo cV29
   anuli candidi cV30.

THE *CONQUISITORIA ABDOMINALIA* ([*FU*]-*MU* 腹募)

A number of foramina situated on the abdominal side are complementary in polarity and function to the *inductoria dorsalia*. In these the structive aspects of a given orb or organic sphere find their purest and most powerful expression, for, as the name *mu* 募, *conquisitorium*, suggests, in them the specific energy of the orbs is structively collected and accumulated. Consequently each *conquisitorium abdominale* has particular significance for the treatment of energetic stagnation and of chronic diseases of the corresponding orb. The *conquisitoria abdominalia* corresponding to the twelve orbs are

Aula media (*Conquisitorium pulmonale*) cP1
Atrium pectoris (*Conquisitorium pericardiale*) Rs17
Conquisitorium cardiale Rs14
Conquisitorium hepaticum cH14
Conquisitorium lienale cH13
Conquisitorium stomachi Rs12
Prima clusarum (*Conquisitorium intestini tenuis*) Rs4
Porta lapidea (*Conquisitorium tricalorii*) Rs5
Conquisitorium vesicale Rs3
Cardo caeli (*Conquisitorium intestini crassi*) cS25
Sol et luna (*Conquisitorium felleum*) cF24
Porta pyramidis (*Conquisitorium renale*) cF25.

THE [*FORAMINA*] *RIMICA* (*HSI* [*-HSÜEH*] 郄穴)

In certain folds or interstices of the extremities (Chinese: *hsi* 郄, Latin: *rima*, English: fissure, cleft) physiological energy may accumulate and stagnate. By influencing the foramina which coincide with these clefts, the so-called *foramina rimica*, it is possible to exert a deep-reaching influence on the circulation of energy through the cardinal conduits and their orbs. The *rimica* are of particular significance for the treatment of severe and persistent diseases and ailments. A *rimicum* is situated on each cardinal conduit and on the *cardinales impares retinentes et ascendentes*, as shown in Table 22.

THE [*FORAMINA*] *NEXORIA* (*LUO* [*-HSÜEH*] 絡穴)

Luo is one of the rare words for which we have introduced two different normative equivalents in order to adequately render its meanings in different contexts: (1) "net," "reticular," in Latin: *reticularis;* and (2)

Table 22. The *Foramina rimica* and Their Locations

Cardinális	*Rimicum*	
pulmonalis	*extremitas cavi*	cP6
cardialis	*rimicum yin minoris*	cC6
renalis	*fons aquarum*	cR5
fellea	*monticulus externus*	cF36
hepatica	*urbs media*	cH6
tricalorii	*genus conventum*	cT7
pericardialis	*porta rimica*	cPC4
lienalis	*domus lienalis*	cL8
intestini crassi	*amnis fovens*	cIC7
vesicalis	*porta metalli*	cV63
intestini tenuis	*senectus felix*	cIT6
stomachi	*monticulus septi*	cS34
Sinarteria impar		
retinens yin	*ripa spissa*	cR9
retinens yang	*copulatio yang*	cF35
ascendens yin	*cursores copulati*	cR8
ascendens yang	*yang tarsi*	cV59

"to attach," in Latin: *nectere, nexorius*. We must, however, keep in mind that both terms go back to one and the same Chinese concept. The contact between a yang or outer orb (*orbis aulicus sive speciei*) and a yin or inner orb (*orbis horrealis sive intimae*) in a functional yoke depends on the linkage between outer and inner cardinal conduits (*cardinalis speciei, cardinalis intimae*). This linkage is established by means of the reticular conduits (*luo-mo*) that attach (*luo*) to the cardinal conduits. Every reticular conduit originates in a foramen situated on the cardinal conduit,[151] called the [*foramen*] *nexorium* (*luo-*[*hsüeh*]).[152] The *nexoria* play a key role in energy exchange within the functional yokes, and thus quite generally in the diagnosis and therapy of disturbances of metabolism in the wide sense. The

Table 23. The *Foramina nexoria* and Their Cardinal Conduits

Cardinalis	Nexorium	
pulmonalis	lacunae	cP7
cardialis	vicus communicans	cC5
lienalis	caput metatarsalis hallucis	cL4
hepatica	canalis teredinis	cH5
renalis	campana magna	cR4
pericardialis	clusa interna	cPC6
intestini crassi	pervium obliquum	cIC6
intestini tenuis	adminiculans orthopathiam	cIT7
stomachi	abundantia	cS40
fellea	lumen ac splendor	cF37
vesicalis	yang flectens	cV58
tricalorii	clusa externa	cT5
Sinarteria		
regens	incrementum et vigor	Rg1
respondens	cauda columbina	Rg15
Reticularis		
magna lienalis	magnum lienalis	cL21

[151]See p. 214 above.
[152]*Ling-shu* 10/1036ff.

nexoria already mentioned, and their respective reticular conduits, are shown in Table 23.

THE FIVE INDUCTORIES (*QUINQUE INDUCTORIA, WU-SHU* 五腧)

All cardinal conduits either originate or terminate at the tip of an extremity. According to a theory set forth in the first two chapters of the *Ling-shu*,[153] the energy circulating in a given cardinal conduit first flows weakly from its "well hole" (in Chinese: *ching* 井, in Latin: [*foramen*] *puteale*) situated at the tip of the extremity, and then at each joint increases in quantity, until it finally constitutes a powerful river running through the body.

This theory has proven of practical use within narrow topological limits: nevertheless it clearly contradicts the general classical rules on the directions of the cardinal conduits.[154] This contradiction can only be resolved empirically.

Starting at the tip of the extremity, the first five foramina of each cardinal conduit are assigned the conventional standards

Table 24. Locations of the Five Inductories and Their Correspondences

Location of the Foramen	Name	Correspondence on a Yin Cardinal Conduit	Correspondence on a Yang Cardinal Conduit
Fingertip/tip of the toe	*foramen puteale* (*ching* 井)	Wood[a]	Metal
Basic phalanx	*foramen effusorium* (*hsing* 滎)	Fire[b]	Water
Metatarsus/metacarpus	*foramen inductorium* (*shu* 腧)	Earth[c]	Wood
Forearm/lower leg	*foramen transitorium* (*ching* 經)	Metal[d]	Fire
Elbow/knee	*foramen coniunctorium* (*ho* 合)	Water[e]	Earth

[a] *Ching* = *puteus* = well.
[b] *Hsing* = *effundere* = to flow out.
[c] See the parenthesis on p. 336 above.
[d] *Ching* = *transire* = to pass.
[e] *Ho* = *coniungere* = to unite.

[153]1/909f; 2/915ff.
[154]See pp. 205–206 above.

of yin, yang, and the Five Evolutive Phases (see Table 24). Thus the points nearest the extremities are implanted even more deeply within the graduated system of therapy.

In therapy the foramina related to the evolutive phases may be influenced in the direction of either the production sequence (Sequence I) or the conquest sequence (Sequence II). If, for example, a pathological repletion of energy is diagnosed in the *orbis pulmonalis*—which corresponds to the evolutive phase Metal—the sensitive point that corresponds to Water, the *foramen coniunctorium cardinalis pulmonalis,* may be needled, in accordance with the rule "in case of repletion the 'child' is drained." If, to the contrary, an exhaustion of the energy in the *orbis pulmonalis* has been diagnosed, the rule "in case of exhaustion the 'mother' must be replenished" is applied and the sensitive point corresponding to Earth, *foramen inductorium orbis pulmonalis,* is given preferred attention. These relations reflect the order Earth–Metal–Water in Sequence I.

To facilitate comparison, the Five Inductories of the twelve cardinal conduits are brought together in Tables 25 and 26.

Quite independently from the cardinal conduits on which they are situated, the Five Inductories are ascribed therapeutic affinities solely on the basis of their corresponding evolutive phases. This implies an influence on the unfoldments (*perfectiones*) of the orbs and their pathology. Thus it is considered that

the *foramina*	should be given attention in case of
putealia	repletion, plethora of the epigastrium
effusoria	heat and fever in general
inductoria	fatigue, pains in the joints
transitoria	difficult respiration; chills and flushes
coniunctoria	*contravectio ch'i* [circulatory troubles] including disturbed excretory functions, urinary incontinence, diarrhea, collapse

THE *FORAMINA* [*CH'I*] *ORIGINALIS* (*YÜAN-HSÜEH* 原穴)

The *foramina* [*ch'i*] *originalis* (*yüan-hsüeh*) are likewise mentioned in *Ling-shu* 1/912f and 2/919ff. Their name, according to *Nan-ching* 5/144f, is explained by the fact that the *ch'i originale* (activated *ch'i nativum*[155] stored in the *orbis renalis* and distribut-

[155]For these terms see the entries on p. 172.

Table 25. The Five Inductories of the Yin Cardinal Conduits

Cardinalis	Foramen puteale (ching): Wood	Foramen effusorium (hsing): Fire	Foramen inductorium (shu): Earth	Foramen transitorium (ching): Metal	Foramen coniunctorium (ho): Water
pulmonalis	metallum structivum cP11	linea piscis cP10	vorago maior cP9	emisarium transitorium cP8	lacus ulnaris cP5
pericardialis	impedimentale medium cPC9	medium palmae cPC8	tumulus magnus cPC7	foramen intermedium cPC5	lacus curvus cPC3
cardialis	impedimentale minus cC9	aula minor cC8	impedimentale laetitiae cC7	foramen responsivum cC4	mare minus cC3
lienalis	canidor occultus cL1	urbs magna cL2	candidum maius cL3	monticulus tali cL5	fons tumuli yin cL9
hepatica	lanx magna cH1	interstitium ambulatorium cH2	impedimentale maius cH3	altare medium cH4	fons curvus cH8
renalis	fons scatens cR1	fons draconis cR2	rivulus maior cR3	amnis recurrens cR7	vallis yin cR10

Table 26. The Five Inductories of the Yang Cardinal Conduits

Cardinalis	Foramen puteale (*ching*): Wood	Foramen effusorium (*hsing*): Water	Foramen inductorium (*shu*): Wood	Foramen transitorium (*ching*): Fire	Foramen coniunctorium (*ho*): Earth
intestini crassi	*yang extremum* cIC1	*interstitium alterum* cIC2	*interstitium tertium* cIC3	*rivulus yang* cIC5	*stagnum curvum* cIC11
tricalorii	*impedimentale clusae* cT1	*porta suci* cT2	*insula media* cT3	*tigris volans* cT6	*puteus caelestis* cT10
intestini tenuis	*lacus minor* cIT1	*vallis anterior* cIT2	*rivulus posterior* cIT3	*vallis yang* cIT5	*mare parvum* cIT8
stomachi	*laetitia repressa* cS45	*vestibulum internum* cS44	*vallis demersum* cS43	*rivulus liberans* cS41	*vicus tertius pedis* cS36
fellea	*yin penetrans pedis* cF44	*rivulus coercitus* cF43	*lacrimarum instantium pedis* cF41	*divisio carnis* cF38	*fors tumuli yang* cF34
vesicalis	*yin supremus* cV67	*vallis communicans vesicalis* cV66	*os ligatum* cV65	*olympus* cV60	*medium lacunae* cV40

Table 27. The *Foramina* [*ch'i*] *originalis* and Their Reticular Conduits

Cardinalis	*Foramen* [*ch'i*] *originalis*	
intestini crassi	*valles coniunctae*	cIC4
tricalorii	*stagnum yang*	cT4
intestini tenuis	*foramen carpium*	cIT4
stomachi	*yang impedimentalis*	cS42
fellea	*agger monticuli*	cF40
vesicalis	*os pyramidale*	cV64

ed throughout the organism under the aspects of *ch'i genuinum,
constructivum, et defensivum* by the influence of the *orbis tricalorii*)
concentrates with particular intensity in these foramina. In
other words; the *foramina originalis* represent sensitive points
through which the physician may directly and profoundly
influence the native constitution of an individual. They are all
situated in the metacarpal or metatarsal regions. Every cardinal
conduit has a *foramen originalis,* but as a rule those of the yin
cardinal conduits are identical with one of the Five Inductories
(*quinque inductorioria*). We may therefore confine ourselves to
an enumeration of the *foramina originalis* situated on the *cardinales yang* (Table 27).

THE *FORAMINA CONVENTORIA (HUI-HSÜEH* 會穴)

According to a theory set out in *Nan-ching* 45[156] the eight
principal constituents of the organism (yang orbs, yin orbs,
ch'i, hsüeh, and so on), even though they are already associated
directly and indirectly with numerous foramina, is each
represented "generically" by a particular foramen. In this
sensitive point, called *foramen conventorium* (*hui-hsüeh* 會穴),
the specific energy of the constituent is concentrated, and thus
is accessible to directed and intensive therapeutic measures.
Practitioners often avail themselves of this possibility, especially
in the event of fever diseases, as the commentator Ting Te-
yung noted in the Sung period.[157] The eight principal constit-

[156]*Nan-ching* 4/112–114.
[157]P. 114.

Table 28. The Eight *Conventus* and Their *Foramina conventoria*

Conventus	Foramen conventorium	
orbium horrealium	conquisitorium lienale	cH13
orbium aulicorum	conquisitorium stomachi	Rs12
ch'i	atrium pectoris	Rs17
hsüeh	inductorium praecordiale	cV17
ossium	radius magnus	cV11
medullae	campana suspensa	cF39
nervorum	fons tumuli yang	cF34
sinarteriarum	vorago maior	cP9

uents (*conventus*) and their corresponding *foramina conventoria* are shown in Table 28.

THE *FORAMINA COPULO-CONVENTORIA (CHIAO-HUI-HSÜEH* 交會穴)

With the exception of the *cardinalis cardialis,* each *cardinalis* and each *cardinalis impar* shares one, two, or even more of its foramina with other conduits. In these sensitive points, called *foramina copulo-conventoria (chiao-hui-hsüeh),* the different energies flowing in the conduits concerned meet (in Chinese: *hui* 會, in Latin: *convenire*) and mingle (in Chinese: *chiao* 交, in Latin *copulare*). By influencing a *foramen copulo-conventorium,* the flow of energy is simultaneously modified in more than one conduit and its corresponding orb. The *foramina copulo-conventoria* are listed at the end of the description of each conduit above.

Conclusion

The preceding account attempts to outline the system of correspondences in Chinese medicine and to lay terminological foundations for more extensive investigations in its vast and immensely rich literature. It is our intention to elucidate in the future the ramifications and the practical applications of these correspondences in the separate disciplines of diagnostics, pathology, acupuncture, pharmacology, and pharmacotherapy. It is our hope that other scholars will join us in this task.

Selected Bibliography

This bibliography includes only sources of general utility. Full citations are given in the footnotes of this book for works cited only in passing. Translations of titles in the first part of this bibliography are enclosed in parentheses. If a translation of the title would not give a sense of the book's contents, a concise description follows the title instead. For the convenience of those who read only Chinese, titles of books written in classical Chinese by Japanese and Korean writers are given in Wade-Giles romanization. No attempt is made to provide provisional dates for well-known anonymous Chinese classics. Cross-references by short forms are provided for any works cited by abbreviated titles.

Chinese Sources

Chen-chiu chi-ch'eng 針灸集成
(Compendium of acu-moxi-therapy), by Liao Jun-hung 廖潤鴻 (1874).
Peking: People's Hygiene Press 人民衛生出版社, 1956.

Chen-chiu chia-i-ching. See *Chia-i-ching*

Chen-chiu chih-liao tz'u-chi-tien chieh-p'ou wei-chih ts'an-k'ao-t'u 針灸治療刺激點解剖位置參考圖
(Illustrations showing the anatomical positions of the sensitive points), edited by Ma Chi-hsing 馬繼興 and drawn by Yeh Yang-hsi 葉仰義.
Peking: *idem.*, 1955, 1957.

Chen-chiu ching-hsüeh t'u-k'ao 針灸經穴圖考
(Illustrated investigations of the *foramina cardinalia* of acu-moxi-therapy), by Huang Chu-chai 黃竹齋. Peking: *idem.*, 1957.

Chen-chiu-hsüeh chiang-i 針灸學講義
(Textbook of acu-moxi-therapy), compiled by Acu-moxi–theraphy Teaching Unit, Shanghai College of Traditional Chinese Medicine. Shanghai: Shanghai Science and Technology Press 上海科學技術出版社, 1960.

Chi-ching pa-mo k'ao 奇經八脈考
(Critical examination of the *cardinales impares* and their pulses), by Li Shih-chen 李時珍 (1518–1593). Peking: *idem.*, 1956, 1957.

Chia-i-ching 針灸甲乙經
(Systematic classic of acu-moxi-therapy), compiled by Huang-fu Mi 皇甫謐 (282). Peking: *idem.*, 1954, 1956, Also cited as *Chen-chiu chia-i-ching*.

Ch'ien-chin yao-fang 千金要方
(Prescriptions worth a thousand), by Sun Szu-mo 孫思邈 (between 650 and 659). Reprint of the Edo igaku reproduction of a Northern Sung edition, Peking: *idem.*, 1955. Cited in some sources as *Ch'ien-chin fang*.

Ching-yüeh ch'üan-shu 景岳全書
(Complete works of Chang Chieh-pin 介賓 or Ching-yüeh, 1624). Shanghai: Shanghai Science and Technology Press, 1959, 1960.

Chou i 周易
(The book of changes). Reprint of the *Shih-san-ching chu-su* 十三經注疏 edition, Taipei: Yee Wen Book Co. 藝文印書館, ca. 1953. Also cited as *I ching.*

Chung-i chen-tuan-hsüeh chiang-i 中醫診斷學講義
(Textbook of traditional Chinese diagnostics), edited by Canton College of Traditional Chinese Medicine. Shanghai: Shanghai Science and Technology Press, 1964.

Chung-i-hsüeh kai-lun 中醫學概論
(Compendium of traditional Chinese medicine), edited by the Nanking College of Traditional Chinese Medicine. Peking: People's Hygiene Press, 1959.

Chung-kuo i-hsüeh shih 中國醫學史
(History of Chinese medicine), by Ch'en Pang-hsien 陳邦賢. Peking: Commercial Press 商務印書館, 1937, 1954.

Chung-kuo i-chi k'ao 中國醫籍考
(Critical examination of the medical literature of China), by the Japanese Tamba Mototsugu 丹波元胤 (compiled in the mid-nineteenth century, first printed 1935 under the title *Iseki kō*=*I-chi k'ao*). Peking: People's Hygiene Press, 1956.

Chung-ts'ang ching or *Chung-tsang ching* 中藏經
(Treasury classic), attributed to the second-century physician Hua T'o 華陀. Shanghai: Commercial Press, 1956.

Ch'un-ch'iu fan-lu 春秋繁露
(Resplendent dew on the Spring and Autumn Annals), by Tung Chung-shu 董仲舒 (ca. 100 B.C.). *Wan-yu wen-k'u* 萬有文庫 edition.

Han-shu 漢書
Official histories of the Han dynasties; the History of the Former Han, *Ch'ien-Han-shu* 前漢書 (compiled by Pan Ku 班固, ca. A.D. 100) and the History of the Later Han, *Hou-Han-shu* 後漢書 (compiled by Fan Yeh 范曄 450). Photomechanical reprint of the Hsü-shou-t'ang 長沙虛受堂王氏 edition. Taipei: Yee Wen Book Co., 1954.

Huai-nan hung-lieh chi-chieh 淮南鴻烈集解
Modern edition of the compilation of philosophical theories prepared under the auspices of the Prince of Huai-nan during the second century B.C., edited by Liu Wen-tien 劉文典. *Wan-yu wen-k'u* edition. The basic work is usually referred to as the *Huai-nan-tzu* 淮南子.

Huang-ti nei-ching. See *Huang-ti nei-ching su-wen; Huang-ti nei-ching t'ai-su; Ling-shu*

Huang-ti nei-ching su-wen 黃帝內經素問
(Candid questions in the Inner Classic of the Yellow Sovereign), Han period. *I-pu ch'üan-lu* edition (q.v.). This work is often cited as *Su-wen*, and the book of which it originally formed a part as *Nei-ching.*

Huang-ti nei-ching t'ai-su 太素
An ancient parallel edition of the *Su-wen*, compiled by Yang Shang-shan 楊上善, Sui period. Photomechanical reprint of a Japanese manuscript written between 1153 and 1163. Peking: People's Hygiene Press, 1955.

Huang-ti nei-ching su-wen i-shih 譯釋
The preceding work translated into modern Chinese with a commentary, edited by the Nanking College of Traditional Chinese Medicine. Shanghai: Shanghai Science and Technology Press, 1959.

I-chi-k'ao. See *Chung-kuo i-chi-k'ao*

I-ching. See *Chou i*

I-ching su-hui-chi 醫經溯洄集
Critical essays on the Chinese medical classics, by Wang Lü 王履 (1368). Peking: People's Hygiene Press, 1956.

I-lin sheng-mo 醫林繩墨
Medical essays, by Fang Yü 方隅, 1584. Peking: Commercial Press, 1957.

I-pu ch'üan-lu 醫部全錄
Typeset reprint of the medical chapters of the *T'u-shu chi-ch'eng* 圖書集成 encyclopedia of 1726. Peking: People's Hygiene Press, 1959–1963.

I-sheng 醫賸
(Medical odds and ends), by Tamba Motohiro 丹波元簡 (mid-nineteenth century). Reprint of the *Huang-Han i-hsüeh ts'ung-shu* 皇漢醫學叢書 edition. Shanghai: Shanghai Science and Technology Press, 1954.

I-tsung chin-chien 醫宗金鑑
(The Golden Mirror of Medicine), printed under imperial auspices in 1742. Peking: People's Hygiene Press, 1957, 1959.

Kuan-tzu 管子
Heterogeneous philosophical writings ascribed to a statesman of the seventh century B.C., but in reality of more recent date. *Chu-tzu chi-ch'eng* 諸子集成 edition. Peking: Chung Hwa Book Co. 中華書局, 1954.

Lao-tzu chiao-shih 老子校釋
(Collated and annotated text of the *Lao-tzu*), edited by Chu Ch'ien-chih 朱謙之. Shanghai: Lung-men lien-ho shu-chü 龍門聯合書局, 1958.

Lao-tzu pen-i 老子本義
(Basic meaning of the *Lao-tzu*), by Wei Yüan 魏源 (1794–1856). Peking: Chung Hwa Book Company, 1954.

Lei-ching 類經
(Classified classic), the contents of the *Nei-ching* arranged by subject, compiled by Chang Ching-yüeh 張景岳, 1624. Peking: People's Hygiene Press, 1957.

Lei-ching t'u-i 圖翼
(Illustrated "wing" to the Classified classic), by the same author. *Idem.*, 1958.

Li chi 禮記
(The record of rites). *Shih-san-ching chu-su* edition (see under *Chou i*).

Ling-shu 靈樞
Second part of the *Huang-ti nei-ching*, of which the *Su-wen* is the first part. *I-pu ch'üan-lu* edition (q.v.). Sometimes referred to as *Ling-shu-ching* 經 or *Hüang-ti nei-ching ling-shu*.

Ling-shu-ching pai-hua chieh 白話解
(The *Ling-shu* explained in modern colloquial Chinese), by Ch'en Pi-liu 陳璧琉 and Cheng Chuo-jen 鄭卓人. Peking: People's Hygiene Press, 1963.

Lü-shih ch'un-ch'iu chi-shih 呂氏春秋集釋
Modern edition of the philosophical compilation of the third century B.C., by Hsü Wei-yü 許維遹. Peking: Wen-hsüeh ku-chi k'an-hsing-she 文學古籍刊行社, 1933, 1955. Referred to as *Lü-shih ch'un-ch'iu*.

Mo-ching 脈經
(Classic of the Pulse), by Wang Shu-ho 王叔和 (second half of third century). Shanghai: Commercial Press, 1956.

Nan- ching chi-chu 難經集註
(Classic of medical problems, with collected commentaries), by Lü Kuang 呂廣 and others. Shanghai: Commercial Press, 1955. The basic work is referred to as *Nan-ching*.

Nei-ching (Huang-ti nei-ching). See *Huang-ti nei-ching su-wen; Huang-ti nei-ching t'ai-su; Ling-shu*

Nei-ching chiang-i 內經講義
(Lectures on the Inner classic), edited at the Peking College of Traditional Chinese Medicine. Shanghai: Shanghai Science and Technology Press, 1964.

Pao-p'u-tzu nei-p'ien 抱朴子內篇
The inner philosophical writings of Ko Hung 葛洪, ca. 320. Reprint of the *P'ing-chin-kuan ts'ung-shu* 平津舘叢書 in *Wan-yu wen-k'u*. This work and the *Pao-p'u-tzu wai-p'ien* 外篇 (Outer writings) are often referred to collectively by the title *Pao-p'u-tzu*, although originally they were separate books, and are so printed in the collection cited.

Pin-hu mo-hsüeh 瀕湖脈學
The pulse studies of Li Shih-chen, 1564. Reprinted together with *Chi-ching pa-mo k'ao*, listed earlier.

Po-hu t'ung-i 白虎通義
(The Comprehensive Discussions in the White Tiger Hall), report of a philosophical conference held A.D. 79. *Wan-yu wen-k'u* edition. Also referred to as *Po-hu t'ung*.

P'u-chi fang 普濟方
(Universal prescriptions), compiled by Chu Su 朱橚 and others, 1410. Typeset reprint. Peking: People's Hygiene Press, 1959–1960.

Shan-hai-ching 山海經
(Classic of mountains and seas). *Ssu-pu pei-yao* 四部備要 edition.

Shang-han-lun chiang-i 傷寒論講義
(Lectures on the Treatise on cold lesions), compiled by the Chengtu College of Traditional Chinese Medicine. Shanghai: Shanghai Science and Technology Press, 1964. The basic work for this and the next item is referred to as *Shang-han-lun*.

Shang-han-lun yü-i 傷寒論語譯
(Colloquial translation of the Treatise on cold lesions), by Jen Ying-ch'iu 任應秋. *Idem.*, 1959.

Shih-chi 史記
(Records of the historians), completed early first century B.C. Reprint of the Ch'ien-lung Palace Edition of 1739. Taipei: Yee Wen Book Co., 1954.

Shu-hsüeh-hsüeh kai-lun 腧穴學概論
(Compendium of foraminology), compiled by Lu Shou-yen 陸瘦燕 and Chu Ju-kung 朱汝功. Shanghai: Shanghai Science and Technology Press, 1961.

Szu-pu tsung-lu: I-yao-pien 四部總錄醫藥編
(General inventory of literature: Section on medicine and pharmacology). Shanghai: Commercial Press, 1955. Referred to as *Szu-pu tsung-lu*.

Su-wen. See *Huang-ti nei-ching su-wen*

Su-wen i-shih. See *Huang-ti nei-ching su-wen i-shih*

Su-wen shao-shih 素問紹識
(Complementary glosses on the Candid questions), by Tamba Mototaka 丹波元堅. Reprint of the *Huang-Han i-hsüeh ts'ung-shu* edition (see under *I-sheng*).

Su-wen-shih 素問識
(Glosses on the Candid questions), by Tamba Motohiro. *Idem.*

T'ai-su. See *Huang-ti nei-ching t'ai-su*

Tung-i pao-chien 東醫寶鑑 (Korean, *Tongŭi pogam*)
(Precious mirror of Eastern medicine), a Korean encyclopedia, compiled by Hŏ Chun 許浚, 1613. Reprint. Peking: People's Hygiene Press, 1955.

Wu-yün liu-ch'i 五運六氣
(Phase energetics), by Jen Ying-ch'iu. Shanghai: Science Hygiene Press 科學衛生出版社. 1959, 1960.

Yün-chi ch'i-ch'ien 雲笈七籤
A Taoist encyclopedia, ca. 1023. *Ssu-pu ts'ung-k'an* 四部叢刊 edition.

Western Publications

Gerhard Bachmann
Die Akupunktur, eine Ordnungstherapie. 2 volumes: text and illustrations. Ulm, 1959.

Hermann Braus (ed. Curt Elze)
Anatomie des Menschen. 3rd edition. 3 volumes. Berlin, Göttingen, Heidelberg, 1954–1960.

Wolfram Eberhard
"Beiträge zur kosmologischen Spekulation Chinas in der Han-Zeit," *Baessler Archiv,* 1933, *16*.1: 1–100.

Otto Franke
Geschichte des chinesischen Reiches. 5 volumes. Berlin, 1930–1952.

Marcel Granet
La pensée chinoise. Paris, 1934 (1950). All references are to the 1934 book-size edition.

———

Etudes sociologiques sur la Chine. Paris, 1953. A posthumous collection of articles that had previously appeared in diverse journals.

———

Fêtes et chansons anciennes de la Chine. Paris, 1929.

Franz Hübotter
Die chinesische Medizin zu Beginn des 20. Jahrhunderts und ihr historischer Werdegang. Leipzig, 1929.

Pierre Huard and Ming Wong
Chinese Medicine [original text in French], World University Library. London, 1968.

Joseph Needham
Science and Civilisation in China. 4 of 7 volumes published to date (volumes I–IV.3), Cambridge, England, 1954–1971.

Articles by the Author
"Die energetische Terminologie in den chinesischen Medizinklassikern," *Sinologica,* 1965, *8*.4: 184–210.

"Farbemblematik in China," *Antaios,* July 1962, *4*.2: 154–167.

"Untersuchungen einiger philosophisch-wissenschaftlicher Grundbegriffe und Beziehungen im Chinesischen," *Zeitshcrift der deutschen morgenländischen Gesellschaft,* 1961, *110*.2: 422–452.

"Wissenschaftliches Denken im alten China: Das System der energetischen Beziehungen," *Antaios,* March 1961, *2*.6: 532–551.

Index

VERMONT STATE COLLEGES

0 0003 0656133 3

DATE DUE

DEC 15 2000		
FLL 4/1/09		
GAYLORD		PRINTED IN U.S.A

DISCARD